DISTANT VISION

VISION

ROMANCE AND DISCOVERY ON AN INVISIBLE FRONTIER

Library of Congress Cataloging-in-Publication Data

Farnsworth, Elma G., 1908-

DISTANT VISION; Romance & Discovery on an Invisible Frontier / by Elma G. Farnsworth.
      p.   cm.
      Bibliography: p.
      Includes index.
      ISBN 0-9623276-0-3 : $24.95
      1. Farnsworth, Philo Taylor, 1906-1971. 2. Television history. 3. Inventors—United States—Biography. I. Title

TK6635.F3F37 1989
621.388'0092—dc20

                              89-16032

For Kenny

DISTANT VISION

ROMANCE AND DISCOVERY ON AN INVISIBLE FRONTIER

By

Mrs. Elma G. "Pem" Farnsworth

PEMBERLYKENT
PUBLISHERS, INC.
SALT LAKE CITY, UTAH

Table of Contents

FOREWORD
  by Utah Senator E. J. "Jake" Garn ix

ACKNOWLEDGEMENTS x

A WORD FROM THE AUTHOR xi

PROLOGUE xiii

CHAPTER ONE
  The Shell of a Man 1

CHAPTER TWO
  Dame Fortune Smiles 4

CHAPTER THREE
  The Other Woman 13

CHAPTER FOUR
  Philo, the Boy 23

CHAPTER FIVE
  Hollywood 43

CHAPTER SIX
  Big Chance 56

CHAPTER SEVEN
  202 Green Street 66

CHAPTER EIGHT
  Image Dissectors 76

CHAPTER NINE
  A Picture 85

CHAPTER TEN
  Backer Talk 93

CHAPTER ELEVEN
  Phil Meets the Press 101

CHAPTER TWELVE
  Friction 110

CHAPTER THIRTEEN
  Television, Inc. 117

CHAPTER FOURTEEN
  Enter RCA 128

CHAPTER FIFTEEN
  First Licensee 135

CHAPTER SIXTEEN
   Troubles in Paradise 147

CHAPTER SEVENTEEN
   Patents 153

CHAPTER EIGHTEEN
   TV Goes Public: Recognition Abroad 159

CHAPTER NINETEEN
   W3XPF on the Air 170

CHAPTER TWENTY
   S.O.S. from Baird 178

CHAPTER TWENTY ONE
   The Last Straw 192

CHAPTER TWENTY TWO
   Company Reorganized 204

CHAPTER TWENTY THREE
   Dashing of Hopes 215

CHAPTER TWENTY FOUR
   Boxes for Bullets 224

CHAPTER TWENTY FIVE
   Forest Fire! 238

CHAPTER TWENTY SIX
   Rescue Attempt 245

CHAPTER TWENTY SEVEN
   ITT Takeover 255

CHAPTER TWENTY EIGHT
   Old Trails; New Directions 265

CHAPTER TWENTY NINE
   Back at Square One 276

CHAPTER THIRTY
   Fusion 284

CHAPTER THIRTY ONE
   Ultimatum 298

CHAPTER THIRTY TWO
   Back to the Woods 311

CHAPTER THIRTY THREE
   Philo T. Farnsworth Associates 322

CHAPTER THIRTY FOUR
   Curtain 329

ADDENDUM 334

EPILOGUE 341

BIBLIOGRAPHY 342

APPENDIX 345

INDEX 351

Foreword

Pem Farnsworth has given us a fascinating and very intimate account of two remarkable lives in this insightful book. We learn in these pages that Philo T. "Phil" Farnsworth, best known as the father of modern electronic television, was aware of its potential before he began his work developing the apparatus necessary to accomplish the first transmission. Indeed, he was still a young man. He envisioned a world that would shrink to a global community, where people of all nations would share a simultaneous awareness of worldwide developments. Phil also maintained a keen interest and hope for television's role in educating our youth.

There have been numerous events that have underscored the significance of television in our day and age. Of course, most of those who were alive in 1969 can remember how they sat or stood, along with a large percentage of the entire world, before a television and witnessed man's first step on the surface of another heavenly body.

The spring of 1990 saw the tearing away of the Iron Curtain, symbolized most vividly by the fall of the wall between East and West Germany. Through television, we were able to see that wall come down; to see the faces of the people who were able to move freely across those borders; to hear and feel their joy and gratitude. Since then, we have been able to witness, again almost first hand, the successive transformation of communist dictatorships into fledgling democracies.

Television not only gave us the ability to witness these incredible events, but also provided much of the momentum that enables that wave of democracy to continue to spread, even as these words are written. And not only to spread, but to become firmly rooted in the minds and consciousness of people throughout the world, and now irrevocably a part of the fabric of humanity.

But there was much more to Phil Farnsworth than even his incalculable gift of television. This book also tells of the man himself, and his personal struggles and personal accomplishments. It tells of his character and his uncompromising morality, and his warm humanity.

Beyond a celebration of Phil Farnsworth's life, this book offers a message to the future generations: That however much time and energy and resources we invest in pursuing the ongoing quest for technical excellence, we must always bear in mind the fundamental importance of our humanity. We must not seek new technologies purely for the sake of redefining the "possible." We must seek technical excellence because it is the means of contributing to the improvement of our fellow man, and of the human condition.

—Senator E.J. "Jake" Garn

Acknowledgements

First and foremost, I am indebted to my son Kent and his wife Linda, who have devoted the past two and one-half years to this project. Without them and their daughter, Camille Sebastiane Farnsworth, this book may never have been finished. With Kent's untiring efforts and software expertise, he made it possible to format, style and even typeset the manuscript in-house; to my daughter-in-law, Linda, for the countless ways she has assisted and sustained us; to Paul Schatzkin and Georja Skinner who not only bought stock to launch this project, but contributed materially to the final stages of the book; to Senator E. J. 'Jake' Garn for his excellent foreword; to my late son Philo, for his early input to my manuscript, and who, with the help of Paul, Georja, and many friends, organized the fiftieth anniversary celebration of the first all-electronic transmission of television on September 7th, 1977, at Foothill College in Los Altos, California; to my son Russell and his wife Rose Kaplin, for their corrections and considerable editorial comment; my everlasting gratitude to Claude and Agnes Lindsay, Laura F. Player, and Lincoln (Phil's brother-in-law, sisters, and brother), for their encouragement and financial support; to Arch Madsen, Don Gale, Dr. Rees and Lois Anderson, David Duffin, Thomas Brown, and all my friends and relatives for their prepaid orders for both the regular and Collector's Editions; to the following for taped interviews and advice: my brother, B. Clifford Gardner, George Everson, Rear Admiral (retired) Frederick R. Furth, LeRoy Wentz, Tobe and Rom Rutherford, Seymour 'Skee' Turner, Arch Brolly, George Huffnagle, Donald Pike, Harold Burnhardt, Edy and Harold Heastan, Gene Meeks, Ray and Toni Bart, and others associated with Phil in his later years; to Fred and Diana Lane, for their editing and purchase of books (Fred even helped Kent, Linda, and Mark Scott build a nice work room from my carport); to my sister Rhae, whose nightly calls never fail to cheer me; to Kent's daughter Jennifer; to Philo's children, Mark, Maya, Matt, Philo Krishna, Arjuna (A.J.), and Vajra for their love and encouragement; to their mother, Diana Lopez, for her loving devotion to them; to my many understanding good friends, especially Ruby Swallow; to many-talented Cindy Hudson, who designed and formatted DISTANT VISION, for her complete dedication to the work; and finally, my love and gratitude to Ralph W. Thompson, Sr., my patient and long-suffering chief editor, who coaxed and teased a better book from my memory, while insisting that as far as possible the story be told in my own words; to Leni Davenport, who inspired the dust jacket design and to Kent for following his inspiration and seeing it to completion. I wish to express my gratitude to Bonneville International Corporation for making the first printing of DISTANT VISION possible. There are so many more—forgive me if you are not mentioned; I appreciate your total support and encouragement, and I love you all.

A Word from the Author

An individual can achieve anything his mind can conjure up, provided he is willing to expend the necessary time and energy.

That a farm-bred boy of fifteen might conceive an idea so complex as electronic television while large companies were spending millions on television transmission by spinning discs was so unlikely as to be ludicrous. Yet Philo's great faith in himself and in his project left no room in his mind for doubts. Philo Taylor Farnsworth made the first modern electronic television transmission on September 7th, 1927, at age twenty-one, in his simple loft-laboratory at 202 Green Street, San Francisco. The image was simply a line, but Philo had proved his point.

Not quite a year later, he demonstrated two-dimensional transmissions in a press conference on September 2nd, 1928. The Philo Farnsworth story immediately captivated the public fancy, and for years everything he did was reported in the press.

The object of this book is not to discredit others who have added immeasurably to the development of television over the years, but to tell the story of the life of Philo T. Farnsworth. Much that has been written about this remarkable man is as one-dimensional as that first electronic television transmission. The intent of this volume is to add another dimension, so that Philo might begin to receive full credit for his many contributions to world culture. Many world encyclopedias have given him credit only for inventing the first television camera tube, when actually he invented the first complete electronic television system, from transmitter to receiver. Although his patents have long since expired, his six controlling patents are still used today. Indeed, if they were to be removed from present day television, we would be left with . . . just a radio.

Regardless of how the reader sees Philo Farnsworth, he saw the future clearly. In 1926 before he made his first television transmission he began telling us how television would change the world. He said it would break down barriers between countries, and when world television could show one country how the other lived and what their problems were, differences could be settled around a conference table instead of on a bloody battlefield, thus creating a global community. He told how our ability to get an education, see world news, sporting events and movies in our own living rooms would obliterate illiteracy worldwide. Television and the dedicated news correspondents undoubtedly played a large part in the triumphant tumbling of the Berlin Wall, leading to a general demand for democracy around the world. How my husband would have rejoiced with us about this.

Philo Farnsworth gave the world many things besides television. He contributed materially to the beginnings of space-age science in the fifties and gave us other badly needed things such as the Isolette (first baby incubator) and the first crude electron microscope. The diversity of his contributions to society reflects not only the diversity of his interest but his conviction that we all have God-given talents, which we are duty bound to develop for the good of all people.

Behind the story of Philo's contributions to mankind is a rare tale of faith, courage, integrity, and character that should be an inspiration to young and old alike.

It was no secret that I planned to write the truth about Philo and his contributions to our culture. I wanted the world to know this humble man as I knew him and had been collecting documents and making notes for some time. He often talked about his early life, and we frequently discussed the times we had shared. Since he made a habit of dictating to me, I always had pen and paper handy but felt inadequate to write a book worthy of him. When I suggested I hire an experienced biographer to write his story, Phil brought me up short with, "You can do it if you really want to, but you can't write about me without writing about us, we are one person." Little did I dream that this would be our last such conversation.

It is my fervent hope that I have met with some small success in this effort. If I have helped just one person to realize that he can achieve his highest goal if he is willing to exert the necessary effort, I will consider my work to have been worthwhile.

Sincerely,

—Elma "Pem" Gardner Farnsworth

Prologue

Lewis Farnsworth tenderly kissed his pregnant wife and, saying the cows had to be milked, picked up his lighted lantern and milk bucket and left the cabin. As he walked toward the corral in the gathering dusk, he thought of his young wife, Serena. She had married him after the death of his first wife, Amelia, and had been a good mother to his two sons and two daughters. Now she was due to give birth to their first child.

As he pulled back the top fence pole to climb into the corral, he heard a voice call his name. Turning, he saw what appeared to be the familiar figure of Amelia, standing a few feet away. Lewis rubbed his eyes and shook his head. As he reopened his eyes, the apparition began to speak. "I have come to tell you that Serena's child is one of God's special spirits; great care should be taken in his upbringing." Lewis started toward her, but having delivered her message, Amelia faded from sight, leaving Lewis shaken and still unable to trust his senses. However, by the time he had finished the milking, he knew that, while Amelia was an apparition, her message was not only real, but must have been of great significance to bring her to him.

When Lewis told Serena what he had seen and heard, she looked at his pale face and shaking hand and suddenly knew that something very special was happening to them. They decided this was a sacred experience, one to be kept close to their hearts between the two of them.

CHAPTER 1

The Shell of a Man

Phil managed to cast a last, weak smile toward his daughter-in-law Linda as the gurney bearing his motionless body was rolled out the back door to the waiting ambulance. Soon after the ambulance began moving, I pressed my fingers to his wrist but could find no pulse. Frantic, I searched with every ounce of tactile sense I could bring to bear . . . still no pulse.

"Driver," I shouted, "his heart is not beating!" "We'll be at the hospital soon," the driver announced. The vehicle's speed increased, but only slightly. It was as though we were moving in a sea of molasses.

We arrived at the emergency room of the LDS Hospital after what seemed a millennium. The attendant staff recognized all the signs of big trouble right away. A young resident placed a stethoscope on Phil's chest for only a moment, then wheeled around and in an oddly subdued way yelled, "Call the code! We've got a code blue here!"

In the next instant, a small platoon of white coats burst through the emergency-room doors. I was pushed out of the way as the circle closed around Phil. I stood to one side, astonished. My mind recoiled as though I had just suffered a completely unexpected blow. While the army in white coats swarmed around the still form of my husband, someone directed me away from the chaos to a room nearby where I could sit down. When I regained a semblance of composure, more like an emotionless state of controlled hysteria, I called my son Kent and informed him that his father's heart had stopped. "I'll be right there," he said.

I am not sure whether I called anyone else or not. I was comforted by the presence of my sister Lois and brother-in-law Dr. Rees Anderson. Rees was Phil's physician, so I knew everything possible was being done. As I sat there, I concentrated on projecting to Phil a will to live. It seemed that the anguish in me was somehow tied to him.

More time passed; then I was led to an elevator which took me to the floor where Phil lay in the intensive care unit. Each time I tried to see some light in the situation, my hopes were quickly dashed by overheard pieces of conversation or by the look on someone's face.

When Kent arrived, I tried to tell him what I knew, but instead I wound up telling him mostly what I didn't know for sure. Rees came to the door and said we could come in now to see Phil, warning us that he was unconscious and gravely ill. They had managed to restart Phil's heart, but it had been stopped too long. His brilliant brain, which had given so much to the world, had sustained irreparable damage.

Phil was still lying on the gurney. Nearby, a respirator made a repetitious click . . . clack . . . hiss . . . as it pumped air into his damaged lungs. A faint beep was audible from the cardiac monitor, tolling each of his heart's attempts to maintain his life.

Before me lay the shell of the man with whom I had spent most of my life. Phil, once so vibrant and alive, had been so starved in recent months by his inability to handle food that he had wasted away to less than ninety pounds: his skeletal frame clearly bulged through his pale skin. My heart shriveled to a leaden lump in my chest to see him like this. With a slight negative movement of his head, Rees eloquently conveyed the hopelessness of the situation.

Phil was dying! I fought this notion, but as I saw his fragile condition, hearing the faint beep of the heart monitor and the incessant click . . . clack . . . hiss . . . of the respirator, any hopes I might have harbored quietly slipped away. I have no idea how long we stood there. Rees's eyes expressed the thoughts I knew he could not bring his lips to speak.

The next thing I remember, we were in the hospital chapel. I believe Rees said a prayer, but I remember none of the words he said. A cold, empty feeling came over me. I searched desperately within my soul for something to remove this terrible weight and pain that had taken full residence in every atom of my being.

We returned to the small waiting room. Kent, suggesting that he should probably call his brothers and tell them what was happening, disappeared. I was comforted by his helpful presence of mind, but still I agonized. The strong bond that had linked Phil and me so closely was tugging at my heartstrings. Rees stood beside me. Painfully aware that it was my decision, I managed to form the words: "Let him go, Rees."

As my mind began to clear, I realized that Phil might already have gone; only the body and its autonomic systems were sustained by machinery. What I had seen in the ICU was just an empty shell. I slowly came to accept the fact that Phil's spirit was already beyond the veil of our awareness.

Fearing I would collapse, Rees told Kent to take me to Lois, who was waiting for me at their home. I went reluctantly, Kent guiding me through the hospital corridors and out the door. Suddenly I felt that cold, empty feeling again, as though something vital had departed from me . . . I knew then Phil was gone.

CHAPTER 2

Dame Fortune Smiles

P em, Darling, can you be ready to be married in three days?"
I had been called to the neighbor's telephone—only about one in six households had such a luxury back in 1926. I had run all the way, because I knew Phil would never call me unless it were a matter of great importance. My mind had raced ahead of me, but of all the dire—or delightful—things my mind could conjure, this was not one of them. My head reeled, and I clutched the mouthpiece of the telephone box on the wall for support.

We had been engaged since my birthday, February 25th, but had agreed to continue our education at least another year before taking the profound "till death do us part" step of marriage. Now, here it was only the 24th of May, and Phil was saying we should be married in just three days!

Recovering from the shock, I responded. "Phil Farnsworth! You've got to be kidding! Of course I can't be married in three days . . . or three weeks, for that matter! Who would take care of my family?"

Young Phil and Pem

Phil cut me short with, "Not another word. I'll take care of everything. Call your father and tell him I must see him in Provo tomorrow evening. Don't worry; I'm not crazy. See you tomorrow at six!" He was gone. I walked home in a daze. As the import of what Phil had said sank in, excitement welled within me. Could it be that he had found backing for his television invention?

Dear, sweet, generous Phil! Six inches taller than my five-foot-two, he had broad shoulders, a lean body, and deep blue eyes that could look right into me. His sandy-colored hair had a tendency to curl, making it a bit unruly, and his broad, infectious smile revealed strong white teeth. Added to this, he had all the fine qualities of the Eagle Scout that he was. No wonder I loved him so much. As for his cryptic phone call, something big must have happened. Phil was too level-headed to think we could get married otherwise.

As I walked slowly back to the duplex my family shared with the Farnsworths, my gaze was drawn heavenward to the top of Mt. Timpanogos in my need for something solid to steady my racing mind. This monolith of the

The duplex shared by the Gardner and Farnsworth families as it appeared in 1978

Wasatch range towered protectively over the town of Provo, home of Brigham Young University, the center of learning responsible for bringing both Phil's and my family here.

Suddenly, the reality of the situation came back to haunt me, and a leaden feeling weighed me down. My mother had been dead just four months, and to leave my family at this time was unthinkable. Daddy had found it necessary to take a job in the coal mines at Castle Gate, some distance away, to support the family, and my brother Cliff, just older than I, was working with Phil in Salt Lake. My older sisters, Verona and Olen, had married and moved away. My brother Art, just younger than I, was still recovering from an emergency appendectomy. Next in line was dear, quiet brother Alton, still having a hard time dealing with the loss of our mother. Then there were my three darling little sisters, Ruth, Rhae, and Lois—twelve, ten, and eight, respectively. Trying to be brave, they were like three little lost lambs. Inadequate as I felt, I was all they had. How could I leave them? There was just one answer: I couldn't! And that was that!

We had moved here for educational reasons. Although Provo was a thriving college town, many of the students attending BYU came from rural communities beyond the reach of power lines. For example, in the small town of Jensen in northeastern Utah, where I had lived my first fourteen years, the only electric lighting was the Delco system in our chapel, and I had never heard a radio, except through earphones attached to the crystal set my brother Cliff had made.

In this environment, it is small wonder that Phil's attempts to stimulate interest in his television ideas were greeted with disbelief, skepticism, and just plain insulting ridicule. No doubt his youth and the very unorthodox nature of his invention prevented him from finding a sympathetic ear.

I was pretty sure that if Phil had obtained backing for his television ideas, it must have come from his bosses, George Everson and Leslie Gorrell, professional fundraisers from California. Their broad experience might make them susceptible to Phil's ideas. They had already been impressed by Phil's ingenuity. They had hired Phil to help them organize a Community Chest Campaign for Salt Lake City. During his interview, Phil had told Mr. Everson he was not interested in doing the actual canvassing but that he knew the city (he had worked on a street cleaning crew). He offered to manage the survey of the downtown area. George Everson was a congenial fellow with the average substantial build of a man in his early forties who enjoyed good food and spent his weekends playing golf to keep fit. Above all, he was good at business and at judging people. Phil's proposal was not exactly what he had in mind, but Mr. Everson was impressed by Phil's personality and forthright attitude. He hired him out of a roomful of other applicants and gave him the responsibility of contacting the management of each business in the area to get the names of the officers who would later be officially approached for support of the Community Chest.

Phil had come home the following weekend bursting with the good news. This was a definite step up the ladder of success. He had also been given the authority to hire his own helpers, and for his assistant he selected my brother Cliff, who had become his best friend.

Phil and Cliff had seen some very rough times together trying to bring in money to help their respective families. They had worked on harvesting and logging crews, among other things. Just before Phil found his job with the Community Chest, he had been working for the Felt Electric Company at a mere subsistence wage. Phil and Cliff built crystal radio sets, Cliff working through the day in the basement of Mrs. Thomas's boarding house where they lived and Phil working with him in the evenings. They had been able to sell all the radios they could build, but they had to supply the parts from their sales, which frequently meant going without meals, so their output—and income—was very low.

As activity peaked during the big rush week at the Chest, Phil had even hired his sister Agnes, who was my best friend, and me to help in the office. On payday he left us to the last. Then, saying this was "only a portent of things to come," he ceremoniously handed us each our eighteen dollars in *gold pieces!* None of us had ever *seen* a gold piece before this.

Phil had stayed in the city to finish the campaign, and I had returned home to Provo to care for my family. Now, only a week later, my mind was in turmoil at the prospect of getting married so soon, but I somehow survived the night. The next evening when we had my father and Phil's mother together, Phil silenced their well-founded objections with a plea to hear him out. This is the story he told:

Phil, Pem, Cliff, and Agnes

As they were sitting around the large table in the office completing a late mailing at the Community Chest, Mr. Everson asked Phil about his plans for the future, assuming he would be going back to college. Phil told him he was unable to continue his education because of family respon- sibilities. Cliff was aware of Phil's reluctance to talk about his invention. Even Cliff and I had known him more than a year before he told us about it. So Cliff took Mr. Gorrell aside and told him Phil had some interesting ideas he should hear about. Leslie Gorrell was a young, tall, smartly dressed man-about-town, with blond hair and a stylishly thin mustache. His friendly sense of humor made him easily approachable. In answer to his query, Phil admitted he had an important invention, but since it was not yet patented, he was not free to talk about it. Phil's reticence only fanned the interest of Mr. Gorrell.

After further questioning, Phil told Mr. Gorrell and Mr. Everson he had a way to produce television electrically, with no moving parts. His efforts to obtain backing had been so discouraging that he had considered selling his invention to a magazine in the form of an article, even though he knew if the idea appeared in print, it would become unpatentable.

They wanted to know more. The term *television* was completely new to them. Phil told them that up to that time, only crude methods— cumbersome spinning discs—had been devised to send pictures from one place to another. Seeing their interest and deciding that might be just what he had been looking for, he got their promise to hold what he was about to tell them in confidence and then launched into a description of his electrical system.

He told them that by manipulating electrons in a vacuum tube he could change a visual image into a stream of electrical current, transmit that to another vacuum tube at the receiver, and on a fluorescent screen turn the current back into the visual image again. Thus one would be able to see as well as hear what was happening on radio.

Phil's heart sank as he recognized in Mr. Everson's reaction the same disbelief he had encountered so many times before. Les Gorrell, on the other hand, was a young graduate civil engineer. Although this hardly qualified him in electronics, he at least was able to grasp something of what Phil was telling them. He took Phil aside and plied him with questions. Later, he told Mr. Everson he thought it would be a good idea to take a closer look at this "television thing."

The next day Phil was invited to dinner, and this time Mr. Everson began to get a glimmer of something that might be of some real consequence. As George Everson related in his book, *The Story of Television*:

"Young Farnsworth at this time looked much older than his nineteen years. He was of moderate height and slight build and gave the impression of being undernourished. There was a nervous tension about him that was probably the result of financial worry and frustration in not making headway in his scientific pursuits.

"As the discussion started, Farnsworth's personality seemed to change from that of a clerk too closely confined to his work. His eyes, always pleasant, began burning with eagerness and conviction; his speech became fluent to the point of eloquence as he described with the fire of earnestness this scheme that had occupied his mind for the last four years. He became a supersalesman, inspiring his listeners with an ever-increasing interest in what he was saying."

Phil's burning desire to prove his television ideas had finally found sympathetic ears. I was near to bursting with excitement at this good news. He squeezed my hand and motioned me to silence. Daddy and Phil's mother sat as if mesmerized. They had promised to hear Phil out, and he was anxious that they hear the whole story before making any decisions.

"We talked into the night," Phil continued, "with the result that Mr. Everson has agreed to invest six thousand dollars to get the project to the point where it could be evaluated by people more competent than they to judge the commercial value of my ideas. It seemed highly probable to them that if a young boy of fifteen could conceive this method of television, surely the well-trained scientists from the large corporations must have thought of it and might even be developing it.

"I told them these same fears had plagued me, but at BYU I read the *Bell Technical Journals* and other scientific journals to follow closely the work being carried out in this field. I assured them that my work was original, and I was as confident that it would work as I was sure the mechanical systems had about reached their maximum capability.

"They seemed impressed by my familiarity with the state of the art and decided to put some money behind my ideas. They said I probably had a really great invention, and if radio could take such a rapid hold on the public fancy, how much greater would be the impact of television!

"We've decided to form a partnership to be known as Everson, Farnsworth & Gorrell. I, as the inventor, am to have 50 percent of the venture, while the remaining 50 percent will be divided between Everson and Gorrell. Mr. Everson told me that this looked to be a great opportunity to cash in on a big thing, but in the event nothing came of it, he would take his loss and say nothing. I thought that was pretty generous of him."

"Oh, Phil! How absolutely wonderful!" I had been sitting on the edge of my seat, barely able to contain my excitement through all this narrative. Phil's mother, a kindly person whose many years of hard work on the farm had left their mark on her stooped shoulders and care-worn face, sat stunned. My father, after all the troubles both families had suffered, seemed to be having a problem believing this was real. Phil tightened his grip on my hand and continued his story.

"Everson and Gorrell have another campaign coming up, and they want me to be in California. I like the idea of at least starting in Los Angeles. I have a high respect for some of the scientists at the California Institute of Technology there and hope to get some guidance from them.

"I told them there was one thing I wanted to do before leaving. I didn't want to leave my sweetheart behind, so our plans would have to include a wedding. They hadn't counted on that kind of a complication. When I told them the girl was Miss Gardner who had helped at the Chest, they decided that to have my mind divided between my work in Los Angeles and my girl in Provo might be detrimental to the project. They asked how long this would take; they hoped I could leave that weekend. I assured them I would be ready."

"This is great, Phil! At last you'll have a chance to prove your ideas! I'm so happy for you! It's just incredible!" My excitement was spilling all over the place. "Maybe you could go now and I could come a little later, when we've ironed out some of the problems." Even as I shared his joy, I felt a sudden, deep sadness at the prospect of his being so far away.

Our parents sat in momentarily stunned silence, no doubt trying to sort out the good news from the shock of our marrying so young and, worse yet, of our going all the way to California.

"No, I wouldn't think of leaving without you, Pem. I know this will be hard on you, Mr. Gardner, but if you could find work in Provo, you could get along, couldn't you?"

"You bet I can, Phil. I learned to be a pretty good cook in my freighting days. I wouldn't stand in your way. This is your big chance, and I know what it means to both of you. The little girls can help me keep house."

A sense of ecstasy enveloped me. Could this really be happening? I was very proud of my big, slightly rough-around-the-edges, compassionate dad. I should have known he would find a way to help us; he always had.

"Thank you, Mr. Gardner; I knew I could count on you," Phil said with a grateful smile, and the eye communication that passed between my sweetheart and my father spoke volumes. My heart sang a blissful rhapsody, and I jumped up to give Daddy a big hug and kiss.

Phil now turned to his mother. "Mother, you've told me of your objections, and I think I know how you feel. I, too, would have more confidence if I had more college training, but I've had to get most of what I have by correspondence, and I can continue to do that. Also, Los Angeles has one of the best-stocked libraries in the country, and I intend to make use of it. As for our youth, as you know, I've earned my own way for the past eight years, and I'm perfectly capable of taking care of Pem. As far as that goes, Pem is a vital part of this venture, and I wouldn't think of going without her.

"Mother, I know how hard it's been for you since Papa died, and I've not forgotten the charge he gave me to take care of you and the family. I'll be able to help you somewhat, from the beginning, and hopefully within a year or two can make you financially independent. I will also be able to help Pem's family. What do you say?"

"I'm sure that if your father were here, he'd say, 'Go, with my blessings,' and that's what I say," was his mother's answer. "But I'm very concerned that you've become increasingly inactive in the Church since your father died. You'll be subject to many temptations in the city, but remember, your Father in Heaven will be a strength and guidance to you if you'll stay close to Him."

"Please don't worry about us, Mother," Phil assured her; "everything'll work out just fine."

Phil still harbored some resentment that his father had been snatched from him at this critical time. He had hoped soon to be able to relieve his parents of their heavy burden of earning a living. Without his father, attending church was not the same. We both had found that moving from a small town where our services were in constant demand to the college town of Provo was a traumatic experience. I found the church a cold, unfriendly place and had finally stopped attending altogether. Forsaking our church activities, however, did not mean we had forsaken our belief in the Mormon Church. This was always with us.

Then Phil changed the subject. "Mother, Pem and I would like to be married at home. Could you arrange for our bishop to perform the ceremony Thursday morning at ten? I have to go back to Salt Lake tonight to help draw up a partnership agreement."

As it turned out, he had to wait until the morning train, because there was the little matter of a marriage license. Phil was only nineteen, so his mother was obliged to sign with him. I kidded him about that; because the age of consent for girls was eighteen, I could sign for myself.

The bishop was to be out of town on Thursday, but Phil's mother knew stake president J. William Knight, who said he would be glad to officiate.

Phil's mother took me to choose a wedding dress. That was my first experience in a dress shop; Mother had taught us to sew our own dresses. Since I owned so few clothes, my wedding dress would have to serve many purposes. We chose a peach-colored, street-length crepe, with accordion-pleated skirt and yoke. It suited me well, and I was very happy with it. A few necessary underthings and a cute nightie Phil's mother insisted I should have completed my trousseau. I was delighted that the money Phil had given his mother had covered it all. From that time on she treated me as one of her own daughters, and she was always Mother Farnsworth to me.

Knowing how worried I was about leaving, Mother Farnsworth assured me that she and Agnes would do what they could to help my little sisters and Alton. Our two families shared a duplex, and they would be close by. My brother Art and Phil's brother Carl had become fast friends.

Wednesday afternoon, Phil and Cliff arrived in style. Mr. Everson had loaned Phil his Chandler Roadster for the occasion. Everyone was in a state of high excitement, but Phil and I were walking on air!

The next day dawned bright and sunny. The May flowers and many blooming shrubs took on more brilliant colors than ever I remembered them before. All the world seemed to join in our celebration. By ten o'clock the house was full of friends and relatives. When I came down the stairs, Cliff pulled me aside and told me, "Sis, don't look now, but your slip is showing." I retreated in some confusion and tightened the shoulder straps on my slip. I felt a sudden yearning for my dear, sweet mother. How I wished she were here to share in my big moment. A warm feeling of comfort spread over me, and somehow I knew she was with me in spirit. I wiped away a tear and hoped I hadn't smeared my mascara.

President Knight arrived as I again descended the stairs. He was a truly spiritual man, and the words he spoke as we stood before him with Cliff and Agnes on either side, as best man and maid of honor, touched us deeply. My heart was pounding in my throat, so I was sure I would only be able to croak when I had to speak. Phil was holding my hand, and I was grateful for his firm, steady presence. I had always felt safe and somehow invulnerable when near him. Now he smiled at me reassuringly and squeezed my hand, his damp palm betraying his outward calm. We then made our vows. Surprisingly enough I heard an "I do" come out of my mouth, and we were pronounced "man and wife."

Everyone was laughing or crying, kissing the bride and hugging the bridegroom, and President Knight caught some of the confusion. In filling out the marriage certificate, he wrote his own name where Phil's should have been. Luckily Phil was able to produce some ink eradicator and the error was quickly corrected, but through the years these smudges served to take us back to that happy day.

After a short reception, we drove back to Salt Lake City with Phil's mother and my dad in the rumble seat. They wanted to see us off on the train next morning. Phil had arranged for them to stay at Mrs. Thomas's boarding house, so he dropped them off there. Then he took me to a modest hotel near the train station, where he had reserved a room.

In the privacy of our room, Phil's exuberance overflowed. He put his arms around me and swung me around several times; then, putting me down, he told me he had to return Mr. Everson's car, because the train was to leave at 6:30 in the morning. He had also been thinking on the way from Provo that he really didn't have enough money to last in Los Angeles until Mr. Everson arrived. He would have to see about that and a couple of other things. Would I mind? He promised he wouldn't be gone long, so of course I said I would be fine.

CHAPTER 3

The Other Woman

Left alone on my wedding night, I welcomed the chance to catch my breath and review the whirlwind happenings of the past three days. As the reality of the moment settled in, I began to recall our courtship . . .

I remembered with great clarity the day Phil and I met. Agnes Farnsworth and I had been good friends since the day we met at Provo High School, becoming even better friends after her father's death. One day in the fall of 1924 she invited me home for a hot lunch. I needed no urging, because my usual lunch was a cold sandwich. As we entered her kitchen, I detected the tempting aroma of delicately seasoned stewed beans. Agnes explained that her mother usually left something for a warm lunch on the back of the wood-burning cook stove. The room was bright and airy, with a well-scrubbed look. The large oilcloth-covered table by the window was surrounded by six chairs. I could visualize heads bent studiously over nightly lessons.

Offering to help, I was shown where to find the things to set two places at the table, and Agnes disappeared to comb her windblown hair. I was interrupted by the entrance of a young man, his arms filled with books. I thought this must be the wonderful brother Agnes had talked so much about, who had recently returned from the Navy.

Embarrassed at being found alone, I went to find Agnes.

We were introduced, and Phil said, "So this is the Pem Gardner you wrote me about." I wondered what she had told him about me. I knew Agnes liked me, so I decided it was nothing uncomplimentary and relaxed. I had ample opportunity to study this young man as he excitedly related to Agnes his good fortune.

"Well, I'm all signed up at the Y, [Brigham Young University] again, Agnes. President Harris made arrangements for me to get a student loan to cover my books and tuition. He also gave me a janitor's job to help with living expenses. I signed up for physics, on top of all my other courses. That will be a breeze, because I went through it with my cousin Arthur, so I have only to go through the motions to get the credit. Wait till you hear this! I joined the chamber music orchestra, and when they had us all try out, I was assigned to the first-chair position in the violin section. That really surprised me. I also crowded in classes in drama and public speaking. Its going to be a busy, lots-of-fun year!"

"Whoa! That's wonderful, Phil! But come and have some of Mother's stewed beans with us. You can tell us the rest while we eat. We have to get back to class."

I had to agree with Agnes—Phil was certainly a brother to boast about. He radiated a sense of strength and vitality, no doubt due to his arduous boot camp activity and, before that, his hard work on the farm. He had a good sense of humor and the deepest blue eyes I had ever seen. Our eyes met, and, frantically searching for something to say that would not betray my dumbness, I blurted, "How did you like navy life?"

"It was quite an experience," he smiled broadly, and his twinkling blue eyes met mine. "I can't say I really enjoyed it, especially when we had drill in dress uniforms in 110-degree weather. On the plus side, though, I learned a lot . . . but I'm glad to be back."

"I'm sure glad you're back, Phil," Agnes said. "We really did miss our big brother."

"What did you like least?" I asked, determined to keep the conversation going.

"I guess it was guard duty. Those guys in the brig acted like animals. They had nothing to do but bait us guards and try to make us angry. Actually, I was sorry for them, but I found I just had to ignore their insults and think of something else."

"That must have been hard to do," Agnes sympathized.

"Well, it did improve my ability to concentrate."

There was that twinkle in his eyes. Yes, I had to agree with Agnes. He was someone special. Viewing him, a college man, from my lowly status of a high school sophomore, I subconsciously put him on a higher level, definitely beyond my reach . . .

. . . As my little daydream ended, I found myself still alone in our little hotel room. More than half an hour had passed, and there was no sign of Phil. Stretched across the big double bed, my mind resumed its wandering . . .

. . . I didn't see Phil again until the Christmas holidays. He had been hired by the Bates Furniture Store. One of his duties was to deliver radios and install antennas. In those days there were no radio broadcast stations in Utah, and elaborate antennas were necessary to bring in the nearest stations, which were in Denver and Los Angeles.

In those early days of radio, many of Phil's BYU friends, coming from rural farming areas, had never heard a radio. Phil decided to give what he called a "radio party." He invited his best friends and classmates and borrowed a top-of-the-line radio console from the store. Miss Frances Critchlow had been Phil's music teacher in Idaho. Now living in Hyrum, Utah, Miss Critchlow drove her mother seventy-five miles to attend. At Agnes's suggestion, I was also invited to this party.

The highlight of the evening came when the voice over the radio announced that the next three selections would be played for Phil Farnsworth and party in Provo, Utah. This caused excited chatter, and everyone gathered close to the radio. After these were played, Phil tuned to KFI in Los Angeles, where again his selections were played. Then to his great delight, he was able to tune in WLW in Cincinnati, Ohio, which was a treat he was not always able to enjoy. These were then the only stations with enough power to reach into Utah. Phil had written each station and given them the time and named his selections. The party was a huge success. Phil was the man of the hour.

The next spring, my sister Verona and her friend Bill invited Phil, Agnes, Cliff, and me on a picnic up the canyon to Castello Springs. This was our first date. We had so much fun dancing to the nickelodeon that we sang all the way home. When Phil learned that Cliff played the trombone and I the piano, he invited himself over for a "jam" session. These sessions became a weekly habit. We enjoyed playing together, but I considered Phil more Cliff's friend than mine.

It wasn't until the fall that Phil and I had our next date. The Farnsworths had moved to a duplex at 187 North 2nd East. When the other side of the duplex became empty, Agnes and I prevailed on my family to move in. My father who had freighted with Agnes' father several years previously near Vernal, Utah, readily agreed. Our families were very compatible. My mother, who was now in very poor health, really appreciated the kindnesses shown her by Serena Farnsworth.

Phil had signed up at the Y again, and invited Agnes and me to go to a Friday night dance. He danced with us only a time or two but introduced us to several young men, and we found ourselves well occupied. He had many lady friends with whom he danced. The next Friday he took us again. This time he danced a little more often with me. Agnes' boyfriend, Jack Scott, came along to see her home. Phil and I practiced new dance steps all the way home on the sidewalk.

Unable to find a job in Provo, Phil found it necessary to go to

Salt Lake City to look for work. He tried several jobs, including the street cleanup crew. After many attempts to get steady work, he was hired by the Felt Electric Company in Salt Lake. He had a very low starting wage because he was supposed to learn the trade of small electrical appliance repair.

He still came home on weekends and took Agnes and me to the BYU Friday night dances. Soon it was just Phil and me; then he began claiming most of my dances. I was falling in love with Phil in spite of myself, although I held no hope that our relationship would be permanent. I knew Phil had some very big plans and that his great obsession was to get an education. Never had he said anything to give me the slightest hope. At times I was so filled with futility that to be around him was pure agony for me.

That all changed the following winter on Christmas Eve, 1925. My sister Verona and her boyfriend Bill had taken us to Salem, fifteen or twenty miles south of Provo, to introduce Phil and Agnes to our father's parents, Alice and Ira Gardner. They were a special couple, loved by all who knew them. Grandma Gardner was "Grandma" to the entire town.

On the way home, crowded in the back seat with Cliff and Agnes, Phil tightened his arm around me and said, "Pem, I think we were meant for each other."

At that moment, the car chug-chugged and stopped. Bill had warned us he was low on gas, but no service stations were open. We were out of gas and still had more than three miles to go! Before we could get too upset about the prospect of walking home, a car drove up. Phil recognized Dr. Harris, president of the BYU, who kindly gave us a gallon of gas to get us home.

"Well, now you know how I feel. What do you think about us?" Phil continued, ignoring the interruption.

"I didn't think you were serious." I hadn't dared dream this would ever happen.

"I couldn't be more so." Phil assured me, hugging me close to him.

"I have to confess I have loved you more than I cared to admit even to myself." I said, in a voice so low he had to lean close to hear me. I remember my heart was racing so, I could hardly breathe.

We decided to keep this our secret. Phil's mother would worry, thinking he had given up all hope of an education. Anyway, we wanted to continue our education before thinking of marriage. Phil told me he had some important plans for the future and promised to tell me about them soon. Later, when he left me at my door, I could have jumped to the roof and shouted my love for him. He had held me in his arms and *kissed me*! . . .

. . . My mind brought me back to the present and to my loneliness in this impersonal hotel room. I wondered what had happened to Phil.

It seemed to be taking him a long time to return Mr. Everson's car. Oh, well. He would be coming soon, no doubt. Of one thing I was certain: I could depend on Phil. I had found him as dependable as the sun coming up in the morning. Whatever was keeping him was surely not of his doing.

My mind started to wander again. Was I really Mrs. Philo Taylor Farnsworth? I pinched myself to make sure it was not just a dream. No, the orange-blossom-encrusted band next to my lovely engagement ring attested to that . . .

. . . Oh, yes, the diamond. How he managed to buy that was still a mystery. Phil had invited me to come to Salt Lake for my eighteenth birthday, February 25th. I arrived the evening of the 24th and shared a room so kindly offered by a lady boarder.

The next morning, Phil's urgent knocking at the door awakened me at dawn. He wanted me to see something and said I would need a coat and boots because three or four inches of snow had fallen during the night. I dressed in a hurry, wondering what on earth he had to show me at this hour of the morning.

He took me up the Avenues to a trail leading uphill behind the magnificent dome of the state capitol. Leading the way, Phil left a shower of snow behind, flicked from branches whose heavy snow load had bent them into our path. Relieved of their burden, they swung to their former position, leaving the way clear for me to follow. Puffing along behind in my efforts to keep up to him, I tried to imagine what his surprise was this time. He was always springing surprises on me. He only said to wait and see.

As we climbed higher, I called through gasps for breath, "How much farther, Phil? I'm pooped!"

"We're almost there, honey. Here, grab my hand."

Very soon we came to a cleared viewing area. Phil stopped and turned me around to face the valley far below. The sun was just casting a crimson glow on the top of the Oquirrh Mountains across the valley to the west. The view was breathtaking!

The shadows of the taller peaks of the Wasatch mountain range towering protectively over the city on the east stretched across the floor of the valley, giving a bluish cast to the newly fallen snow. Gradually these shadows shortened until the sun rose higher and bathed the city in dazzling white. The nearby bushes were adorned with a myriad of sparkling jewels. We stood arm in arm, enthralled with this magic moment. Phil told me he had stood here many times seeking solace . . . or inspiration.

I was struck by the complete silence. We seemed to be caught in a magic moment of time: not even the chirp of a bird broke the stillness of the early morning air. The only movement was of spasmodic clouds of warm breath issuing from our lungs into the crispy cold, clear air, as they labored to replace the oxygen used by our climb. My heart was pumping so hard I thought surely Phil would hear it, but he made no indication. He slipped an arm around me and hugged me close to him. We stood for some time, mesmerized by the splendor spread before us. Then Phil broke the spell.

"Pem, sweetheart, I have something for you. I wanted to give it to you on your birthday, because if anything ever happens between us, I never want it back."

He took a small blue plush box from his pocket and lifted the hinged lid. I could hardly believe my eyes! There was a gorgeous diamond engagement ring. On each side of the diamond was a pear-shaped sapphire. I was speechless! With an effort I pulled myself together to hear what he was saying.

". . . of course we can't be married right away, because I still have to get more education and get some money together."

"But Phil! You can't do this! I won't let you . . . you can't afford it . . . there's still plenty of time."

"It's all right, honey; trust me. I didn't want to give you a ring we'd both be ashamed of when we're rich, and we will be! I love you so much, honey, and this is my notice to all the young men you meet that you are spoken for."

He silenced any further protests with a kiss and held me in a tight embrace. Suddenly everything fell into place, as though we had been here at some other time. "God was truly in His heaven and all was right with the world." A warm glow filled me and took up permanent residence.

The second day after I returned to my home in Provo, I received in the mail the sheet music to Irving Berlin's new release entitled "Always." Enclosed was a note from Phil saying Irving Berlin could say it so much better than he, but this was what he would have said if he could have found the words. "Always" remained our song, and because it so aptly depicts our life together, I shall include the words:

Verse 1

Everything went wrong,
And the whole day long,
I'd feel so blue.
For the longest while,
I'd forget to smile —
Then I met you.
Now that my blue days have past,
Now that I've found you at last —

Verse 2

Dreams will all come true,
Growing old with you,
And time will fly.

Caring each day more,
Than the day before —
Till Spring rolls by.
Then when the Springtime has gone,
Then will my love linger on —

Chorus:

I'll be loving you, always —
With a love that's true, always —
When the things you've planned,
Need a helping hand,
I will understand, always, always.

Days may not be fair, always,
That's when I'll be there, always.
Not for just an hour,
not for just a day,
Not for just a year . . . but always.

. . . As the music faded from my mind, I found myself still alone in an empty hotel room. Minutes had turned into hours, but there still was no sign of Phil. I began to feel terribly alone—and this was my wedding night! As I lamented my predicament, a little ditty unbidden came to mind:

Was it for this I uttered prayers,
And sobbed and cursed and kicked the stairs,
That now domestic as a plate,
I should retire at half-past eight?

—Edna St. Vincent Millay

With this unworthy thought, I jumped up and began pacing the floor. Phil was undertaking a monumental task. He deserved more support than this! So what if this was our wedding night! There would be long years of other nights. I shut out the little voice whispering in my ear, "Not like this one," and lying on the bed, I willed the tenseness to depart.

As the clock continued to tick away, I remembered the first time Phil had told me about his television invention . . .

. . . Early one Saturday morning, he appeared at my door riding one horse and leading another. I had learned to ride early, as horseback was my only mode of transportation in Jensen, so I leaped at the chance to take a ride. Remembering the lively little mare I had ridden then, I chose the more spirited of the horses. That was a mistake. These were rented "Armory" horses, accustomed to the strong, disciplinary hand of a cavalryman.

Hardly had I hit the saddle when that horse took off on a dead run up the quiet residential street with me pulling on the reins with all my strength. Suddenly, the horse swerved left, leaped a small ditch, and dumped me ignominiously on my cousin's lawn, physically unhurt but thoroughly deflated. The horse just stood there, as much as to say, "Now what do you think of that!" Phil arrived, white with concern for my safety. It was a situation I could laugh at later. Now I was shaken, very embarrassed, and grateful to Phil that he had seen nothing funny about it. He had thought I was just showing off, and didn't race after me for fear of making my horse run away!

With a sadly deflated ego, I traded mounts with Phil, and taking the shortest route out of town, we headed up Provo Canyon. Phil's destination was Bridal Veil Falls. Here, a sizable stream breaking over the towering cliff was parted in the middle by a protruding rock, the water falling in long misty streamers resembling a bridal veil, hence its name. This was a favorite spot for a picnic or, as in this case, a lovers' meeting. Phil tied the horses and found a large rock at the edge of the Provo River which threaded its way down the canyon.

Sitting on the rock, we had a long, intimate talk. In sharing childhood experiences, both having grown up on farms, we found we had much in common. We also shared a common interest in music, since Phil played the violin and I played the piano. He told me all about how he had taken up the violin after his grandmother had persuaded him he could be a great concert violinist—if he would just spend some money he had saved for a violin instead of for a bicycle.

"You've come a long way, Phil. Did you ever really want to be a concert violinist?"

"I thought about it for a while, but this brings me to what I have to tell you."

"That's good. I was beginning to wonder what you brought me up here for."

Phil got up, threw a stick upstream, and watched it bob along past us and on downstream before returning to resume his seat on the rock. I waited patiently for him to collect his thoughts. He began somewhat hesitantly, as though he were apprehensive of how I would react to what he had to tell me. Then he launched into the most incredible tale, far beyond anything I could have ever imagined.

He told me he had dreamed up a way to send pictures through the air along with the sound of radio. He said crude pictures had already been transmitted using mechanical spinning discs; however, he thought the discs were not only cumbersome, but a potential danger to the user. He was going to train something called an "electron" to do the job.

I asked what an electron was. He said it was a tiny particle of matter that was the "glue" that held all matter together, even the rock on which we sat. As he talked, I became uneasy to think of my world of solid rocks, mountains, and even metals being made of atoms whose nuclei were surrounded by dancing electrons. That day, Phil changed my entire concept of the world around me.

He ended with an account of the insulting reactions his story had evoked from people he had attempted to interest in backing him. He had once told a girl for whom he thought he cared. She said she could never marry a dreamer. The man she married would have to be "going somewhere." He said he had not told me before, because he had to assure himself that my reaction would be different.

I listened wide-eyed to Phil's story. I had always sensed a deeper side to him than the fun-loving young man I had come to know, but was hardly prepared for this. While I had not begun to understand all he had said, I believed in Phil implicitly and told him so. Seeing the sincerity and frank honesty shining from those blue eyes, how could anyone doubt him? Had he told me he could fly to the moon, I would have believed he could find a way. In my mind he had miraculously changed from a fun-loving young man to a serious inventor. On the way home I found it difficult to adjust to this new image of him . .

. . . By now several hours had passed since Phil had promised he would be right back. My loneliness was beginning to turn into worry, and my mind filled with thoughts of a sadder time . . .

. . . On Phil's weekend visits he always took time to sit and visit with my mother, whose health was failing rapidly. They became very fond of each other. He often brought his violin over, and he always asked if there were any pieces she would like to hear. She usually chose hymns. Her favorite was the Mormon hymn "Oh, My Father."

On Phil's last visit, suspecting time was running out for Mama, he told her he intended to marry me and take care of me. Later that evening, I went in to sit with Mama. She was so frail that her hands were almost transparent. My heart shriveled within me to see her like this. She reached for my hand. Taking her hand in mine, I bent and kissed her pale forehead. It felt cold and clammy. She smiled her brave, courageous smile.

"Phil told me that he was going to marry you and take care of you."

"Yes, Mama. I have been so in love with him, but he hadn't given me any idea that he wanted us to be more than just good friends until last Christmas. He thought it best not to tell anyone, because we had a few years of education to get behind us before we could think of getting married. I'm so glad he told you."

"I'm very happy for you, dear. Phil is such a fine young man, and you'll make him a wonderful wife. Just love him and be the best you can, and you will have many happy years together."

"I'll try, Mama. You and Daddy have really set us kids a good example.   I have never heard a cross word between you."

"Your father is a good, kind man."

"And you are a remarkable woman, Mama.   How could he help loving you?"

The next morning, January 18th, 1926, this glowing example of womanhood, my mother, passed from this world. We were all huddled together in the kitchen, too numb and grief-stricken to talk, but drawing some measure of comfort in being together. We had always been a close-knit and loving family.

Daddy had shut himself in with Mama, completely shattered and heartbroken.   She had been his love and inspiration all through their life together. Her shining light that had guided us all, now gone, left us adrift. Pulling myself together, with leaden feet I went next door and called Phil and Cliff with the devastating news.   They took the next train to Provo.   Cliff sought the comfort of the family, and with the memory of the loss of his father fresh in his mind, Phil knew how much I needed him . . .

. . . I rejected the unhappy memory of losing my mother and began again to wonder what had happened to Phil. Pacing the room, I became keenly aware for the first time of the four dreary walls that enclosed me and the much-used furniture of the room. I was fast losing the perfume-and-roses ambience that had surrounded me on this, my wedding day. I was the neglected bride . . . where was my bridegroom?

With a start, I realized it was very late, and my thoughts turned from self-pity to alarm for Phil's safety.   What if something dreadful had happened to him?   Now I really began to worry.   I had created a rotating carousel of emotions and had resumed pacing the floor before I heard Phil's key in the lock.

I cut off his apologies with a kiss.   I was so happy to see him alive and well.   Releasing me from a tight embrace, he held me off, and looking deep into my eyes, he said, "Pemmie, I have to tell you there is another woman in my life."   Then before I could faint from the shock, he added, ". . . and her name is 'Television.' The way I see it, my work is going to be taking up most of my time. The only way we will have the time together I would like is for you to work with me. How about it?   It will be very exciting.   We'll be working right on the leading edge of discovery."

"But, Phil, I could never catch up to you, let alone keep up with you."

"You can if you want to bad enough, because I'm going to help you."   He felt bad that he had ruined our wedding night. We decided that since the magic of this all-important night had been lost and our train was to leave at six the next morning, we would celebrate our wedding the following night, on the train enroute to Los Angeles and to our new lives together.

CHAPTER 4

Philo, the Boy

The question is often asked, "How could a fourteen-year-old farm boy ever devise something so technically complex as television?" As improbable as it seems, young Philo Farnsworth not only proved it was possible, but he did it. How could that happen? Was it a matter of early motivation and circumstance, or, as Phil said, was there a certain amount of guidance from a higher intelligence, even God? Phil often referred to the sequence of events that constituted our lives as a "guided tour." Phil's inventiveness was characterized by a series of inspirations that moved him toward some distant vision. So that you may draw your own conclusions, let me begin at the beginning.

Philo Taylor Farnsworth was born August 19th, 1906, to Lewis Edwin and Serena Amanda Bastian Farnsworth at a place called Indian Creek near Beaver, Utah, in the log cabin built by his paternal grandfather, for whom he was named.

The first Philo Taylor Farnsworth had been among the early Mormon pioneers who trekked west across the plains from Nauvoo, Illinois, to the Rocky Mountains in the 1840s. He had been ordained bishop of the group of families sent by Brigham Young to build the town of Beaver (1856) from sagebrush flats. That was his third such assignment, the town of Pleasant Grove being the first, and he also had a large part in organizing the town of Fillmore, which was the first site picked for the state capital. He was later named territorial judge and, along with my own pioneer ancestor Bernard Snow, was among the legislators who composed the state constitution when Utah was admitted to the Union in 1896. At the request of his widowed mother, Agnes Ann Patterson Farnsworth, Lewis named this son, Lewis's firstborn of his second marriage, for her late husband, Philo Taylor. Lewis's first wife, Amelia White, had died, leaving Lewis with four children; Vernessa, Lewis Franklin, Hortense, and Ronald Edwin, ranging in age from

Birthplace of Philo Taylor Farnsworth, Indian Creek, Utah and (inset) Philo at 6 months of age.

Judge Philo T. Farnsworth, Phil's grandfather

Lewis Edwin Farnsworth, Phil's father

fifteen to nine.

Serena was descended from a long line of independent, seafaring Norsemen. Her father, Jacob Bastian, Sr., was a modern viking in blood, in physique, in training, and in spirit—a great Dane of the sea. He was well over six feet tall, rawboned, with a firm chin and deepset, penetrating blue eyes that, in Phil's words, "seemed to look right through you."

In his native village near Copenhagen, Denmark, he was year after year the champion "Barrel King." He was the proudest dancer in his part of Denmark. He and his chosen lady—Gertrude Petersen—were one of the four couples selected to dance before the Crown Prince of the Realm.

*Phil with his mother,
Serena Amanda Bastian Farnsworth,
in 1939 on the sun porch of Cresheim
Valley Road house in Philadelphia.*

As a ship's carpenter and cabinetmaker, he had saved a considerable sum to build a home for his beloved Gertrude. When Gertrude joined the Mormon church and banded with a group of members to sail to the new country of America, Jacob left his wealth, his family, and way of life and cast his lot with the poor Mormon immigrants. They endured a traumatic voyage across the Atlantic Ocean, only to find at the Missouri River they were faced with the appalling prospect of pulling handcarts across the plains to the Great Salt Lake Valley.

The voyage had left Gertrude in poor health, and Jacob wanted to outfit them with the best equipment to make this trip easier for her, but she would not leave her friends. Many of these people had no money for provisions, not to mention a handcart in which to carry them. Jacob bought materials, and with the tools he had brought, built handcarts for these people, and filled them with provisions.

At the end of the long day's journey, he often volunteered to go back over the trail to help stragglers—the sick, the weak, or those who had suffered accidents. Many times it was his own Gertrude whom he had cradled in his arms on a quilt in a sequestered spot until he could return in the cool of the night to bring her into camp when she could better withstand this segment of the journey.

By her faith in God and sheer willpower, Gertrude lived to see her goal, the Great Salt Lake Valley, but died soon after arriving. Broken hearted Jacob was left stranded at age 22, without close friends, or even the ability to speak the language of this new country (Gertrude had always acted as his interpreter). He stayed in Utah out of loyalty, because he promised Gertrude he would do what he could for "her people."

Jacob Bastian was a perfectionist. He always had the strongest and most beautiful animals and the best fruits and vegetables. The Bastian Ranch in Washington (in Utah's Dixie, near St. George—the rapidly growing mecca for the affluent) was, as one grandson described it, a veritable shangrila—an oasis carved from black lava rock and red sandstone. He had brought many fruits, including pomegranates, figs, peaches, and grapes, from California. He even planted mulberry trees and attempted to create a silk industry for the ladies, with silkworms imported by the church from Japan.

A small trickle of water at the base of the vermilion cliffs was dug out and developed into a perpetual living spring. The water was led down into a cistern-like rocked-in reservoir around which he planted weeping willows for shade. An outlet gate from this provided means to water the place. Young people from the entire region came here for gatherings and watermelon feasts.

Serena's mother was Kirsten Hansen, also from Denmark. She had crossed the plains with a later group using handcarts, and as a girl of fourteen had married Jacob. He had built their home, and all of her furniture was lovingly fashioned by Jacob's capable hands.

Kirsten bore Jacob eleven children, five of whom died at a very tender age. She, as an early Mormon wife, corded and spun wool from the sheep and cotton from the local cotton fields. Until the building of the Washington cotton mill, which later produced cloth for clothes, the ladies had spinning wheels and looms for the hand weaving of material they called homespun. This was colored with natural dyes, an art they learned from the Indians. Also from the Indians they learned to make soap from the Joshua trees that were natural to that area. Serena was the ninth child, but the second daughter to reach adulthood. She was not many years older than Lewis's eldest daughter when she undertook the raising of his four children.

The first indication that Philo was a gifted child came at the age of three. Lewis was driving the stage from the railroad terminal at Medina, northwest of Beaver, to the southwestern area of Utah. One day he took his young son to see the large locomotive that pulled the train. As the hissing, puffing, clanking monster pulled into the station, Philo covered his ears in terror and hid his face in his father's coat. Seeing this, the kindly engineer invited Philo up to the cab to see how he ran the train. With considerable misgiving, Philo allowed his father to boost him up to the waiting arms of the engineer.

Apprehension soon turned to fascination as each phase of the operation was patiently explained to him, from the Johnson bar, which opened the steam vents giving power to the engine, to the mechanism that dumped sand on the tracks to give traction or help stop the train. An inquisitive child, Philo was quick to learn. Back with his father, he had many questions.

When they arrived home late that evening, Philo asked for a piece of paper and a pencil. Climbing up on a chair by the kitchen table, and sitting on his heels to make himself taller, he proceeded to make a detailed drawing of the locomotive. This demonstration of photographic memory won him much praise from the older members of the family and no doubt heralded the first seeds of greatness in his young mind.

Philo was six years old when the hand-cranked Bell telephone and the Edison gramophone came to the small town of Washington, Utah, where the Farnsworths now lived. Power lines had not yet arrived in rural areas of the west. To hear the voice of a favorite aunt over a long distance was beyond his comprehension. The gramophone was no less baffling. To hear beautiful music or funny stories by resting a needle on the groove of a black cylinder about the size of a baby's nursing bottle was nothing less than a miracle. To answer his many questions, his father told him these were inventions and that Alexander Graham Bell and Thomas Alva Edison, who had created them, were called inventors. His older half-brothers and half-sisters read to him about inventors from their textbooks. He came to the conclusion that inventors were truly special people, and he hoped that someday *he* could be an inventor.

Philo's entire life was characterized by that hope, that quest, that led him to seek constantly to further his knowledge and understanding. He began learning about electricity from the Sears, Roebuck Catalog, then the "wishbook" of rural families nationwide. Because the toys he coveted, such as motors and trains, required electricity to operate, young Philo decided to make his own electricity. From parts found around the farm he fashioned a sort of "perpetual motion" device. Although it failed to produce electricity, the disappointment was easier for his young mind to bear because he felt he had made an invention.

To proceed toward his ultimate vision required more than a fascination for the electron, a talent for mechanical detail, a thirst for knowledge. Philo needed to develop a faith not only in divine guidance but in himself. He needed to develop the courage and integrity and character to persist in his quest.

Lewis and Ronald, Lewis's youngest son by his first wife, Amelia, were hired to help on a government project of clearing land for a town on the Uintah Indian Reservation in northeastern Utah. Lewis had a brother and several grown sons living in Mountain Home, the nearest settlement. With their help, Lewis and Ronald built a one-room log cabin to house the family. The men needed to camp on the site of the project.

Serena was pregnant with her fifth child, and Lewis was very reluctant to leave her, but they badly needed the work. He told eight-year-old Philo he was to be the man of the house. He was to take the cow to find grazing spots, feed the pigs, milk the cow, and bring in wood for the cookstove. As befitting his new station and to make possible the herding of the cow, Philo was presented with a pony. He took great pride in having his own mare, Tippy. She received careful grooming and ample grazing.

Philo had many character-building experiences in his childhood, but to him one stood out among the rest. One day an important letter came for Lewis. Against her better judgment and with no alternative, Serena allowed Philo to deliver it to the work site, some dozen miles away. Serena had cause for concern, because little Philo would be trekking through the foothills of the Uintah range, where mountain lions and other wild animals were known to wander down from the mountains in search of food. Also, the Lake Fork Creek, usually a clear, easily crossable mountain stream, was an unpredictable hazard. When it rained in the mountains, the stream could swell quickly to many times its normal size.

To reassure his mother, Philo told her about his father's instructions. If Tippy pricked up her ears and snorted, that would indicate the presence of danger. If he let her run as fast and as far as she wanted to, she would get him out of danger. Since there seemed no sign of rain, Serena was reassured.

Philo was up at dawn the next morning. He fed the pigs and milked the cow while his mother cooked his breakfast, then was off in true pony-express style. Upon contemplating the miles ahead of them, he slowed Tippy's pace. Having been warned that mountain lions liked to leap from ledges or trees upon their prey, Philo was ever watchful of such places.

As they reached the Lake Fork, he was uneasy to see the bushes crowding the road and the stream. Allowing Tippy only a few gulps of the clear, fast-running mountain water, he urged her on across the stream. The high praise and warm embrace he got from his father for delivering the letter and fresh-baked bread and cookies his mother had sent made him feel ten feet tall. He dearly loved his father.

After watching the men work a while, Philo started home. Noting the angle of the sun, he urged Tippy along. As Philo came close enough to see the Lake Fork, which was at the bottom of a deep ravine, he was horrified. In the short time since he had crossed it, it had swollen to a raging torrent. The high clouds over the mountains, which had not seemed to be a threat, had caused a flash flood. The fast-moving, tempestuous water frightened Philo. He knew it was dangerous to try to cross, but there was no way to get word to his mother. If he were not home by dark, she would be frantic. He had to do it! More concerned for his mother than for his own safety, Philo summoned the courage to cross the angry stream.

Tippy was a smart mare; she had protected Philo more than once on their daily jaunts in search of grass. Now she hesitated; her every instinct told her not to enter that water. Displaying his inborn ingenuity, Philo tied the reins together, wrapped strands of Tippy's mane around his hands (since he had no saddle, there was no horn to cling to), and urged her into the icy water. Almost at once she was swimming. The swift-running water almost swept the boy from her back; terrified, he dug his toes into her sides and clung for dear life.

Although Tippy was in good shape, they were being swept downstream. Through chattering teeth, Philo kept up words of encourage- ment, "You can do it, girl! You can do it!" He was as much concerned for his beloved mare as for himself.

Eventually they neared the far side of the creek and, getting her footing, Tippy climbed up the bank. When she snorted and began to run through the brush, it was only Philo's strength born of desperation that kept his hold on her mane. Nor did the mare slow her headlong flight until she reached the top of the long hill leading out of the gully. Then she stopped, thoroughly winded.

Philo was soaked to the skin and very, very cold. On the other hand, Tippy was overheated. Steam rose from her as she stood wheezing for breath. Philo slipped from her back and wedged himself between her front legs for warmth. She stood perfectly still, as though she sensed his need. After a while, when Philo could stop shivering, he climbed on her back and they resumed their long trip home.

Meanwhile, back at the cabin, Serena was becoming increasingly uneasy. As the sun went down, she could no longer contain her anxiety. She felt totally helpless. She could not leave her three young children, Laura, Carl, and Agnes, ages two, four, and six; and had she no way to send for help. Unable to wait longer, she had left Agnes in charge of the younger two and started walking up the road, when she saw Philo coming. She felt a welcome relief at the sight of him, but seeing his wet clothes, she had him strip. She bundled him in a quilt and set him with his feet on the warm oven of the cookstove while she dished up a bowl of hot soup. Between sips, Philo related his traumatic adventure. Serena, very much shaken by the realization that her son's concern for her could have cost him his life, silently vowed never again to allow him to take such chances. Philo himself, far from being discouraged by the adventure, was strengthened in his lifelong conviction that he could accomplish whatever he set out to do.

Serena's baby son was born February 12th, 1914, with a cleft palate and lip. Unable to nurse, he swallowed only with great difficulty. His chances of living looked very slim. Lewis took his tiny son in his arms and gave him a father's blessing and the name of Lincoln, for the great man whose birthdate he shared.

Serena was a woman of great courage and determination. She knew help was available in Salt Lake City, if she could only keep her son alive until she gained strength enough to get him there.

For the next week or so she patiently fed little Lincoln drop by drop from an eye dropper. While Lewis took care of the other children, she took the baby to Salt Lake City on the horse-drawn stage. At the Latter-day Saint Children's Hospital, a very able surgeon made the necessary repairs of baby Lincoln's palate and lip. Serena was happy to find that on the trip home, the horse-drawn stage was replaced by an automobile.

Their comfort was cut short, however, when they ran into a severe sleet storm. The unpaved roads turned to potholes of mud up to the hubcaps. It soon became necessary to change to an open wagon with a four-horse team. Through the night, stopping only for warm milk for the baby, Serena held a heavy and quite soggy denim quilt over them as their only protection from the storm.

Serena was in poor health after that, so Lewis moved the family to Vernal, to be near her sister Rhetta. That was a traumatic move for Philo.

Not only were there no facilities to care for Tippy, but horses were not allowed within the city limits. Since they could not afford to pay for her keep, he had to give her up. When she was traded for a bushel of peaches for Serena to can, he was highly indignant, although peaches were a rare treat for all of them. The ultimate insult came when the peaches were found to be wormy.

His father bought him a beautiful pair of roller skates with ball bearings. This was the first time in his life they had lived in a place with sidewalks, and although he took much pleasure with his skates, it did little to assuage his grief for Tippy.

The next year they moved back to Washington in southern Utah, where Serena had spent her youth and where her parents still made their home. Philo adopted several dogy (orphaned) lambs with the idea of raising them for sale and buying a bicycle with the money. They wouldn't have to feed a bicycle, and it would take up very little room. He vowed never to allow himself to become attached to another horse. Perhaps being prevented from keeping his horse underlaid Philo's lifelong trait of loyalty to his friends and associates as well as to his ideas.

With the help of Agnes and his younger brother Carl at bottle feeding time, Philo's lambs grew rapidly. When they were ready for market, Philo went to Grandma Bastian's house to choose a bicycle from her Sears, Roebuck catalog. When he showed her his choice of a bicycle, she agreed it was a fine bicycle, but she had something to show him. Turning to the music section, she pointed to a violin.

"Philo, I know how much you want a bicycle, but with the same amount of money you could buy this nice violin. Wouldn't you like to be able to play beautiful music, like you hear on the gramophone? Some day you could be a great violinist."

Philo left in a very unhappy state of mind. He dearly loved his grandmother and wanted to please her, but he had planned all summer on a bicycle. Now it was so near he could almost feel the air hitting his face as he whizzed along on it. He spent a troubled night, and in his sleep he dreamed he was indeed a famous violinist. Everywhere he played, he was received with great acclaim. The next morning he could hardly wait to tell his grandmother.

By the time the violin arrived, he had made arrangements for lessons. During those early days of screeches and sour notes he was always welcome to practice at Grandma's house. Philo approached learning to play the violin much as he did all the challenges of his life, with a wholehearted effort and dedication.

Philo's best friend, Milo Jones, decided to join Philo in his pursuit of the violin. The two boys took much taunting from their peers, who considered them sissies. One day, on their way home from a lesson, they were accosted by their tormentors, led by the town bully. Using an old tactic to split their attackers, they ran in opposite directions. Although Philo was fairly fast on his feet, he was hampered by his violin. A quick glance over his shoulder revealed the gang leader close on his heels.

Anger at the injustice of it all lent him wings. Putting on a last burst of speed, he laid his precious violin aside and whirled, landing a stiff uppercut on the chin of his pursuer. All the fury built up over weeks of harassment was in that punch. The larger boy went down like a sack of potatoes.

Poised like a prizefighter, Philo stood ready to take on the rest of the gang if necessary. However, seeing their leader unconscious at Philo's feet, they looked at him with bulging eyes. Philo had removed their chief, and they looked upon him with new respect. There was no more heckling. Throughout his life, few things angered or frustrated him more than a sense of injustice such as he reacted to here.

The next landmark pointing him toward his destiny was the eclipse of the sun he experienced in 1918 in Thomas, Idaho. Lured by the booming sugar beet industry, the family packed their worldly belongings in three pioneer-type covered wagons and traveled to Idaho. Ronald and his bride drove the first wagon. Lewis, Serena, and the younger children were in the second wagon. Eleven-year-old Philo drove the third wagon carrying his mother's indispensable sewing machine, their highly prized gramophone, a crate of hens, and a crate of young piglets. They were leading several cows, two horses, and a mare with a young colt. When the colt developed sore feet, it, too, was added to Philo's menagerie.

After five weeks of travel, visiting friends and family along the way, they arrived at Thomas, Idaho, where lived Serena's sister Laura. They were there at the time of the eclipse of the sun, which was total in that area. Three of the older children, including Philo, were confined with measles to a darkened room. Their father smoked pieces of glass over the kerosene lamp so they could view this spectacle without damage to their eyes.

The eclipse was very exciting to Philo, but of even more interest was the story of the English expedition to Sobral, Brazil. The English had built the world's largest telescope there. The object of the expedition was to prove, or disprove, Einstein's theory of relativity. Because the eclipse was to be total also in Sobral, this was a rare opportunity to study the corona of the sun they could not forego.

Their reasons meant little to Philo, for he had never heard of relativity. What really impressed him was that along with two scientists from each of the principal countries of Europe, two German scientists were invited. The war was very real to Philo, for his two half-brothers were fighting with the Allies in France. He thought if scientists could rise above their warring nations to solve a scientific problem, they must be endowed with special qualities. He hoped he could someday become a scientist.

That fall found the Farnsworths in Ucon, a small town a few miles north of Thomas, where the older children entered school. When word came of the signing of the Armistice, Philo and Carl climbed to the roof of the cow shed and rang cowbells until their arms ached. This meant that Lew and Ronald could now return home.

The joy occasioned by the return of the soldiers, however, was soon overshadowed by a devastating influenza epidemic. Few communities in the nation escaped this plague. Entire families were stricken, with no one to care for them. The overworked medical profession was at a loss. Nothing they tried had any effect on this new virus.

In desperation, President Wilson issued a decree. All public gatherings, including schools, were suspended until further notice. Facemasks were to be worn whenever leaving home was an absolute necessity. Powdered sulphur was to be burned on hot wood or coal cook stoves as a fumigant, Lysol was to be added to water for washing hands, and the list went on. Despite all these precautions, death, no respecter of persons, knocked on a great many doors. One of the victims was Philo's dear half-sister Hortense. Her husband brought their two little girls to their grandparents and left, leaving no forwarding address.

This "flu" epidemic killed 21 million people and affected the lives of a billion more, half of the world's population at that time. This was more effective than the Maxim machine gun in blunting Germany's final assault on France in World War 1. Practically the entire Royal Navy was kept in port for twelve days. There were 10,000 cases including Commander-in-Chief His Majesty King George V.

The flu-ridden crew of the American transport *Otranto* were too weak to abandon ship after colliding with another vessel during an Atlantic storm. The ship sank, taking all 431 men with it.

Aboard troopship *Leviathan* a young assistant Secretary of the Navy, Franklin D. Roosevelt, keeled over, and 16-year-old Walt Disney, who had lied about his age to join an ambulance crew, was sent home to recover.

The highest mortality was 12.5 million in India; the lowest was on the South Atlantic island of St. Helena, Napoleon's last home, and a U. S. naval training station in San Francisco Bay where drinking fountains were sterilized hourly with blow torches.*

In the spring of 1919, Lewis moved his family to the 240-acre Bungalow Ranch of his brother Albert, in the Snake River Valley, near Rigby, Idaho. Philo was overjoyed to find the ranch powered by a Delco power system. Of equal or greater importance to him was the stack of radio, popular science, and semi-technical magazines he found in the attic of his new home, left by the former owner who had installed the power system. What was excess baggage to him was manna to the book-starved Philo. These magazines opened up a whole new world for him. There had been no libraries to visit, and there never seemed to be money for anything beyond the bare necessities of life.

The first things to catch his eye were Albert Einstein and relativity.

---

* My family in Jensen, Utah was going through this same ordeal. People were dying, but none would expose themselves to this very contagious disease to lend a helping hand. Seeing the helpless suffering of friends and family, my parents, Bernard and Alice Gardner, became ministering angels. Mother made huge pots of nourishing soup, and Daddy, disregarding the chances he was taking, carried it into stricken homes and did what he could to relieve the suffering people. Upon arriving home he always gargled with antiseptic and washed thoroughly in strong lysol water. Neither he nor any of our family was stricken, however, his beloved sister Elma, for whom I was named, was one of the many victims.

He found an article by Robert A. Millikan stating why Einstein's theory of relativity was based on wrong principles. Then in the next issue of *Science and Invention*, Philo found an answer to Millikan's charges, an article written by the master himself, Dr. Albert Einstein.

Dr. Einstein's clear and simplified explanation of his theory hit a responsive chord in young Philo. To his twelve-year-old mind, uncluttered by preconceived scientific notions, relativity seemed perfectly logical. He was so impressed by it that he committed it to memory. From then on it colored all of his scientific thinking. It broadened his horizons and helped him think in larger dimensions, giving him a unique vantage point from which to view a problem.

The farm's Delco power system fascinated Philo. The former owner had installed it to power hay stackers and grain loaders. None of the new owners understood enough about it to keep it running, however. This necessitated frequent and expensive visits from William Tall, the man who had installed it. Each time Mr. Tall came to service the generator, Philo carefully observed everything he did. He had to know how the generator made electricity. It was not in his nature to take such things for granted. Learning how things worked was essential training for later understanding how to develop his own ideas into functional processes.

One day the generator stopped again, and, since it had recently been serviced, Uncle Albert lost all patience with it. He, his grown sons, and Philo's father, Lewis, discussed the situation. His sons said it would be impossible to operate the ranch without it. Twelve-year-old Philo stepped forward and offered to fix it. Interrupting the derisive laughter of his cousins, his father said, "Why don't you give Philo a chance, Albert? What do we have to lose?" Lewis was very proud of this son, the firstborn of his second marriage. He knew that Philo would not have offered had he not been fairly sure of what he was doing. He was also keenly aware that Philo's confidence in himself usually brought results.

Reluctantly, Albert agreed, then watched apprehensively as Philo took the mechanism apart. Calling for some kerosene, Philo carefully washed away the heavy oil deposits, which he suspected to be the culprit, and reassembled the generator. The chance of letting his father down worried him more than whether the generator would work; however, he had watched Mr. Tall work on the generator and was pretty sure of what he was doing. Asking for their lightest weight oil, he applied it sparingly. He had a very interested audience as he stood back and, with an outward show of confidence, pushed the "on" button. An audible sigh of relief was heard as the generator came to life and ran like new. Uncle Albert slapped Philo on the shoulder and pronounced him officially the "engineer in charge of the generator." When his father hugged him and said, "Good work, son," the pride swelling within him almost burst his buttons.

One of Philo's household chores was pushing the to-and-fro handle of the family washing machine. This required standing for what seemed to him to be forever, pushing and pulling the long wooden lever that agitated the clothes in the tub. This emancipated his mother from the drudgery of scrubbing them on the corrugated washboard. Eager to have more time for his magazines, Philo rewound the armature to a burned-out motor he found in the shed and connected it with pulleys to the washer. *Voila!* It worked!

As anyone who has rewound an armature can tell you, this was not a small undertaking. It took a boy with a purpose and a large bag of tricks to attempt such a task. He also hooked up the motor to his mother's sewing machine, but she preferred her own foot power. Nonetheless encouraged, he installed lights in the barn, illuminating his early morning and nightly chores.

One day he read an article about sending pictures along with sound by means of radio signals through the air. Keep in mind this was in 1919, and radio was still in swaddling clothes. The method described used the Nipkow spinning disc with a spiral pattern of holes through which the image to be transmitted was scanned. To thirteen-year-old Philo, the method seemed clumsy and inadequate. There had to be a better way.

Bit by bit he collected information that eventually led him to discover that mysterious, vitally important particle called the electron, the study of which would define his life. After Phil's death, his oldest son, Philo T. Farnsworth III, described his father's whole life as "a romance with the electron." No one ever put it more succinctly.

Each day, Philo tried to imagine a way to use electrons to eliminate the mechanical method of transmitting pictures. After his chores were finished, he hurriedly ate his supper to get back to his private loft and his most prized possessions, the magazines. While he gleaned much information this way, he was left with still more questions. In searching for a way to earn money to buy books, he read in Hugo Gernsback's *Science and Invention* magazine about a national contest for ideas to enhance the comfort of the automobile. Cars in those days were crude affairs and could use some ideas. The prize was $25, a handsome sum to a farm boy.

At this time, Philo was operating a horse-drawn hay mower. This gave him much time to think as day after long day, he drove his team around and around the hay field. A large part of this ranch was planted in hay and grain because Uncle Albert raised race horses. So when one field was finished, Philo went on to the next. Nor was he finished when that crop was all mowed, because then the first field was ready with the second crop of hay. They even had a third crop of hay that year, because of the early spring. Philo was alone in seeing this as a bit of bad luck—he was the one who had to mow it. Nor was his day finished when he came in from the fields and cared for his team. He still had the milking to do and animals to feed. Although the repetitive, mechanical nature of his chores freed his mind for contemplation, the drudgery of the work motivated him to plan that neither he nor his family would be bound to the farm.

Philo was given the job of preparing the large field reserved for potatoes. To save time, he was using a three-gang disc and a three-horse team. Philo's father cautioned him to be careful, because at times the third horse was inclined to be skittish. After the first row, the horse on the left (sometimes called the wheelhorse), well trained in such work, dutifully followed the row already made. Noticing that, Philo began to relax and let his mind wander to the contest. His only contact with cars had been the Model "T" Ford belonging to the father of his best friend, Milo Jones, in Washington, Utah. The only horsepower with which he was familiar was the kind powered by oats and hay.

Then he remembered hearing of cars being stolen. If he could find a way to prevent car theft, he would stand a pretty good chance of winning that $25. In studying the properties of the electron, he had learned that moving electrons could produce magnetism. If he could magnetize certain parts within a car's ignition lock, could it be that the key would also have to be magnetized in order to unlock it? Everything he had learned about magnetism told him this was so.

An uneasy feeling about Philo had alerted his father, who was even now approaching the field. What he saw made his blood run like ice water in his veins. Philo's concentration had made him unmindful of the third rein, which had slipped from his hands and was dragging on the ground. Lewis remembered a fatal accident in just this type of situation when the horse was startled and began to run. The driver had been thrown back and cut to pieces by the sharp discs.

Knowing better than to shout or run, Lewis set a course to intercept Philo as he approached the end of the row. It required all of his willpower to maintain a steady walking pace. Not until his father grabbed the horse's rein did Philo become aware of his predicament. He took in the situation at a glance, but his need to tell his father his good news was more important than his own safety. He jumped from his seat, yelling, "Papa, Papa! I've got it! This idea will win the prize!"

"Philo! You could have been killed!"

Lewis, still shaken by thoughts of what might have been, had little patience for hearing his son's idea. After supper that evening, however, he found Philo sitting on the floor of his attic room surrounded by magazines.

"I'm sorry I didn't listen to your idea this afternoon, son. I really want to hear it."

"That's OK, Papa; it was dumb of me to drop the rein, but I really think I've got a swell idea."

"Let's hear it." Lewis cleared a place and sat down on the floor.

"Here, Papa; this tells about the contest." He handed a copy of *Science and Invention* to Lewis and pointed to the open page.

"I've been reading about electrons and how to magnetize metals. I think if I magnetize the ignition of a car, you can't unlock it unless you also magnetize the key."

"Hmmm, sounds like a good idea—if it works, but do you think it's good enough to win a national contest? You'll probably have a lot of competition."

"I know, but I'm pretty sure it'll work, and I think it's worth a try. Do you know where I can find an ignition to try it out?"

"No, I don't, but why not ask your cousin Kent? He seems to have a finger on most everything going on around town."

The next morning, Philo went in search of his cousin. Kent, several years older than Philo, was an accomplished horseman and something of a hero to Philo. Not finding Kent at the corral, Philo was ready to leave when he saw Kent coming up the field on a dead run with two horses, one foot on the back of each. Philo held his breath. He had seen this cousin whom he idolized perform riding stunts before, but none so blatantly tempting fate as what he was now witnessing. Stopping in a cloud of dust, Kent jumped lithely to the ground.

Philo struggled to regain his composure; it would never do to let Kent know he had never witnessed anything like this before in his young life. Then he asked his question.

"Heck yes! I know a guy that just wrecked his car. I hear it's a mess. I'll take you there. Mount up!" Taking the reins of the proffered horse, Philo climbed up and followed Kent, staying far enough behind to avoid the clods and mud thrown by the flying feet of the horse ahead.

At their destination, they were led out by the barn to view the remains.

"Sure! You can have it, if you can get the durned thing out," Philo was told. "It's no good to me. Let me get you some tools."

Philo triumphantly carried home the ignition with not one but two keys and, best of all, with Kent's praise ringing in his ears. Neither Kent

Philo T. Farnsworth,
age 13

nor the car owner had expected Philo to meet with much success in this endeavor. Their skepticism was typical of that which followed Philo the rest of his life. Only his close associates, who had seen time and again how he managed to turn his visions into reality, failed to be surprised at the success of his ideas.

He caused quite a stir at home when he proved his point. With certain changes he made in the ignition, the only key that would turn it on was his magnetized key. It was necessary to have this witnessed by a notary public, who turned out to be the president of the local bank. He was so impressed that he had a reporter and photographer come over from the *Rigby Star.* The resulting article and picture made Philo a local celebrity.

As Philo predicted, his idea won the prize, but by the time the money came in the fall, his need to replace his boyhood knickers for a long-pants suit was more urgent than his need for books. He was then playing the violin in a four-piece orchestra formed by Frances Critchlow, his music teacher, to fill the local need for dance music. Philo, a fourth-year violin student, was playing very well. Wearing knickers was a sore embarrassment to him in his elevated position.

His need for books was no less acute, but he had wangled the job of driving the school wagon on the five-mile route from his side of town. This job enabled him to make a down payment on a set of books on electricity, which he paid off at fifty cents a week. He also made five dollars every Friday night by playing in the orchestra.

In the spring of 1921, Lewis purchased a 140-acre farm in Bybee, four miles from Rigby. Philo again operated a disc, this time with a single disc and two horses. He enjoyed the early morning hours, making a habit of rising early and studying from four to five when the house was quiet. He was out with the first sleepy chirping of the birds to milk the cows and feed the animals and was in the field with the first rosy glow of sunrise.

He filled his lungs with the fresh, dewy Idaho air. It was a beautiful clear day, with just a few fleecy white clouds to break the deep blue of the sky, and he had all morning just to sit on the disc seat and think. As usual, his thoughts turned to how he might train electrons to convert a visual image into an electrical image so it could be sent through the air. He knew this had to be done in a vacuum. He had read of a man named Braun who had made a crude vacuum tube and who had produced light by directing an electrical beam to a surface coated with photosensitive material. He had also read that an electron beam can be manipulated in a magnetic field.

As he turned the horses for another row, he looked back along the even rows he had made in the damp earth. A thought struck him like a bolt out of the blue! The tremendous import of this revelation hit him like a physical blow and came near to unseating him. He could build the image like a page of print and paint the image line after line! With the speed of the electron, this could be done so rapidly the eye would view it as a solid picture! He could hardly contain his excitement. After mulling this idea around in his mind all this time and piecing it together one piece at a time, it had fallen together like a puzzle! Philo's constant seeking had borne fruit. In later years he was to consider this inspiration the first major turn in the "guided tour" leading him to his "distant vision." He humbly acknowledged an influence beyond himself.

When he told his father about this inspiration, Lewis advised him to keep it quiet. His older cousins already considered Philo as something of a wool-gathering dreamer of dreams, not to mention a bit odd. While Lewis placed great faith in this son of his, he had not the ability to understand the concept. His-never-to-be-forgotten advice to his son was, "It's all right, son, to have your head in the clouds, so long as you keep your feet firmly planted on the ground." Lewis's advice to Philo to keep things to himself was often reflected in Philo's career as scientist and inventor. Whenever he was pressured into revealing his ideas before they had been implemented to his satisfaction, the reaction of his critics was frustrating.

He and his father had worked very hard on their farm, resulting in a very good harvest. However, the great post World War I depression hit, and there was no market for their farm products. Unable to make the payments, they lost the farm.

In September Philo entered high school, determined to cram in all the knowledge possible. After signing up for all the science and math available to him, he tried to get admitted to the chemistry class. Because this class was strictly for seniors, he was turned down by both the teacher and the principal, to whom he had appealed his case. Philo decided to show them what he could do. By midterm he had completed his science course and Algebra I. His science teacher, the redheaded, energetic Mrs. McCoy, now petitioned the principal in Philo's behalf. His algebra teacher, who had suffered an eye injury, asked Philo to be his eyes in teaching the class. Philo agreed to do it but asked if he could take Algebra II at the same time. His algebra teacher also spoke to the principal about the chemistry class, but to no avail.

Going to the chemistry teacher again, Philo asked if he could just sit in on the class. He needed a knowledge of chemistry for his work. The teacher, Mr. Justin Tolman, gave in, thinking Philo would soon lose interest. As Philo shortly began taking part in the discussions, it was

Rigby High School, where Philo attended. It was here that he revealed his television invention to Justin Tolman.

apparent that he had a better grasp of the subject than did many of the seniors. Mr. Tolman now went to the principal, proposing that if Philo could be given credit for the class, he (Mr. Tolman) would spend an hour after school each day to catch him up on what he had missed.

Mr. Tolman got more than he had bargained for. Philo's questions went far beyond chemistry. Mr. Tolman had answers for many of them, and better yet, he could lend Philo books from his personal library. Mr. Tolman later recalled that one of these books, covering the kinetic theory of matter, Philo almost wore out. To quote Mr. Tolman, "He would devour what was in these books and come back for more."

Mr. Tolman said he happened one day to walk by the study hall door to find Philo at the blackboard deep in an explanation of Einstein's theory of relativity to classmates who should have been deep in their lessons. Although this was an infringement of school rules, Mr. Tolman was caught up in what Philo was saying and stopped to listen. Tolman said it was the most clear and concise explanation of Einstein's relativity theory he ever heard, before or since.

As Mr. Tolman told it later, his curiosity was very much exercised. He knew there had to be something behind Philo's urgency to learn. It was not until late February that Philo had his television ideas to the point of talking about them to anyone except his father. One day Mr. Tolman came to their after-school session to find Philo at the blackboard, which was filled with diagrams and equations. That day Philo explained his invention to Mr. Tolman and drew a diagram of his Image Dissector (camera) tube on a page of his pocket notebook, which he tore out and gave to Mr. Tolman. This incident and the notebook page years later were significant in a patent suit concerning the Image Dissector.

After his discussions with Mr. Tolman, Philo was more convinced than ever that his approach to television was workable; he was equally convinced that he needed much more education before he would be able to make his ideas work. High school was no longer sufficient for his needs—he was determined to start college as soon as possible.

Soon after the disclosure to Mr. Tolman, Philo left school to help his father with the spring planting. Lewis had leased the Kinghorn ranch not far from Bybee. With the help of Philo and a hired man, they raised a bumper crop that year, and with the improved economy, they made enough profit to pay off all of the family debts.

As always, however, money continued to be a problem, and it was up to Philo to earn enough money for college. During the summer of 1922, he completed a correspondence course from the National Radio Institute to earn an electrician's license, which he immediately put to good use. Learning from his brother Lew that the Oregon Short Line railroad needed electricians, he found a job there as a junior electrician. With his first paycheck, he signed up for four courses from the University of Utah correspondence school.

Lewis and Serena moved the family to Provo in the fall of 1922 to help Ronald, whose dear wife Violet had died, leaving a small son and daughter. The next fall Philo joined them; however, at Provo's Brigham Young University (BYU), he was told he lacked sufficient credits in history and English to enter. They enrolled him as a special student to complete his high school credits.

Lewis had made a down payment on a large home near BYU because Serena wanted to take in student boarders. They had no trouble filling the house, two to a room. The students were mostly from the Rigby area, except for Philo's cousin Arthur Crawford, who roomed with him. Philo was very disappointed when he was not allowed to take physics. As a second-year student, Arthur was taking the course and having problems with it. Philo helped him through the course. Arthur said later, "Phil was a mathematical wizard, and he had no problem at all with physics. He finished the entire course with me." Of course Phil got no credit for it.

Shortly before Christmas 1923, Lewis was confined to his bed with pneumonia. He and Ronald had been employed in another ground-clearing project, this time at Soda Springs in southern Idaho. Lewis had driven his team home to Provo in an open wagon through a blinding blizzard, arriving wet and half frozen. Serena got him into a hot bath and then to bed. By morning he was burning up with fever. The doctor Serena called in said it was a very serious case of pneumonia. The patient must be kept warm, confined to bed, and given as much liquid as he could manage. Beyond cold cloths on his head to help break the fever, nothing more could be done. The sort of medicines upon which we now rely were not available for another two decades or more.

Serena followed the doctor's orders and added some of her own "family" remedies, but nothing seemed to be of much help. As Philo watched the strength gradually drain from his much-loved father, he was filled with a dire sense of foreboding. During the Christmas holidays, Philo took every opportunity to slip into his father's room and sit quietly by his bed. At times when his father was more alert, Philo tried to strengthen his will to fight for life by telling him of the ambitious plans he had for the family's future. Then as his fever-ridden father drifted off to sleep, Philo sat quietly by, deriving comfort from the feeling that just being near might be of some help.

During these times, he often let his mind dwell on the happier days, like the freighting trips they shared. Lying under the stars, Lewis, an avid amateur student of astronomy, would point out our sister planets, the Big Dipper, Cassiopeia, and show Philo how to use these constellations to locate the North Star. Philo learned to recognize the Little Dipper, the Hunter and his dog, Cignus, and others. Not even the chilling cry of the coyote could shake the sense of security he felt in the presence of his big, self-sufficient father. He remembered one night in the high mountains, when in the light of the dying camp fire they saw the glowing eyes of a sizeable wild animal. His father had kept a fire blazing all night to keep any lurking animals at bay.

Then there was another trip when sitting around the campfire after their evening meal, they were visited by several Indian braves and a very beautiful girl who seemed to be his own age of ten years. It was apparent that this was not the first time his father had met these people, because Lewis offered no objection when they asked to take Philo to their hidden village. They called themselves Paiutes (Pah-utes), and in their village Philo remembered seeing fine crafted pottery, beadwork, and carvings. The men were tall and proud, and the women carried themselves with dignity. The girl his age was the only child in sight. She seemed to be the daughter of the chief.

These people spoke little English, so he could only guess by their actions what was going on. He participated in sort of a ritual ceremony which culminated in a chieftain's headdress being placed on Philo's head and the men performing a ceremonial dance around him. Then the headdress was removed and the chief said some solemn words to him before he was returned to his father. He often pondered the meaning of all this. Could it have been an awareness of Philo's destiny such as Lewis had received at Philo's birth?

On January 8th, 1924, after charging Philo with the responsibility of caring for the family, Lewis slipped from the world of the living on to his next estate in the great beyond. Philo's world crashed around him. The loss of his beloved father was almost more than he could bear, but he kept his deepest feelings from the family, in an attempt to buoy them up. His mother was in shock for many weeks, confined to bed, taking no interest in what went on around her.

Philo spent many sleepless nights. When his grief became unbearable, he rose from his bed and walked the three miles to the cemetery. It was only by baring his soul in prayer to his Father in Heaven to give him strength that he derived any comfort. Gradually, he gained enough peace of mind to continue his studies at the university. Then a kindly professor loaned him two books to read, *As a Man Thinketh,* by James Allen, and Ralph Waldo Emerson's *Essays on Compensation.*

In the forty-seven short pages of *As a Man Thinketh*, Philo discovered words of wisdom by far more precious than diamonds or gold. From the opening sentence, "As a man thinketh in his heart so is he," to the end, the message of this book struck a highly responsive chord in his grief-stricken mind. He savored every word. On page nine he found:

"Man is always the master, even in his weakest and most abandoned state; when he begins to reflect upon his condition, and to search diligently for the law upon which his being is established, he then becomes the wise master, directing his energies with intelligence, and fashioning his thoughts to fruitful issues. Such is the *conscious* master, and man can only thus become by discovering *within himself* the laws of thought; which discovery is totally a matter of application, self-analysis, and experience.

"Tempest tossed souls, wherever ye may be, under whatsoever conditions ye may live, know this—in the oceans of life the isles of Blessedness are smiling, and the sunny shore of your ideal awaits your coming. Keep your hand firmly upon the helm of thought. In the barque of your soul reclines the commanding Master; He does not sleep; wake Him. Self-control is strength; Right Thought is mastery; Calmness is power. Say unto your heart, 'Peace, be still!" (From *As a Man Thinketh* by James Allen.)

Emerson's laws of compensation also hit a very responsive chord in Philo. He learned from Emerson one gets out of life what one puts into life, no more, no less; and one must to his own self be true.

Through these profound gems of thought, he was comforted. He put them to use in his life and from them derived great benefit. These and other insights into the laws of nature served to give him inspiration and an ever-growing inner courage and self-confidence that sustained him then and in the years to come. Philo was determined to be his own master, relying not on convention but upon his own intelligence and the laws of thought to bring his ideas to fruition. His dedication to hard work showed his determination to put into life all he could. He struggled against tremendous odds to remain true to himself—to his "distant vision." These books were recommended reading for friends and later for the people who worked with him. They were *required* reading for his sons.

Philo finished his year at BYU; then, unable to find work, he joined the Navy, hoping to get into officers' training at Annapolis and get his education that way. It was there that he dropped the "o" from his name to prevent his being called "Fido." He passed the Annapolis examinations second highest in the nation, or so he was told by his commanding officer, but by this time he had decided Navy life was not for him. His mother pleaded "widow's hardship," and as the family breadwinner he was given an honorable release. He then returned to BYU, and this is when we met.

CHAPTER 5

Hollywood

As the train for Los Angeles traveled through the fertile Utah Valley, we felt very much in tune with nature. Farmers were busily plowing fields for planting, and the fresh green color of fields planted the previous fall gave promise to the rich, brown, newly turned earth.

How like the awakening of spring were we. The seeds of Phil's television ideas, which he had nurtured for the past five years, were on the verge of sprouting and bearing fruit. Also we were, through our marriage, experiencing an awakening. Life was taking on new meaning to us. The sight of so many newborn wobbly-legged lambs, calves, and colts nuzzling their mothers delighted us.

"I feel like that little colt over there," I told Phil, "a bit wobbly and unsure of myself. It's hard to believe I'm really a married woman. In a way, I still feel like that little girl from Jensen."

"That's part of your charm, sweetheart. I worked very hard while on the farm, all the while striving to do something to liberate me from its tedium. I'm excited with the prospect of our future. We will be learning and growing together. Remember, we are limited only by our ability to envision the goals we set for ourselves."

"I know you've set some very lofty goals. That is what scares me."

"Don't worry about it; you'll do just fine!" Phil said, tightening his arm around me. This was so comforting, with my head on his shoulder,

I gave in to the feeling of complete happiness that filled me to overflowing.

The spell was interrupted by the porter announcing lunch was being served three cars ahead. All this was new and exciting. We negotiated the transition from car to car, with the rush of air, the loud clanking of the couplings which moved and shifted under foot. As Phil opened the door of the dining car, we were met by a broadly smiling, scrupulously attired Negro steward. We were led down the aisle between white linen covered tables with gleaming silver and flowers. On every side were smiling, white-coated Negro men.

The first black person I had ever seen was our very pleasant and helpful porter. I marveled at the smooth way the stewards manipulated their loaded trays along the crowded aisle. In those days, the Southern Pacific Railroad boasted chefs and service equal to those of the best restaurants. This was especially true on their City of San Francisco and their City of Los Angeles trains, on which we were riding. I had never tasted such delicious food, although I suspect that my taste buds, along with all of my senses, were enhanced by that love-engendered ambience that surrounded us.

Back in our seats, I asked Phil what had led him to thinking about such subjects as television.

"I guess I had decided it would be nice to be an inventor when I first saw a hand-cranked telephone and gramophone. I was only six years old, and these things seemed like magic to me."

"I was five or six when the first gramophone came to Jensen," I interjected, "someone had brought it to play for dances. I don't think we had telephones until several years later. I don't know when electricity came to Jensen, but it was after we left. They did have electric lights in Vernal then."

"The Delco power system on the Bungalow Ranch in Idaho was the first time we had electricity. Pem, I couldn't wait to find out how power was made. Then the more I learned, the more I wanted to know. I was in seventh heaven when I found all those radio and popular science magazines the former tenant had left in our attic. We never had money for books."

"We didn't have much money either, but Mother was a schoolteacher before she married Daddy, and she managed to buy a few books. She read to us in the evenings. During the school year, we had to finish our lessons first, so we older kids would help the younger ones with their lessons so Mother could read longer."

"Your mother was a very special lady, Pem."

"I'm so happy you had an opportunity to know her, honey, and I only wish I could have known your father, though he is beginning to emerge as I get glimpses of him through your eyes. But go on."

"I was only thirteen when the idea first came to me to use electrons to take the moving parts out of television, and although Papa didn't understand much of what I was talking about, he encouraged me. I made another invention about the time I came to Provo. I called it the Vernier Dial. The nearest radio stations were in Denver and Los Angeles. Back in those days you had to have a pretty good radio to bring in signals. There was a lot of static. My idea was to use the Vernier principle by using a second smaller dial on top of the regular dial. You could tune in to the frequency you wanted with the larger dial, then use the top, or fine tuner to sort out the static, leaving just the signal you were after."

"That sounds like a good idea. What happened to it?"

"I wrote to a patent attorney by the name of O'Brian who advertised in *Science and Invention Magazine* about it. He said if I sent him drawings and two hundred dollars, he would file my patent for me. I had spent all my savings for entrance fees and books at the "Y", but Papa offered to give me the two hundred dollars. I knew how hard he had worked for this and how much the family needed it, but I knew the Vernier dial would sell. In fact, I had hopes that it would even finance my television research. So I made Papa a half owner and sent the money and drawings to Mr. O'Brian . . . and waited. Those were anxious times. It wasn't until after Papa died in January that I got a letter from Mr. O'Brian saying my idea was already patented."

"I'm so sorry, Phil."

"I was sure that Mr. O'Brian had just stolen my idea. The Vernier dial came on the market later, and it looked exactly like the drawings I had sent. Those were tough times. Mother was still in shock from Papa's death. She had lost all interest in what went on around her. Agnes and our cousin Freda Sainsbury, who lived with us while attending college at the Y, kept things going. Mother was boarding several BYU students, so Agnes had to quit school in January to take care of Mother and cook for our boarders."

"Agnes and I met on registration day at the Provo High School. Since we both come from small towns, we felt a little lost, and we found in each other a kindred soul. I missed her when she quit. Phil, did you know that our fathers hauled freight together the year you lived in Vernal? I didn't know until later it was Agnes's father whose family he went to see when he said an old friend had died."

"I can understand why our fathers had a high regard for one another. They had many similar qualities. I find in your father the same kind of trust my father had in me. I really appreciate that." There was that sad look again he always had when speaking of his father.

"Coming back to your television invention. I think that is just incredible."

"Yes, I know. I've heard that from everyone I've told before. They thought it was too incredible to believe. My father warned me when I first told him about it that people would be skeptical. But I have learned a lot in the last six years, and I know I can do it."

"I've no doubt that you can, Phil. I have complete faith that you can do anything you set your mind to do."

Later that evening, with the clickity-clackity of the train on the rails in our ears, Phil talked about his all-too-short time at Brigham Young

University. He had enjoyed his orchestra and drama classes, especially his role in the play, *The Taming of the Shrew*; however, he really concentrated on gleaning all possible information from Dr. Milton Marshall and Dr. Carl Eyring (pronounced eye-ring), his math and chemistry professors.

When he told them about his ideas of broadcasting not just sound but sound and pictures, they were very skeptical. They both warned him he was over his head. Indeed, the idea was way over their heads at the time. Small wonder they doubted his ability to do it. Nevertheless, they did their best to answer his incessant questions, even though many dealt with subjects unfamiliar to them.

"Weren't you discouraged at their reaction to your ideas?" I asked when he had finished.

"I was more disappointed than anything. I had hoped to find in them someone who could understand what I was talking about. Their disbelief made me only more determined to show them I could do what I said I could."

Seeing the resolute set of his jaw, I had little doubt he would do just that. "I really have married a remarkable man," I thought to myself.

Phil went on to tell me about his chemistry project at BYU, an improved method of refining oils.* Dr. Eyring advised him to stick to his oil project and said if it were successful, it would make him a fortune.

"I made encouraging progress on my chemistry project until my part-time job ran out, and there was just no work to be had in Provo. I had to go to Salt Lake to find work to help my mother."

Phil awakened me very early the next morning. He had raised the blind of our compartment window to show me the passing panorama of palm trees and vast geometrical orange groves. We were actually in California! As the train clickity-clacked along, I felt the encircling protective mountains of my native Utah being pleasantly replaced by a rosy land of promise.

We arrived in Los Angeles on Saturday morning, May 29th, 1926, filled with high expectations for the future. We were two ecstatic young people, so in love, delighted with only a glimmer of what was to unfold before us.

The first night, Phil treated me to the luxury of the Hotel Lankersham in the heart of the city. We spent the day walking around, taking in the sights and window shopping. From our seventh-floor room, we could see the sprawling city reaching far into the distance. As night came and lights glimmered over the landscape, the city took on an air of mystery . . . all those lights!

I wondered about the people who lived behind those lighted windows. Were they dramatic people such as I had seen in the movies? Or just ordinary people like me, with ordinary problems? Then the thought struck me that right here in this room was the potential of changing the lives of all those

---

*In 1925, the oil industry was sorely in need of modernizing its refining processes. A few years later, as new methods were implemented, Phil was gratified to see that the industry was following a path similar to the one he had been researching at BYU.

people out there. How many other world-shaking ideas lurked behind other lighted windows? When I mentioned that thought to Phil, he said, "That does lead one furiously to think." Then, "Come on to bed, we have a big day tomorrow." The next day, to conserve our funds, we moved to an efficiency apartment while looking for a larger place where Phil could begin his work.

Harry Cartlidge, Mr. Everson's friend and fellow campaigner, invited Phil to meet him for lunch on a movie lot where he was conducting a fund-raising campaign for the benefit of retired movie folk, who, once adored, had since been cast aside by a fickle public and were now down on their luck. Before leaving for his appointment, Phil took me to a small grocery store down the street. Keeping our list to a bare minimum, Phil suggested I cook a pot of beans for dinner.

Left alone, I basked in the realization that this was our first home. What did it matter if our first meal consisted chiefly of beans? I had never cooked beans (mine was a meat-and-potatoes family), but I thought they must require a long time. With the beans on to cook, I sat down to write notes to our families to let them know we had arrived safely.

As dinner time approached, I became increasingly agitated. Those beans must have been retrieved from some Egyptian sarcophagus. They showed no signs of softening. Phil found me in a bridelike state of tears, which spilled over when he came in asking if dinner were ready. He dried my tears and said he had forgotten that his mother usually soaked beans overnight.

We ate dinner at a small restaurant down the street, and, while waiting for our order, we scanned the evening paper for apartments. When Phil had asked Mr. Cartlidge for advice on where to look for an apartment, he was told that Hollywood might be the best place for us. There were many small houses there, and the rent was reasonable. Phil found one which seemed to be just what we were looking for. Anxious to begin his work, he called and asked if we might see the apartment that evening. The lady on the phone said that would be fine and gave Phil instructions on how to find the place. On the long street car ride out to Hollywood, I heard all about his day at the movie lot.

Phil and Mr. Cartlidge had lunched at the commissary, where Phil was introduced to Jack Benny and his lovely wife, Mary Livingston. Mary's normally auburn hair had been dyed green. Yes, green! This was not unusual in those days of black and white movies. The movie industry was experimenting with "pan" film. Green gave just the needed shade of gray. Their experimenting at times produced some very weird effects, not always conducive to a healthy lunchtime appetite.

He also met Pat O'Brien and Tom Mix, both longtime box-office favorites. Phil told me of his excitement in meeting these legendary actors. It seemed unreal that they were after all just plain living and breathing people with whom he was shaking hands.

After lunch, he met Bette Davis. It was she who had originally suggested the fund-raising benefit and had backed it all the way. She was one of Phil's favorite actresses. He had a feeling of worshipful awe upon meeting and talking to her. He also had an idea that his television work might spark some changes in the life of Miss Davis, as well as the entire movie industry.

The apartment at 1339 North New Hampshire street, on the lower floor of a fourplex, proved to be even better than expected. The living room was of fair size and comfortably, if simply, furnished. Phil quickly took over the dining table to set up more equipment, but fortunately there was a small breakfast nook in the kitchen. A hall led from the dining room past the bedroom to the back door. In the rear was a carport with four stalls. The accommodating landlady gave Phil permission to do light shop work there. The rent was fifty dollars a month, including utilities.

We left after being assured that the apartment was ready and we could move in the next day. When I lamented the loss of the rest of our week's rent in our present place, Phil reminded me it was only ten dollars a week, and it would have been more than that for one night at the hotel.

Sitting in front of a cheery fire the first evening in our new home, we decided the only thing lacking was a piano. Phil said he would rent one. Always when physically possible a man of his word, he rented one the very next day. Such indications ever-enlarged a certain solid warm glow somewhere deep inside me and further cemented the enduring bond that was growing between us.

Phil found his thoughts came more easily while playing the piano or violin. He had memorized a number of piano selections such as "Nola" and "Under the Double Eagle," but he usually played by ear, composing as he went. As for the violin, Fritz Kreisler was his idol. Phil liked to play many Kreisler classics as well as other classical music. He also enjoyed popular and semiclassical numbers. We spent many an evening together, with me accompanying him at the piano. We found music and songs a very satisfying way to communicate. The harmony in our songs reflected in the feelings of harmony between us.

I often played when I was sad, homesick, or glad, and found emotional relief by venting my spleen on the piano when I was angry. One evening as we were playing "There'll Be Some Changes Made," Phil said, "Play it as you do when you are angry." I was unaware he had been so attuned to my emotional outbursts.

We soon learned to find our way around the Los Angeles area by bus, but I was somewhat intimidated by the city and seldom ventured off by myself. A city this size was unfathomable (though strangely tantalizing) to me. Also, deep down inside me, I held in awe the challenge before us. Phil's air of confidence and self-assurance soon dispelled all feelings of insecurity, however. He harbored no illusions about the tremendous job ahead. Hard work held no terror for him; he had always recognized it as an integral part of his life. In fact, he was in his glory.

We spent the first few days in the Los Angeles Library. Not yet financially able to acquire the books he coveted, Phil was thrilled to find so much material on subjects that had been causing him concern. To an inventor, knowledge is a tool. Phil was up to his elbows in tools and was totally enraptured. He researched carefully the workings of the human eye, for he needed to know how rapidly a television image had to be reconstructed at the receiver in order to fool the eye into seeing it not as a series of dots but as an instant and complete picture. The electron was clearly the only thing fast enough to fulfill this requirement.

Phil usually explained as he went along. Now his ideas began to emerge from the realm of magic into something quite plausible, even to me! The excitement continued to build in me; the plausibility became real; I was rapidly becoming aware that this was no magic . . . it was going to work!

The next Sunday, Phil gave me my first glimpse of the Pacific Ocean. We took the street car, by way of two transfers, to Venice Beach. He could hardly wait to share his thrill of riding the fastest and highest roller coaster there. Unfortunately, I shared none of his fascination for such an assault on my system. After the first ride, I was happy to watch from a nearby bench. As I watched him climb to the summit of the tallest peak, then plummet with blinding speed to the bottom, I wondered about our future. When Phil reached his lofty goals, how long could we ride the crest of the wave? There would undoubtedly be some downward plunges, and just as surely there would be other mountains to climb. I decided that with Phil's fighting spirit and my incurable optimism, we should be fine.

Phil's Navy tour in San Diego and his friendship with a Navy pilot had afforded him several flights out over the ocean. I found seeing the ocean for the first time a mind-expanding experience. Phil took this opportunity to explain some of the deeper laws of nature.

He told me that for a long time atoms had been thought to be the

Phil and Pem in California soon after their marriage.

smallest structural unit holding matter together. Then it was discovered that inside the atom was a nucleus with electrons dancing around it. The number and position of the electrons determined the kind of material of which the atom was a part. He said he thought there were even smaller units to discover, probably as much to learn through a microscope, as we developed better instruments, as through telescopes. To be with Phil was always a learning experience.

Walking up the beach, we thrilled to the vastness and living energy of the ocean. Despite the carnival atmosphere of Venice Beach, we shared visions of invisible tropical islands somewhere out there, far beyond the horizon. Subtly, Venice Beach slipped away; we were somewhere . . . sailing through our imaginations . . . somewhere lovely. Phil vowed that one day we would sail across the ocean and spend a heavenly holiday on one of those tropical paradise islands.

Going home on the overcrowded street car that evening was complete chaos. Tired little children were crying for their supper and bed. Tired parents, worn to a frazzle by trying to keep an eye on their children on the crowded beach, did little to quiet them. By the time we reached our transfer point, our nerves were also wearing thin. We decided never again to take a street car to the beach.

As Phil continued to gather the material he needed for his experiments, a glittering array of crystals, prisms, and lenses was set up on the dining room table. With an arc lamp as a source of light, he was able to study light refraction. It was interesting to see how many ways he could bend light rays through these crystals. The results of these experiments were carefully recorded in his notebook—a habit he continued meticulously throughout his lifetime.

Upon the arrival of Phil's partners, George and Les (as they wished to be called), the activity in the apartment accelerated, due to their help in locating hard-to-find items. Les was on home turf here; his parents still resided in the area.

One of Phil's highest priorities was someone to build his Image Dissector tube. He and George found a glassblower and gave him the necessary materials and instructions. While waiting for the tube, they collected materials for winding deflecting coils to direct magnetically the electron image beam. They found a hand-operated coil winder with a counter to record the number of turns. This instrument needed to be very accurate to focus the image on the sensitized cathode with as much force as possible without overheating it.

George, wishing to hurry the work along, asked if he might help by winding the coils. Phil appreciated his offer, but warned him it was a very messy job. Each layer of wire must have a layer of shellac to insulate and hold the wire in place. The shellac was an orange-colored goo with the consistency of honey and a disgusting smell. Now, George was a very fastidious person. His hand-tailored suits lent him an air of elegance, punctuated by a carefully trimmed and tailored mustache. Volunteering for this job was proof positive of his enthusiasm for the project.

George insisted, so Phil set him up in the back yard. Les, not wishing to be outdone, offered to make professional drawings from Phil's sketches. After all, he was a graduate mechanical engineer. Phil suggested I take some pointers from Les, so I could take over later when Les was not there. He and George had several more campaigns scheduled.

That afternoon, after getting George started on the coils, Phil went back to his notes. Les and I were at the drawing board Les had borrowed from a friend. George, elbowing his way in through the back door to ask Phil a question, interrupted us. His hands were covered with a layer of rich orange-colored shellac.

It's not hard to imagine how suspicious our operation must have looked to an outsider. Strange packages were being brought in, and the curtains were drawn for demonstrating the light relay. Even the coil winding in the back yard must have looked suspicious to an imaginative mind. So I should not have been surprised when the doorbell rang and I opened the front door to find two of the largest policemen I had ever seen filling the doorway. George, not wishing to be caught in such a state of messiness, headed for the back door.

"We've had a report that you're operating a still here," the leader said. His stern, accusatory stare, calculated to intimidate the most hardened criminal, bored right through me.

As soon as I could find my voice, I asked them to wait; I would get my husband. These were prohibition days, and operating a still was very much frowned upon—to say nothing of being entirely illegal. Phil invited the officers in and asked what he could do for them. They repeated their accusation, so he began telling them what he was really doing.

They shook their heads perplexedly when they saw Phil's setup and walked on through the dining room toward the back door. Then we saw George with his hands up, his progress out the back blocked by two more burly arms of the law. They had stopped him with, "Oh, no ya don't, buddy!" They thought he was trying to escape, as in many respects he was.

The spokesman from the front door relieved the situation by saying, "It's okay, Joe; there ain't no still here. They're doing somethin' kookie they call electric vision or somethin', but they ain't got no still." They left then, and there was laughter about the incongruity of the situation, though the house hushed quickly and we were again absorbed in our work.

We learned later that the LAPD had not given up the search. The next door neighbors were the lovely young starlet Hazel Keener and her mother. According to an account Mrs. Keener gave me over the back fence the next morning, Hazel had just finished playing the lead opposite Harold Lloyd in *The Freshman*, a silent movie. Home from the morning's filming, Hazel had donned something comfortable and was lounging on her bed with a book and an apple.

The police went through the Keener cottage much the same as they had ours until sight of the nubile Hazel prolonged their search. They looked under the bed and peered into closets, anything to delay their departure.

The next afternoon, Hazel invited me to ride over to the shopping area with her. When she chided me for being raided for a still, I replied, "At least they didn't look under my bed and in my closets." We had a good laugh about that. Later, we learned that they had indeed found a still a short distance away.

Meanwhile, George succeeded in finishing the magnetic focusing coils. He was justifiably proud of his achievement and won high praise from Phil. Then he and Les left town for a few days, leaving George's Chandler Roadster for Phil to use.

The Sheik, starring Rudolf Valentino, was premiering at the newly opened Grauman's Chinese Theater. Phil decided to treat me to the excitement of a Hollywood premiere. It was a lovely starry evening, and with the Chandler's top down, we could enjoy the cool night air. The Hollywood Hills were mostly wooded, with few houses to clutter them. For miles around, we could see the searchlights crisscrossing the sky, advertising *The Sheik*'s opening.

At the theater, crowds were gathering. We joined the throng straining at the ropes to catch a glimpse of the celebrities. Long lines of chauffeur-driven limousines arrived, carrying gorgeously gowned and bejeweled movie queens. The gentlemen were elegant in their top hats and swallow-tailed suits. I gazed at this splendor in wide-eyed wonder. I am sure Phil was impressed too, though there was little outward evidence. He had an inborn sense of dignity, and his new responsibilities were adding to his maturity.

When the feature was over, Mr. Valentino came on stage to receive his acclaim. The audience went wild. It was a standing ovation. Backing offstage after taking his third bow, he brushed against a tall Chinese urn. When this elegant piece of Chinese art began to topple, a gasp of dismay rippled over the audience.

Valentino managed to save the urn, but in so doing, he lost his balance and fell into the orchestra pit. A groan echoed around the theater. He was helped back to the stage, insisting he was unhurt, but said he couldn't say as much for the bass drum that had broken his fall.

In those days, one never knew what one might run into in Hollywood. This was forcibly brought to my attention one day, as I was walking along a deserted street lined with shops, each with an apartment above it. Suddenly, a beautiful young woman burst from a doorway, not ten feet from me, with a terrified look on her face. Her long hair streamed behind her as she ran. Close on her heels was a sinister-looking man with a long-bladed knife in his hand. Before I could recover enough to think what I should do, they were around a corner a short distance away. Looking around for any kind of help, I spotted a camera crew across the street. To my embarrassment I had walked squarely into the middle of a movie scene.

Knowing Phil and I were two movie-struck kids, George took us to the Brown Derby Restaurant, a favorite place for movie people to frequent, where newcomers went to see and be seen. At the next table, Boris Karloff, noted character actor, was entertaining four young lovelies. George also identified a number of other movie people in the room. I decided they must have left most of their glamor with their makeup artists, but upon thinking it over, I felt they had a right to be just plain Janes and Joes if they so desired. To turn the situation around, no one would suspect that the unassuming young man beside me was about to change the world with his wonderful invention.

George also treated us to a sumptuous dinner at Victor Hugo's elegant restaurant. He said we should be exposed to the more opulent side of life to prepare us for our future.

I had prepared lunch for George and Les several times before I discovered George to be an excellent cook. He appeared one day with a bag of groceries and announced he was going to make his specialty for lunch. It turned out to be an impressively tall, fluffy omelette with asparagus in a rich, tasty cream sauce. It was a true gourmet delight, not to mention a bit of a surprise!

One day George caught me putting into the garbage my first attempt at baking a pie. My sister Olen had been the pastry cook at home. After I was left with the responsibility for my family's well-being, I had no time for pastries. To make me feel better, George told me we all had to learn. Taking me to an open-air fruit market, he selected some giant boysenberries, the first I had ever seen. Back at the apartment, he baked a pie that would have held its own with those of the best of cooks. I have found that bachelors who have a taste for fine food often develop into superb cooks.

Meantime, Phil continued with his preparations. He installed a motor generator in the garage to provide the required DC power for the television experiment. He and George scoured the city for the tubes and other components for building the test equipment, which Phil mounted on a chassis in his closet workroom. Finally, the glassblower called to say the Image Dissector was finished. It had taken more than two months of trial and error on the part of the glassblower and many consultations with Phil. After all, never before had such a tube been built, and it stood as a credit to the patience of the glassblower and Phil's determination. The precious tube was brought and installed with great care into the circuit.

At last the day arrived when Phil was ready to test his idea. George and Les were on hand to see the results of the summer's work. Making sure everything was connected, Phil started the generator. There was a Bang! Pop! Sizzle! Then smoke and terrible acrid smells began to rise from the assorted devices! Phil quickly cut the power, but it was too late. He had not anticipated the large surge of power that starting the generator would produce. He had blown every tube in the circuit, including the Image Dissector! Numb from shock at seeing all his work erased in one swoop, he turned a stricken face to George.

Although obviously disappointed, George hid his own feelings, and putting a hand on Phil's shoulder, said, "That's too bad, Phil."

Les added, "Of all the tough luck!"

My heart went out to Phil. I knew what a terrible shock this was to him. I could see the thoughts whirling in his head. Was this to be the end of his dream? After this careless blunder, would George and Les still believe in him and his ideas? A brief, profoundly thick silence prevailed.

"I should have known better!" Phil blurted through stiff lips, "I should have turned the power on before I connected the tubes." Motioning toward the charred mess, "That's all I have to show you for your investment, George."

"I really didn't expect as much from it as you did, Phil," George, said comfortingly, "but it is too bad we didn't at least get to see the results of the first test."

"Hey," Les broke in, "It's not the end of the world! We still have Phil's ideas! Let's sit down and decide what to do about it! Heck, George, you're a fundraiser! You can scare up at least enough money to prove Phil's point."

I could see that Phil was deeply touched by this show of confidence in the face of what had just happened. Because the underlying theories behind Phil's concept of electronic television were beyond their understanding, they had put their trust in Phil and his impeccable integrity, and it had withstood the test.

They decided the first thing to do was for Phil to draw up a formal disclosure describing his invention. Les offered to make a comprehensive drawing to go with it. Aware of the dangers of doing that, Phil said to be safe he should first disclose his invention to a good patent attorney. They thought that was a good precaution. Then George said he would like a scientific opinion about the potential worth of the invention, before approaching anyone to ask for money. Also, there was the El Paso campaign commitment in September, so no time should be lost.

Within a week Phil had completed his disclosure, which included every aspect of his invention. Les had the drawing ready. He had called some attorney friends in Los Angeles for recommendations of the best patent attorney in town. The firm with the best rating was Lyon & Lyon, the principals being Leonard and Richard Lyon.

An appointment was made for George with senior partner Leonard. After hearing the Farnsworth story and looking through the disclosure, he gave George this advice, "If you have what you think you have, you have got the world by the tail, but if you don't have it, the sooner you find this out the better. You can waste a lot of money on a scheme of this kind. You bring your young genius in here. My brother Richard, the technical brains of our outfit, will arrange for a qualified man from the California Institute of Technology to join him in passing judgment on the merits of these ideas."

Several days later, George, Phil, and Les appeared at the office of Lyon & Lyon. Waiting for them were Leonard and Richard Lyon and Dr. Mott Smith of Cal Tech. After introductions were made, Leonard suggested they sit down and let Phil tell them about his ideas.

Hesitantly feeling his way at first, Phil soon warmed to his subject. In clear, concise language, he outlined his invention. It soon became apparent that he knew more about the subject than either of the technical men present. To quote George, "Phil completely overwhelmed them with the brilliance and originality of his concept." No doubt his infectious charisma helped considerably.

As Phil talked, Richard Lyon walked up and down the room, pounding his hands together behind his back. At a pause in Phil's explanations, he stopped and exclaimed, "This is a monstrous idea! The daring of this young man's intellect!"

The conference went on for hours, Phil dispatching each question with assurance and authority. When they seemed satisfied, George took the floor. He asked if, in their opinion, these ideas were scientifically sound. Dr. Smith answered thoughtfully, "Yes." To George's question, "Is it novel?" Richard replied it very probably was; at least he knew of no patents along these lines. Leonard suggested that a patent search would reveal any work in progress. George told him to go ahead with it.

As a clincher, George asked Dr. Smith if he thought the idea was feasible and what its chances were of reaching a commercial stage. Dr. Smith answered that it would be difficult, but he could see no insurmountable obstacles at this time. With that conclusion, the meeting was adjourned; a scheduled half-hour conference had escalated into virtually the entire afternoon.

The partners left the meeting feeling they really did have the world by the tail. Privately, Phil's confidence was greatly bolstered by "besting" these specialists in the fields of science and patent law. Later, when we were alone, he recounted all that had happened and told me of his concern about the tremendous responsibility of making television available to the world. It would be a powerful tool, to be used in ways we could not even imagine.

CHAPTER 6

Big Chance

"Thought allied fearlessly to purpose becomes creative force: he who KNOWS this is ready to become something higher and stronger than a mere bundle of wavering thoughts and fluctuating sensations; he who DOES this has become the conscious and intelligent wielder of his mental powers."

-Allen

Back at the apartment, after the interview with the patent attorneys and Dr. Mott Smith of Cal Tech, the three partners, Everson, Farnsworth, and Gorrell, sat down to discuss the next course of action. Although George's faith in Phil was still strong after the disastrous results of the first attempted demonstration, today's conference added further proof and justification of his faith in Phil's ideas.

"After what happened this afternoon," George said, with a note of relief in his voice, "I can go ask for money with a clear conscience. How much do you think you will need to get us a television picture, Phil?"

Phil had thought long and hard about this difficult question. He was keenly aware that this was a very crucial time in his career. It would be comforting to know he had enough money to safeguard the project; however, to ask too much would mean such a discouraging job for George that the project would be doomed to failure. Failure! That was a word he refused to contemplate. All his life he had been accustomed to do with little and make that little do much. Now he braced himself and answered, "A thousand dollars a month for twelve months."

"Phil! Be realistic!" George exclaimed. "I don't believe you're allowing for any contingencies."

Phil said he had thought a lot about it, and with no unforeseen problems, he could have a picture in six months. The other six months were to give him time to work out any problems. He ended with, "I don't think there's anything that can stop me as far as the work goes."

Les, with his usual attitude of encouragement, commented, "With that kind of confidence, how can we lose?"

"You must realize we have spent money at twice that rate this summer," George reminded them.

"Yes, I know that, George," Phil acknowledged. "This experience is part of the reason I think my budget is real. I don't say it'll be easy, but I think I can do it."

"Well," said George, "I think we'd better be on the safe side and ask for twenty-five thousand dollars."

"You're right, George," Les agreed, "and you can raise twenty-five thousand dollars as easily as you can half that amount on a thing like this." George agreed, and they shook hands on it. They left, with George saying he would be leaving the next morning on his search for backing funds.

Alone in our apartment, Phil was jubilant. He whirled me around the living room once, and then stopped suddenly with a serious expression on his face.

"Honey, we are two lucky people to find men like George and Les to help us. I have no doubt that George can raise the money. Neither do I doubt that I can fulfill my promise to them, but I have a lot of research to do at the library. I want to be all primed and ready to begin work when the time comes."

"You will be, sweetheart, but first sit down and tell me all about your interview with the patent attorneys."

He launched into a detailed account of all that had been said. When he came to the part where Richard Lyon got up and began pacing, he said at first he was nervous, not knowing what to expect. When Mr. Lyon stopped and said, "This is a monstrous idea," Phil said he held his breath; this could go either way. When he heard the words, "The daring of this young man's intellect," relief flooded over him like a warm shower. This spontaneous reaction to his ideas further bolstered his courage. In my mind's eye I could visualize this scene, Phil's brilliant blue eyes flashing with the realization that at last his ideas were getting the recognition they deserved. He continued to answer their questions with confidence derived from his years of thought and study.

"Phil, darling, I'm so proud of you! It was obvious that George and Les were also very pleased. Come here! I have to kiss you!" Phil came over and kissed me soundly, then held me in a tight embrace. That evening we spent hours with the violin and piano, pouring out our love, joy, and excitement through our music.

Phil and I spent most of the next week in the Los Angeles Library. In his research, Phil was always running into some new property of the electron, which he would point out to me. I was expanding my own knowledge and understanding of what he was doing. Soon, these fascinating particles of energy became almost as real to me as they were to him. He made copious notes, since he was unable to purchase his own books. That he vowed to correct at his earliest opportunity. Although I had never taken shorthand, I developed my own shortcuts and was able to be of considerable help to him.

As weeks passed and we heard nothing from George regarding his fund raising, Phil became uneasy. He knew from his own experience that few people at this time had even heard the term *television*. Also, he was painfully aware of the effect his youth would have on prospective investors. Knowing the calming effect playing the violin had upon him, I sat at the piano and started playing one of his favorite numbers. That usually compelled him to pick up his violin, but now he was too much on edge, nervously going from one thing to another. We needed relief from the heat and tension that were mounting daily.

Les came by in George's Chandler. When he found no news from George, he offered to drive us to the Santa Monica beach for a swim. On the way, he entertained us with some of his silly songs and ballads. Les had often joined us around the piano at the apartment. Soon we were all in a jolly mood. We even tried some barber shop harmony. We arrived at the beach in a much better frame of mind. After an hour or two of fighting the high waves, we returned to the apartment much more relaxed, with renewed hope of what the morrow might bring.

The morrow brought George . . . and many tales of approaches and rejections; however, a friend of his in Santa Barbara had arranged an appointment with a Los Angeles group that occasionally financed scientific research. George was to see them that day.

With Phil's brochure in hand, George went to keep his appointment. He left the brochure to allow the group to ascertain whether the ideas were indeed original. After a period of anxious waiting, the report came back that the Westinghouse Corporation held many patents on television and probably controlled the entire art.

Of course, this report was misleading and probably calculated by Westinghouse to discourage competition. In any case, it was a terrible blow to George. It took Phil two days to rebuild George's faith in the project. Phil had just completed an up-to-date study of the *Bell Laboratory Journals*. Bell Labs (the AT&T Research and Development division) had reported only its mechanical method of transmitting images. The financing group had based its report on the recent purchase of the Alexander M. Nicolson television patent, which used an oscillating mirror-type transmitter and a Braun-type cathode-ray tube at the receiver. There is no evidence that this was ever actually built, and it posed no threat to Phil and his all-electronic television system.

Before his last lead, George had intended visiting Jesse B. McCargar, vice-president of the Crocker Bank in San Francisco, who had acted as financial manager on George's organizing campaign for Californians, Inc. This looked like a good place to go for advice. At the Crocker Bank, he learned that Mr. McCargar was away on vacation.

George's face must have mirrored his disappointment, for as he passed the desk of Mr. J. J. Fagan, executive vice-president of the bank, that gentleman asked if he could do anything to help. A colorful character of the California Gold Rush days, Mr. Fagan had been a moving force in rebuilding the city of San Francisco after the disastrous earthquake and fire of 1906. He still retained some of his old habits and mannerisms, one of which was chewing tobacco. According to George, his aim was perfected to the degree that he rarely, if ever, missed the gold spittoon in the corner. He had a droll sense of humor, and his unfailing fairness in business dealings had gained him much respect in the San Francisco business community.

Aware that Mr. Fagan had the reputation of being the most shrewd and conservative banker on the West Coast, George at first refused Mr. Fagan's offer of help. He explained that he had come to talk over a matter with Mr. McCargar. Finally, however, he accepted the invitation to sit down and talk about it. He began by warning Mr. Fagan this was nothing to do with regular banking procedures; it was just plain "wildcatting—and very wildcatting at that!"

Mr. Fagan listened thoughtfully as George told about Phil and his invention. "Well, that's a damn fool idea, but someone should put some money into it," he said, then added, "someone who can afford to lose it." As George often recounted, after his many rebuffs in trying to raise money, even this much encouragement was music to his ears.

Now, thinking over people who might like to take a flyer on such a venture, Mr. Fagan discarded them one by one. "I know a fellow who might be interested," he said finally. "You come in tomorrow, and I'll fix you up with an appointment."

It turned out that the "interested party" was an engineer charged with the job of looking into the merits of the proposal for Mr. Fagan. Very excited about the idea, the engineer suggested George bring his inventor in. He would arrange an appointment with Mr. Roy Bishop, a local engineer-turned-capitalist, whose opinion was highly respected.

A luncheon meeting was arranged at the Palace Hotel, San Francisco's oldest and best, and George had Phil came up from Hollywood. Phil arrived looking very much the poor inventor that he was. George, whose sartorial elegance was a matter of great pride with him, decided something had to be done.

Taking Phil into the Knox Shop, one of the city's best men's clothiers, George told the salesman to fix Phil up with a complete outfit. Phil was keenly aware of his shabby clothes, remembering how self-conscious he had been when he was obliged to wear knickers to play in the orchestra when the other boys wore long pants. But his sense of pride now led him to protest George's generosity. George silenced him by saying it was for the good of the cause.

George insisted the alterations be made and the suit be ready by the next morning. Therefore he was able to take a very different-looking young man to their luncheon engagement. Topped with a good haircut and a smart snap-brimmed hat, Phil not only looked but felt like a confident young man who had places to go and knew he could get there.

Their luncheon lasted two hours, and they spent the remainder of the afternoon in Mr. Bishop's office. Mr. Bishop and Mr. Fagan's engineer, who had been present through lunch and the following conference, expressed considerable interest in Phil's ideas and had many questions. All of these Phil answered with unhesitating conviction; however, Mr. Bishop said he had grave doubts that Phil would be able to bring his invention to a commercial conclusion.

Phil recognized Mr. Bishop's obvious reluctance and, addressing him directly, spoke with confident defiance: "I'm sorry, Mr. Bishop, that you don't see the possibilities for this invention that I do, or that you doubt my ability to make it happen. Thank you for your time and the very nice lunch." At this, Phil packed up his papers and, hat in hand, motioned to a visibly shaken George that he was ready to leave.

As Phil strode deliberately toward the door, Mr. Bishop called to him, "Wait a minute." Phil and George waited at the door, Mr. Bishop engaged an associate in a whispered conversation. Finally, he said "There is one more opinion I would like to have, that of Harlon Honn, an engineer." Mr. Honn was working on a new type of refrigerator that was being funded by Mr. W. W. Crocker. He offered to call Mr. Honn immediately and suggested they meet later that afternoon at George's apartment.

Later, comfortably seated in George's elegant apartment high up on California Street, Phil once more launched into a description of his invention. Mr. Honn was most enthusiastic, thought it was a wonderful idea, and was sure it would work. He agreed to go right home and make a written report for Mr. Bishop. Although it was apparent that Mr. Honn's expertise in electrical engineering was somewhat lacking, Phil hoped that his report would be comprehensive. On the other hand, Phil had found it almost impossible to change the mind of a so-called qualified person already set in his own convictions. Those steeped in convention are often so wary of change that their vision of progress is very limited.

Phil's fears proved groundless. After reading the report, Mr. Bishop called to say he was very pleased with it and would like to think it over until Mr. McCargar's return. That was fine with George and Phil.

A few days later, they were summoned to the board room of the Crocker Bank. Upon their arrival, George was greeted warmly by his friend, Jesse B. McCargar, a Crocker Bank vice-president, who told him confidentially he thought they were going to put up the money. He then took them to meet the Crocker Bank officials gathered for the conference. These were William H. Crocker, president and founder of the bank; his son, William W. Crocker, vice-president; James J. Fagan, executive vice-president; and Mr. Willis, a vice-president. Also present were R. J. Hanna, vice-president of Standard Oil of California, and Roy N. Bishop. George and Phil were much impressed by this prestigious group.

Mr. Bishop, leading the meeting, asked Phil just what he proposed to do.

Phil answered that he planned to do for sight what radio had done for sound and then went on to explain. "It isn't as simple as it sounds. The image must be broken up into thousands of pieces, or elements. These individual elements must be converted into varying electrical charges according to their light values. These charges are amplified and transmitted to a receiver, where they must be reassembled into their original light values in their exact original relationship. All this must be done rapidly enough to appear to be a simultaneous operation."

To their questions of "Is television new?" and "Why hasn't someone done it before?" Phil gave them a short history of television.

"In the 1880s there were many patent applications on various ideas for sending images through the air, none of which were very effective. Then on January 6th, 1884, Paul Nipkow, a Russian working in Germany, applied for a German patent number 30105, which disclosed the first mechanical method of transmission, using a perforated spinning disc. From that time to the present, many patents had been granted on television, all relating to similar mechanical systems. Phil explained that none of these ideas were capable of attaining the speed and resolution that acceptable television transmission would require.

Phil told them the speeds required just to transmit a picture of the quality of poor newsprint would be so great that any mechanical method would be inadequate. He then explained how he intended to use the tremendous speed of the electron to accomplish it.

The assembled financiers still had questions. Phil picked up a newspaper from the table and explained the method used to print the picture. Calling their attention to the fine dots making up the picture, he explained that a slick magazine picture required much better definition. In fact, it might require as many as a quarter of a million dots of much smaller size.

In the system that Phil proposed, a picture would be scanned one line at a time in a succession of dots and focused on a sensitized plate in his Image Dissector, where electrons would be released in proportion to the brightness of the individual picture elements: if the dot on the picture was black, no electrons would be released; if white, a maximum number would be released. This stream of electrons would then be transmitted to a cathode-ray receiving tube to be reproduced on the photosensitive surface one line at a time.

"To get that kind of definition over television," Phil continued, "a complete picture must be transmitted at the rate of about thirty per second. That would require approximately 7,500,000 dots, or elements, every second. I'm sure you can imagine that this speed is beyond the capacity of any mechanical device. Of course it would have to be very carefully synchronized with the transmitter, or you would have a lot of mush on your screen."

Phil's listeners confessed they still understood very little of what he had told them. Nevertheless, because he seemed confident, they would take his and Mr. Honn's word for it. Mr. Bishop asked how much it would cost. Phil told him he thought a budget of a thousand dollars a month for a year would do it, but to be safe, he would like a total of twenty-five thousand dollars.

Mr. Bishop doubted that would be enough, but they finally decided to go with that amount. They further agreed it was to be Phil's show. He was to have complete charge of his work, since, as Mr. McCargar commented, what Phil planned "would probably give a trained engineer heart failure."

The backing syndicate proposed to put up the money and act as trustees for 60 percent of the venture. Of the remaining 40 percent, Phil was to have 20 percent and George and Les were to divide the other 20 percent. That was a hard pill for Phil to swallow, for he had been determined to keep control of his invention. His only hope was that somehow later on he might be able to buy back some of the outstanding interest in his work. In any case, as things looked now, he saw no choice but to go along with the deal. At least he would be the largest single stockholder.

These matters settled, the meeting was about to come to a close, when Mr. Bishop turned to Phil and George and said, "This is the first time anyone has gotten money from this bunch without putting something on the table for it. In this case, all we have are the ideas in this young man's head. You can bet we'd better treat him like a prized racehorse."

Phil dispatched a telegram to my brother Cliff in Baker, Oregon, saying he had a job for him and to take the next train to San Francisco. When I opened the door to Phil's knock, I could hardly recognize him as the same apprehensive young man who had left me a few days before. He was wearing his new clothes, and he was very handsome. He swung me around several times, taking my breath away; then, putting me down, he began telling me the good news.

By the time he had reported all that had happened to him, I was so excited I could hardly contain myself; I began dancing around the room. He caught me and waltzed me around until I was so dizzy I could hardly stand. Then he informed me we were to drive George's car to San Francisco early the next morning.

Next day we were up at dawn. I had packed all of our clothes in one bag so Phil could have our only other suitcase for his books, drafting tools, and papers. Phil packed the Chandler, but had no room for the bag containing our clothes, so he tied it to the fender well on my side of the car.

Within the hour we were on our way, rolling along between orange groves. Soon the sun peeping over the hills bathed the countryside in a rosy light and released the fragrance from the dewy blossoms on the trees. It was heavenly, as if God were putting a benediction on us and our rosy-looking future.

Our hearts were filled to overflowing. Phil pulled me over closer to him and hugged me tight, saying, "Are you happy?" In answer I started to sing, "Looking at the World through Rose-Colored Glasses, Everything is Rosy Now." Then he chimed in with the tenor and finished the song with me. This was followed by "I Want To Be Happy But I Can't Be Happy Till I've Made You Happy Too," "I Have Built a Dream House," and of course our song, "Always." This was a very satisfying way of expressing our love and exuberance, and we sang until we were hoarse.

Then after a long silence, Phil began talking of his plans for the future and of what television would do for the world. He saw television as a marvelous teaching tool. There would be no excuse for illiteracy. Parents could learn along with their children. News and sporting events could be seen as they were happening. Symphonies would mean more when one could see the musicians as they played, and movies would be seen in our own living rooms. He said there would be a time when we would be able to see and learn about people in other lands. If we understood them better, differences could be settled around conference tables, without going to war.

"Wait!" I interrupted him, "I thought you said television could be sent only in a straight line. How are you going to get it across the ocean?"

"We'll find a way, even if we have to relay it using captive balloons." Phil had an answer for everything.

The beautiful California countryside was enhanced by our enchanted mood. The colors seemed fantastically more brilliant than they had been just yesterday. The world was our oyster, and we were going to do such marvelous things it would never be the same.

I was fascinated by what lay ahead of us, but beyond this fascination, I was filled with the wonder of this young husband of mine and considered myself the luckiest girl alive. It was hard for me to realize that this was actually happening to me. I asked Phil why he had chosen me for a wife, with all of the ambitious plans he had for the future.

"Well," he answered, "It could be because I love you very much. Also, I saw in you many of the same qualities possessed by your dear mother, and I don't think I could do better than that." I doubted that I could ever be the woman my mother was. She was a talented, generous, outgoing woman, with the patience of Job. Her strength was no doubt gained from her schoolteaching years before marriage and raising nine lively children. Her glorious high soprano voice was equally effective in leading the singing in church, taking leads in musicals, or calling her family in from the fields for dinner. Papa confessed delaying at times just to hear again her voice calling his name. In later life when her health began to fail, she faced life's problems with faith, courage, and a light-hearted optimism. She was certainly a good example of what I should like to be.

"Anyway," Phil continued, "we are both young and we can grow together. I want you to be a part of everything I do."

We stopped in San Luis Obispo and had the Chandler oiled and lubricated while we ate lunch. After filling our gas tank, we continued on. About fifty miles on our way Phil abruptly pulled off the road.

"We've lost our suitcase! All our good clothes are in it, including my new suit!"

A sick feeling came over me, and I cried out, "And that's not all! It had my wedding dress in it too!"

"I must not have tied it on very well at the garage." Phil reproved himself.

"But Phil, I would have seen or heard it if it had fallen on the way; I think someone must have taken it while we were in the rest rooms at the filling station."

"Well, we can't go on without it, so we'll just have to go back," Phil decided, turning around and doubling back over our route. Although we carefully retraced our steps and questioned the people at both the garage and service station, we found no trace of the missing suitcase.

I pleaded with Phil to report our loss to a policeman and have those places searched, but he said dejectedly, "What chance would we have? We are strangers, and these people are local residents with businesses here. Just whom do you think they would believe?" Hopelessly we got into the car and again started for San Francisco.

The loss of our clothes was enough, but just now when all those people were putting their trust in him to do something no one had ever done before, this act of carelessness was inexcusable.

"George may not pass this off so lightly as he did my fiasco in Hollywood, when I blew the whole shebang by not letting the generator warm up before turning things on."

"You're being too hard on yourself, sweetheart. Chalk that up to inexperience and go on from there. It was a hard blow, but the lesson you learned may prevent worse catastrophes later."

As we drove along now, the whole world seemed somehow different. Gone were the light hearts and song. We rode in silence for some time, Phil grimly bent on covering miles as fast as possible. Finally, he voiced his thoughts with, "How can I ever face George? How can I face anybody in these old clothes?" We had saved out our old comfortable clothes for traveling.

"You won't have to face George for a while," I tried to comfort him. "Didn't you say he and Les left for another community chest campaign in El Paso, Texas? By the time he returns, we will have figured something out."

"The only thing I can think of is to look up George's friend, Lynn Mowatt. George introduced me to him and said if I needed help before he returned, to call on Lynn. I'm ashamed to tell him that I carelessly lost our clothes."

It was late when we drove slowly through Paso Robles looking for a place to sleep. Just beyond the business section, we spotted an inviting hacienda-style hotel covered with flowers. We were shown to a pleasant room, clean and airy, with a comfortable bed.

We hit the road early the next morning to make up for lost time. Cliff was very much on our minds. Phil's telegram had instructed him to wait for us at the corner of California and Powell streets from noon to one o'clock every day until we arrived, and this was the third day. We hoped he would still be waiting at the appointed rendezvous.

From Salinas, we took the coastal route. I was delighted with the scenery; the ocean never failed to stimulate and thrill me. On one stretch, the road resembled a roller coaster. Phil thought it was fun and accelerated to make the effect more pronounced, until I became queasy and he had to slow down. From Half Moon Bay we took the Skyline Highway up through fields of artichokes. It was one-thirty as we entered South San Francisco and we thought again of Cliff. If he had left his post, we had not the slightest idea where to look for him. I said a little prayer that he would still be there.

CHAPTER 7

202 Green Street

Cliff was standing on the corner of California and Powell Streets in San Francisco. The telegram he received from Phil in Baker, Oregon, had said:

HAVE BACKING FROM SAN FRANCISCO BANKERS - STOP - JOB FOR YOU - STOP - MEET US CORNER CALIFORNIA AND POWELL STREETS NOON EACH DAY STARTING SEPT 19 UNTIL WE GET THERE - STOP - PHIL

This was exciting, heady news to Cliff. In Salt Lake City, Phil had said he would send for him as soon as serious backing could be found, and now here it was! It had seemed such an impossible dream, certainly too remote a prospect to hang any immediate hopes on. Nonetheless, the bond of friendship and trust built up during the rough times they had shared in their many jobs together, from farm harvesting and logging to building and selling crystal radio sets in Salt Lake City, brooked no hesitation. Cliff had been staying in Oregon with our sister Verona. He said good-bye to her and to his girlfriend, quit his mill job in Baker, packed his few belongings and fewer dollars, and hopped a train for San Francisco.

San Francisco! He was still more than a little overwhelmed by the city. He looked over at the Fairmont Hotel kitty-corner across the street.

Towering high in the sky atop one of San Francisco's taller hills, it was filled with people of another world, a world he had never seen. He pondered this a bit, then turned to scan the downtown buildings and the beautiful bay beyond. Across the bay, he could see towns backed by wooded hills.

This was his third day of waiting patiently for a sign of George's Chandler coming up the hill. There was only the constant flow of people and cars. The noisy little cable cars kept things lively, but all was external, a sea of humanity in which he had no part. He drew within himself and pondered his problems.

He was nearly out of money and would soon be out of a place to stay. He mentally shook himself. Phil and Pem would undoubtedly arrive today. He tried to think of something constructive, like what Phil had in mind to set up as a laboratory and how he could fit in. He had only a vague idea of what was involved in making experimental tubes and such. With nothing but time on his hands, he wondered at length what in the world he could do to help. He felt apprehensive about his own capabilities, but hoped he could jump into the work and find something he could do reasonably well.

Phil and I found Cliff seated on the curb, lost in thought, when we finally reached the appointed corner at 1:40 p.m. September 22nd. Suddenly, Cliff looked up and saw us coming. My heart went out to this lovable, lanky, sandy-haired brother of mine, and I was greatly relieved that he was still at his post. Amid the joyful reunion, as I made room for him beside me in the car, I asked what had made him look up before we even reached him. He had seemed so absorbed in his thoughts.

"Oh," he answered, "I recognized you easy enough; George has a leaky muffler . . . sounds sporty as all get-out."

As Phil drew away from the curb, Cliff asked if we could pick up his bag to save paying another day's lodging. Finding the address, we waited in front of the shabby hotel while he got his bag. He was back shortly wearing a big grin, and as we drove away, he said, "You know, there are some pretty nice people in that place. This morning, I told the lady at the desk I was about broke and if my friends didn't show up today I'd have to find a cheaper hotel. Do you know what she said? She said, 'There are cheaper rooms south of Market Street, young feller, but I'd rather trust you till your friends come than see you go down there. That's a real rough neighborhood.' What do you think of that? She surely was nice."

This evidence of the friendliness of our adopted city warmed our feelings toward it. Phil drove us around to see a few of the sights and thrills that are so much a part of the unique flavor of this city by the Golden Gate. The seven hills upon which the city was built were totally covered with row houses, the fronts of which were painted in pastel colors in an attempt to lend them some individuality. An occasional apartment building offered some diversion in architecture. Some streets became so steep they ended in steps near the top. Such places offered a spectacular view of the entire Northern Bay area, from the Golden Gate to the Dumbarton Bridge far to the south.

Eventually, we came to Sansome Street and almost at once turned onto Green Street. The street at this point was a mere alley of less than 100 feet, ending at the foot of a sheer cliff which formed the eastern side of Telegraph Hill. A two-story brick building occupied the entire north side of the street. The bottom floor housed a garage and a carpenter shop, and the second floor carried a sign proclaiming it to be "THE CROCKER RESEARCH LABORATORY."

"Behold," Phil said, gesturing grandly at the sign, "the future home of electronic television. Come on; let's go in and look around." So saying, he led the way, with Cliff and me close behind. The stairs led to a short central hallway. On the right was a closed door; the open door on the left revealed two men at work.

"That's Mr. Honn," Phil said. "Let's go in and say hello."

Mr. Honn, a pleasant man of stocky build and bushy hair, greeted Phil warmly and introduced his associate, Mr. Morse. He was a tall, dignified gentleman who had designed a refrigeration system which he was developing with Mr. Honn.

"Welcome to the Crocker Laboratory," was Mr. Honn's affable greeting. "If we can be of any help to you in getting settled and going, let us know."

"By all means," added Mr. Morse, "and feel free to use our telephone and restroom while you're getting set up."

Phil thanked them for their kindness. He knew he would doubtless need that help in getting oriented and organized to the point where he could begin his work.

Phil led us across the hall to his allotted space. As he put the key in the lock and opened the door to that bare loft on September 22nd, 1926, we felt we had opened the door to opportunity. Looking at Phil as he gazed around the empty, sunlit chamber, I could almost read the thoughts running through his mind:

For five long years Phil had struggled, through the shock of losing his beloved father, through the frustration of earning a living and supporting his family while trying to further his education. Now the challenge he had dreamed about was at hand. Though he had made every conceivable effort to prepare himself for this day, he feared he was still lacking in the experience necessary to complete the monumental task before him. But I knew that the immense energy of his vision would save him from giving up in the face of whatever pitfalls and discouragements lay ahead. At this point, producing an all-electric television system seemed to be a straightforward matter. There was nothing that could stand between him and his goal.

The loft was roughly twenty by thirty feet. Two sides of this room were mostly in windows, giving good light. The ceiling was the high roof, raftered by huge beams. There was little resemblance to my idea of what a laboratory should look like, but to Phil it was beautiful. From the time he was assured of backing, he had been busy thinking of how he would proceed and what he would need to do it. He had made good use of his time at BYU. The setup of the chemistry and physics labs was indelibly engraved on his mind. Since vacuum tubes were the heart of his television system, a means for making them was of the highest priority.

Pacing his way around the empty space, Phil outlined what had to be done to prepare the way. They would need a large, sturdy table on which to set up a glassblowing system, with a sink nearby. That could go toward the north wall but out in the room far enough to allow working space on all sides. Benches for parts assembly and circuitry should be in the same general area. That would give access to the same bench drills and spot welders. The west wall would do nicely for them.

202 Green Street, site of Crocker Research Labs.
This is the location where Phil built his first television system.

He would get the carpenter downstairs to build them a rest room while he and Cliff built the work-benches, shelves etc. Suddenly we realized it was dinner time, and we had no idea where we were to stay the night or where we were to live.

"We might find an apartment on the other side of the hill if the rent is reasonable," Phil suggested. "What do you think, honey?"

"Well," I hesitated, "if you really want to know, I would rather be out of the thick of things a little. I feel too lost in such a big city." I had been more comfortable in Hollywood. The atmosphere there was more relaxed, people moving with a sort of languor. Suddenly transplanted to San Francisco, I felt like a mole in a stirred-up ant hill. Phil had noted this change but had attributed it to the cool, crisp weather of the area.

"Would you like to live across the Bay?" Phil asked. "We could look in Berkeley, and if that's too expensive, we could try Oakland. Commuting wouldn't be much of a problem. The ferries run about every fifteen or twenty minutes during rush hours." This sounded exciting to me.

"What do you think, Cliff?"

"You do what you think best, Phil; I don't know much about this place." Then he added with a touch of his laconic humor, "That is, except for what I could see from my corner observation post at California and Powell."

We decided that since the hotels were probably cheaper across the Bay, we would take the ferry and start looking for apartments the next morning. That settled, Phil drove to the ferry building. This venerable structure was one of the few to remain standing after the devastating earthquake and fire of 1906. With its high clock tower, it still looked up Market Street with considerable presence. We joined the line of cars waiting for the Oakland ferry and were soon directed to our place on board.

All this was exciting and filled with a sort of magic for all three of us. We investigated the huge paddlewheels mounted midships that propelled the boat along, then went to the rear of the ferry to watch the sun setting behind the San Francisco skyline. The tall buildings silhouetted against the crimson sky were a breathtaking sight, and we stood enthralled. I had a strange feeling of being suddenly caught up in a fantastic dream, as though destiny had touched me with a magic finger. From the enraptured look on the faces of Phil and Cliff, they must be sharing these same feelings.

Phil broke the spell by saying we were nearing Oakland and should return to the car. Then, as we faced the Berkeley Hills, we had another thrill. The sun was shedding its last rays on houses dotting the hillside. Amidst the rosy glow, the windows reflected the light as though they were fierce eyes looking down upon us. We would have lingered but were urged along by people flocking back to their cars.

We ate dinner at a cozy cafe and upon inquiring about hotels were directed to the St. Mark's Hotel at 394 Twelfth Street. While it could never be confused with the famous hotel of that name in San Francisco, it was presentable, and Phil engaged two rooms. By the time Phil had registered, Cliff was deeply engrossed in the radio account of a boxing match. The lobby was filled with avid fans. As Phil gave him his key, he said, "Hey! This is the big one between Dempsey and Tunney; I was afraid I'd missed it! I'm going to stay down and hear it through." Phil said he was tired from the drive and would see him at eight for breakfast.

The next morning, Cliff related the story of the now famous "long count." College man Gene Tunney had surprised everyone by unexpectedly winning the fight with a knockout, thus taking the title from longtime world champion Jack Dempsey. Cliff, along with the majority of the fans, had thought Tunney had little chance against the "Champ."

Armed with the morning rental ads, we set out to find an apartment. Apartments in Oakland that were within our budget failed to meet our standards. We ended up driving around the Berkeley University of California Campus. With the top down on George's roadster, we could soak up the campus ambience. Noting the dreamy look on Phil's face, I asked, "A penny for your thoughts?"

"Oh, I was just wishing I'd been able to finish college. It's harder, and you're more likely to leave gaps that will show up later, when you dig it out for yourself."

"And you miss the social side of it, the whole college life. I know you enjoyed the BYU dances."

"Yes, especially after you came into the picture.   But I wouldn't have had time for sports. Still, it would have been nice to start out with more of a foundation. There's so much I need to know."

"I shouldn't have come into the picture so soon."

"Don't misunderstand me, Pemmie; I wouldn't trade my present situation for a dozen college degrees! Especially if it meant losing you. We'll get by."

We looked at the remaining apartments on the list without success, and our hopes of living in Berkeley were beginning to dim. On an impulse, Phil turned east on Derby Street, in the vicinity of the university football stadium. Almost at once, I spotted a "FOR RENT" sign on a charming little brown, shingle-sided house with white shutters. The house number read 2910.

"Honey, that's sure to be over our budget," Phil warned.

"Probably," I agreed, "but let's look at it anyway, just for fun. I'm so tired of looking at musty apartments."

We were greeted at the door by a spry little lady who looked to be in her sixties and proved to be the owner. She didn't want to rent to students. When Phil told her he was an inventor and would be working in San Francisco on a method of sending sight with the sound of radio, she was impressed. She was anxious to rent her home so she could be with her ailing sister in Los Angeles. She could be packed in time to take the evening train if we wanted to move right in. The rent was $62.50, complete with linens, dishes, and all furnishings.

We had set $50.00 as a limit for our rent, but this house had two bedrooms. If we invited Cliff to live with us, he could make up the difference. There was even a fireplace and a small den with day-bed and desk. Phil offered to take our new landlady, Mrs. Knapp, to her train. Consequently, that evening we were comfortably installed in our new home.

Feeling the necessity of budgeting our monthly salary of $200.00, we came up with the following:

OUR FIRST MONTHLY BUDGET

Phil's mother's rent in Provo	$35.00
Our rent	62.50
Food	45.00
Transportation & lunches	45.00
Savings	40.00
Total	$227.50
Cliff's contribution	27.50
leaving	$200.00

Phil hated to see his mother doing housework for a living and vowed to change that at the earliest opportunity.

In his anxiety to get the lab organized, Phil was up early the next morning. He and Cliff took the first ferry to San Francisco and planned to be home for dinner by seven.

The dinner was ready on time, but there were no boys. From my window, I could see the ferries dock out in the Bay. On the Berkeley side, a train trestle ran far out in the shallow water to a point where the depth could accommodate the boats. A commuter train called the KEY Route met the boats at the pier to transport the passengers to and from Berkeley.

As the trains arrived and still the boys did not come, I became very worried. What if there had been an accident?! I felt totally isolated and completely helpless. I built a fire in the fireplace to cheer me up. They would probably be cold.

They arrived about ten-thirty, full of apologies.

"There just was no place to stop, and since Mr. Honn had gone home, we had no way to call you." Phil explained.

Everything was fine now that they were home. I told them to sit by the fire while I warmed dinner. Later, as we sat around the fireplace, Phil brought us up to date on his plans.

"I'm anxious to get organized to the point where we can begin making Image Dissector tubes."

"Do you think we can do it?" Cliff wanted to know.

"It shouldn't be too difficult," Phil assured him, "I fooled around with making glass-to-glass seals and simple stuff like that at BYU, and I think I can learn to do it."

"Once you get the tube made, then what?" Cliff asked.

"We'll have to amplify the picture signal and build a receiver tube to turn the electrical image back into an optical image."

"I'll bet that's easier said than done," was Cliff's comment.

Phil admitted they had their work cut out for them. Even so, he intended to have a fully electrical television transmission in a year just as he had promised, and nothing was going to stop him. (The word *electronic* was not yet in general use.)

"I don't know just what I can do to help most," Cliff said, "but I have two willing hands, and I'll sure do anything I can." That, of course, Phil already knew.

"You've got a lot of get-up-and-go, Cliff, which we'll need more than anything, and I know from experience that you pick things up very easily. You'll make out just fine; don't worry."

Cliff assured him he would do his "damnedest!"

Phil sat thinking for a time, then made a statement.

"I'm going to enroll in some correspondence courses at the University to fill in some of the holes in my hit-and-miss education. How about you two joining me?"

"Sure, I have a few holes myself," Cliff agreed with a chuckle.

"Me too!" I chimed in, "I'm in worse shape than either of you."

We all agreed that Monday would be a good time to sign up.

The next day was Sunday. Phil announced there would be no work at the lab on the Sabbath except in dire necessity. This didn't mean he would not be busy. Although Phil maintained a deep faith in God, somehow going to church was not the same after his father died, and he had lost interest. I could understand this, because the death of my mother had affected me the same way.

We took a ride to explore the area. Around the Berkeley hills we came upon a natural Greek theater built with stone stage and seats arranged up a semi-circular hillside. Phil was delighted with this. He stepped up on the stage and launched into some dialogue from the Shakespeare play *The Taming of the Shrew* in which he had performed at BYU. It was evident he had memorized much more than his own part. Cliff and I were quite entertained.

Monday morning saw the boys up early and off for San Francisco. The lab was rapidly taking shape. Scientific and trade supply houses were located, and supplies, tools, and equipment started flowing in. The place immediately took on the look of a functioning work area. This progress served to fan to a fine flame Phil's long-thwarted desire to get going on a Dissector tube.

One evening he announced that the next day they would make their first attempt at building a Dissector. Accompanying the boys to work the next morning, I was greatly impressed when they ushered me into the lab. I commented on the size (4x10 feet) and obvious solidity of the glassblowing table. Phil explained that since both delicate glasswork and a working vacuum system were to be installed thereon, such bracing was required to limit vibration. They had also installed sink and toilet, as they proudly pointed out.

Among the tools and materials laid out on the table were several ring stands, heavy steel bases with an upright rod on which were fastened asbestos-sleeved clamps. Onto one of these, Phil had clamped a glass tube blank, about eight inches long and three inches in diameter, with a rounded end. Phil had tried to find blanks with really flat ends, but was told, "They don't make them like that." It was the first of many times he would be hearing that, which of course meant "make it yourself." The end of the tube needed to be flat and optically clear to prevent distortion in the televised image. Phil went ahead with what was available because his first job was to prove his theory in order to sophisticate his design.

I should point out here that experimental glassblowing is an undertaking noted for being fraught with disappointment, periodic rage at the perversity of inanimate objects, and peril to any time schedules. Certainly, it is better left, if one has the choice, to masters of the craft. But Phil saw no choice. He was not afraid to tackle anything, certainly not on the grounds of prior inexperience. Much of his innocence and determination goes with the inventor's territory. Cliff had a lot of the same kind of directness, and it grew in the lab and around Phil.

Holding up a round piece of very fine-meshed metal screen with a wire ring around it, Phil explained, "This is a cathode. Here the light rays are converted to an electron image. It must be placed in the end of the tube blank as the first step. The heavy wires you see sticking out on each side are leads which must be sealed through the wall of the tube. This is called a glass-to-metal seal. That's what we're going to try now."

Lighting his torch and adjusting it, he gave instructions.

"Cliff, get a good hold on the cathode with those long-handled forceps. Now slip it in the tube to within about a half-inch of the end. When I get the glass softened, you push the wire on that side of the cathode slowly through the glass, OK?"

"Gotcha," Cliff acknowledged. Phil now lit a Bunsen burner and played the flame gently over the tube blank. He explained that this was necessary both in heating and cooling the glass in order to prevent strains that would cause cracking. Now he moved the hotter flame of the oxygen torch nearer to the glass, and a small red spot appeared.

"Are you ready, Cliff?"

"Say when."

"Now!"

Cliff pushed gently and the wire slid smoothly through the molten spot on the tube.

"Can you straighten it a little so it's parallel to the end of the tube? Fine. Now, hold it steady while I cool it down." As the glass solidified, he changed back to the cooler flame and bathed the whole tube. Finally, his hands shaking, he put the torch down and said, "That was good, Cliff. That gives us a photo-cathode in place." But as he spoke, a crack appeared.

They tried it again, and this time they got a little further, but the same thing happened. All through lunch, Phil was introspective. Cliff and I respected his silence, very much aware that the problem rested squarely on his shoulders. Upon returning to the lab, Phil decided that the type of glass was complicating the problem. He thought soda-lime glass would be easier to handle while they were learning.

While he and Cliff went to pick up the glass and some other supplies, I cleaned the floor and was on the second row of windows when they returned.

"Say, this is a big improvement," Phil said appreciatively. He decided to experiment with the new glass before trying another tube. His seals were a little lumpy but solid enough to satisfy him. Then they made some more cathodes, to be ready for another try the next day. Phil said he was sorry he had been unable to produce a tube for me. I told him not to be discouraged—this was only the first try; tomorrow things would go better.

At six they were ready to call it a day. Having missed the six o'clock ferry, we had time to study the block-long relief map of the San Francisco Bay Area, housed in the Ferry Building. It was a work of art. It included the entire city of San Francisco, even down to the principal buildings.

My prediction was faulty. The next day they met with no more success than the day before. They came home discouraged. After relating the failures of the day, Phil decided they couldn't go on like this. He hoped in the morning to find some professional help through the university chemistry department. With this off his mind, he brightened a little and said, "What's for dinner?"

That night, we were awakened from a sound sleep by a roaring sound and a jolt that almost threw us out of bed. Phil jumped up saying, "This is an earthquake!" The floor was shaking so that it was difficult to walk, but I started getting dressed as fast as I could. I could hear the excited shouts and other noises of the students of the special education school across the street. Evidently the building had been evacuated as a precaution.

"Where are you going?" Phil asked. I looked around and there he was. He had calmly gone back to bed!

"I'm getting out of here!"

"Oh, come on back to bed; it's all over now."

In my excitement, I had not noticed that the house was no longer shaking. Seeing how unconcerned he was, I got back into my nightie and crawled cautiously back in bed. I had calmed down to the point where I was contemplating sleep, when there was an aftershock. This one was less severe, and with Phil's comforting arm around me, we waited it out.

CHAPTER 8

Image Dissectors

It was Sunday. We had been for a drive, and I was in the pantry selecting food to prepare for our dinner, when suddenly everything around me came alive and started weaving before my eyes. I staggered in to where Phil and Cliff were, saying I felt very dizzy; they would have to wait for their dinner. Phil came and helped me to a chair. Cliff started to laugh.

"That was another earthquake, Pem," Phil now joined Cliff in laughing at the joke Mother Nature had played on me. They told me dishes were rattling in the cupboards and pictures were swinging back and forth. This little shingle-sided house had no doubt weathered many such tremors. It just swayed with the ground waves. We were told this was an after-shock of the temblor that had shaken us up the previous evening. Many broken windows were caused by the last one, but the only serious damage was a perpendicular crack in a high-rise building in San Francisco.

With the reverses of the past week still fresh in their minds, Monday morning Phil and Cliff visited the Berkeley campus of the University of California. They were directed to a Mr. Bill Cummings, head of the glass-blowing lab. Mr. Cummings was a tall, pleasant man of middle age, known for his considerable ability with experimental procedures involving glass and vacuums. He took the time to sit down with the boys and listen to their problems in some detail.

Mr. Cummings found the idea of working on a television tube

intriguing. To their great relief, he agreed to help them between regular university jobs. He said if they would bring the tube elements the following morning, he would put them into a tube and bring it to San Francisco on Wednesday.

He told them they would need a good vacuum setup. He had developed one over the years that worked very well for tube-pumping applications such as theirs. It involved roughing pumps, a high-vacuum mercury-diffusion pump, glassware, traps, and the like. He said if they wished, he would bring the components with him on Wednesday and set it up. Perhaps he could also seal their new tube onto the vacuum line for them then. He gave Phil a list of additional gear and supplies to purchase, saying the most likely place to find special items would be either C. W. Marwidel or Braun Knecht Hyman. Expressing much gratitude, the boys left to put things together.

This sudden switch in fortunes left the boys in a highly elated state, still evident that night as they recounted the events of the day. After purchasing the necessary parts and supplies, they made the tube elements and put together a crude bakeout oven, which was necessary for the pumping procedure.

By Wednesday noon everything was in readiness for the arrival of Mr. Cummings. One last item on the shopping list was liquid air, which was needed to trap mercury vapor from the high-vacuum pump to prevent it from entering the vacuum system. Cliff made the jaunt over to Emeryville, near Oakland, to secure the rapidly evaporating, supercold fluid. That required a minor odyssey involving two streetcar transfers and a ferry ride each way. The bake-out oven and other paraphernalia were ready, and it was with considerable excitement the boys had left for work that morning.

Dinner was ready at seven, but no boys. By nine o'clock I was beginning to worry. When the last ferry pulled in at the dock about midnight, I was in a state of real anxiety. Telling myself they would surely be home any minute now could not dispel my feeling of total helplessness. I vowed never to be put in this position again. I began pacing the floor. With a flood of relief I heard their footsteps and ran to open the door.

With a comforting arm around me, Phil said he knew I would be worried, but Mr. Honn had left early and there was no way to call me. He promised to have the lab phone connected the very next day.

"Thank goodness for that! I was worried sick."

"Pemmie, you'll have to have more confidence in our ability to take care of ourselves," Cliff admonished.

Seeing the tired look on their faces, I told them to sit by the fire while I prepared something to eat.

"No, honey; we ate on the ferry."

"We had to," Cliff chimed in. "Our knees were so shaky we'd never have made it home. Boy, that fire feels good. It gets cold on the ferry at night."

Sitting around the fire, they told of the progress of the day. Mr. Cummings had arrived with the tube as promised and had spent the rest of the afternoon setting up the vacuum system. Then he had sealed the precious Dissector tube on the vacuum system to be pumped. Phil had been reluctant to leave the tube pumping overnight even though he had been assured it would be safe to do so. Though he still feared some unforeseen problem, he had finally left the tube pumping.

"The tube should have a high enough vacuum by tomorrow for me to form the photosensitive surfaces." Phil concluded.

I announced that I was going to see this operation. I could not stand another day of suspense.

Phil was up at dawn the next morning, hurrying us in his anxiety for his precious tube. To save time, we waited to have breakfast on the ferry. The ferry diner's poached-eggs-on-corned-beef-hash specialty was delicious. The diner was also famous for fresh-baked apple pie, which several passengers ordered with their early morning breakfast.

We arrived in the city before the day's activity had really begun. Entering the lab, I was surprised to see the changes. The glass-blowing table had been transformed into a wondrous array of tubing, bulbous appendages with stopcocks, gauges, and instruments. In the middle of this forest of glass and wires was the Image Dissector, star of the show.

Tube labs in those days always had a characteristic ambience of sights, smells, and sounds such as the ever-present "thunk, thunk, thunk" of the vacuum pump. Here was indeed a working laboratory, and I was very impressed.

Phil plugged in a Bakelite-encased cylindrical instrument about the size and shape of a rolling pin. It had a control knob on one end and a short, heavy wire sticking out the other. "This is a Tesla Coil, a tool for testing the vacuum of a tube being pumped. We call it a kicker coil," Phil explained, holding it near the Dissector tube. A thin high-voltage arc jumped to the wall of the tube. He calmly played it over the tube to produce a gaseous cloud inside.

"Well, the tube looks OK, but the vacuum isn't high enough," Phil explained. "The glow you see is the remaining gas ionizing. It needs a few more hours on the pump."

It was midafternoon when Phil decided to take a chance on the vacuum. Sitting on the observation stool Phil had placed for me, I watched as he made the necessary preparations. I felt a sense of destiny moving and wondered if Phil and Cliff were aware they could well be making history at this very moment.. I was really proud of my young husband and very happy he had chosen my brother to help him.

Phil called my attention to his next operation. He lit a small torch and played it on the first of five test-tube-like appendages suspended from the vacuum line as it entered the Dissector Tube. He explained that Mr. Cummings had sealed these tubes on. The first tube contained potassium, a powdered photosensitive material, and this was a purification process.

As he held the torch on the bottom of the first tube, the potassium began to melt and then, vaporize. I watched, fascinated, as he began driving the vapor out of that tube into the next by keeping the glass behind it too hot for the vapor to condense. This process left a noticeable residue in the first tube. As he took the vapor from one tube to the next, fewer and fewer impurities were left. At the last stage there was no residue, and Phil could drive the vapor on into the Dissector.

The problem now was to deposit the potassium vapor on the photocathode without getting it on the other tube elements or the side walls of the tube. That was difficult, because the vapor had a propensity for condensing on anything it touched. The photocathode was fastened to the wall of the tube by a heavy wire through the tube wall. Here I was given my first opportunity to help. My job was to keep the wire cool by holding cotton wrung from ice water

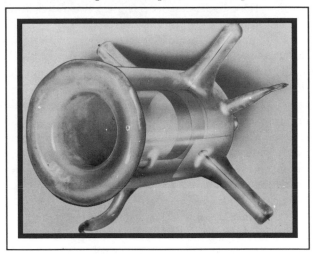

The first attempt at an Image Dissector. Of course, this did not function.

against it. Then Phil was able to keep the walls of the tube warm and drive the vapor mostly to the cathode. When he felt it was enough, he called Cliff to help him with the sealing-off process.

"Mr. Cummings showed me how to seal the tube off the pump," Phil informed me.

"He sure was accommodating," Cliff added. "Couldn't do enough."

The big moment had arrived. I could feel the tension that builds at moments like these, when it is easy to lose the work of hours or days with a single mistake.

When Cliff had warmed the tube with the Bunsen burner, Phil applied his oxy-hydrogen torch, and by melting the connecting tubulation, was able to pull the tube away. Now he held it in his asbestos-clad hand. Laying it on the asbestos-covered bench, he breathed a sigh of relief. The baby had survived its birth.

"I hope I got enough potassium on the cathode. It needs to be a fairly heavy layer."

"That was downright professional," I congratulated them.

"You're prejudiced," was Phil's comment. "I'm afraid that was pretty amateurish. We'll have to do a lot better, if we're to succeed at this game." He connected various batteries and meters to the wires coming from the tube elements. He had two interested observers as he put a light on the potassium photosurface inside the tube and watched a meter. The indicator needle hardly moved.

"I think we're on the right track," Phil said, "but we'll need a much more sensitive meter to measure the output of that tube. We're working in the dark this way. I can see we need a heavier layer of potassium on the photocathode. We'd better get busy on another set of tube elements for Mr. Cummings."

They had been working on this fabrication for a while when Phil looked up, the light of inspiration in his eyes. "Cliff, I know how to do it. We'll get Mr. Cummings to put the tubulation through which we drive the vapor on the *other* side of the cathode screen. Then the vapor will have to go through the screen first. Most of it should deposit there. I'll bet it'll work."

"Sounds reasonable," Cliff said. I realized they had already started on their second model.

The backing syndicate appointed a liaison between them and Phil's day-to-day operations to keep them informed of lab progress and to act as watchdog over the budget. This liaison turned out to be Mr. Albert B. Mann, who appeared the next morning to meet Phil and to see what was going on in the lab.

Mr. Mann, who described himself as an acoustical engineer, was portly, middle-aged, and inclined to be officious. He treated Phil from the start with just enough condescension to set my teeth on edge. Something about that man made me uneasy.

On this occasion he wanted to know how things were going. Phil showed him the equipment setup and the new tube. In explaining things, he mentioned the trouble he was having making measurements with his present instruments. Better versions were well beyond that month's budget. Mr. Mann took his leave, having made so few comments Phil had the feeling he hadn't been much impressed.

The next morning Phil got a call from Mr. Bishop, who asked Phil to come down to his office right away. Wondering what could be wrong, Phil presented himself at Mr. Bishop's office. He was greeted affably and asked to sit down. Mr. Bishop, a direct man, came at once to the point.

"Phil, I hear you're getting that place to look almost like a laboratory, but you're short on equipment."

"Well, yes, I am, Mr. Bishop," Phil admitted. "I need instruments that will enable me to make measurements down around a microampere or so with fair accuracy. Getting set up cost more than I had expected. To stay within budget, such purchases will have to wait awhile."

"Young man, I like your spunk, and I think you're probably going to do just what you said you would." Mr. Bishop became thoughtful and after a moment said, "I lost a son not long ago. He was about your age, and in some ways you remind me of him. He also was interested in radio and electrical things . . . always messing around with some kind of equipment."

Phil contemplated Mr. Bishop's loss with sympathy. The loss of his father still painfully fresh in his mind, Phil thought it must be really hard to lose a son.

"My son had some ideas he wanted to work out, so I bought him three meters he needed for his work. They cost a lot of money and are supposed to be quite sensitive. I'd like you to have them." Reaching into a desk drawer, Mr. Bishop brought out three expensive precision meters. When Phil saw them, he could hardly believe his eyes. They were exactly what he needed. Thanking Mr. Bishop profusely and cradling the precious meters in his arms, he took his leave.

"Well I'll be!" Cliff exclaimed when he saw the meters. "The man must be psychic!"

"They couldn't have come at a better time, that's for sure," Phil agreed. "Now let's see if we can measure the photocurrents directly." While the reading was disappointing, it pointed the way. By quitting time Phil was already making more changes in the next tube.

That evening, Phil told me he would have to get his notes completely up to date. As soon as he had a tube with all the working principles demonstrated, he would have to get Lyon & Lyon to file a patent. He knew he would need accurate notes to justify and defend his patent cases. At the time he could hardly have realized how true that was—and is—for any inventor. Years later, these notes were crucial in defending Phil's patents.

I was given the job of making drawings in his journal from Phil's sketches. My first attempts were so crude that I told Phil he would be better off to use his own freehand sketches. Phil disagreed. He said we were all learning. I would improve with practice.

Phil had told Mr. Cummings he was working against time, but he hadn't expected the commitment he was getting. He told Mr. Cummings there would no doubt be many of these tubes before he was finished. Mr. Cummings again assured him these tubes were just being worked in between university jobs. In any case, Phil's was a fantastic idea, and he admired the courage it took to undertake such a project.

Work continued in this fashion for weeks, Phil redesigning and trying new ideas, Cliff helping to make new elements and taking them to Mr. Cummings. Tubes were now pumped an extra day. The higher vacuum produced better results, and each time they were ready to pump, Cliff made the journey to Emeryville for liquid air.

Cliff was returning one day with a filled container when the thermos liner in the Dewar jar sprang a leak. These containers resembled nose cones from the Flash Gordon era, and Cliff was in a crowded two-car commuter train between Emeryville and Oakland. Clouds of vapor began to spew out of the weird-looking container, causing quite a stir among the passengers around him. Someone shouted "BOMB!" and was about to pull the emergency cord. Cliff, red with embarrassment, said, "No! It's only liquid air! I'll take it outside." Taking it outside entailed standing on a very small step between cars, a very precarious perch. He managed to hold onto the container with one hand and the door frame with the other, around curves and over bumps to the next stop. By this time, his hand was numb from the supercooled fumes. Then he had to get a new container and return for more liquid air.

The Image Dissector became more sophisticated, and the problems of making it work, better defined. Now Phil became increasingly concerned with patent protection for his work. George had talked to the backers, who decided Phil should make further disclosures to Lyon & Lyon and have them prepare an immediate application for a United States Letters Patent. Therefore, on December 7th, 1926, a greatly relieved Phil left for Los Angeles to make disclosures for his first patent.

The fruit of this visit was U.S. Patent Office application number 159,540. It was signed in front of a San Francisco notary on December 21st, 1926 and filed January 7th, 1927. This application contained language and novelty that signaled the beginning of electronic television as a technological and social reality. It issued on August 16th, 1930, as patent number 1,773,980, a number many had cause to remember. In an interview some fifty years later, Samuel Smith, early patent attorney for RCA, recited it unhesitatingly from memory. Mr. Smith said the patent office had no right to grant Farnsworth such broad claims. I reminded him that had Phil not been the first in his field, they would have been unable to do so.

In late January 1927, Phil added to my responsibilities that of secretary. I was to be paid ten dollars monthly, which was used to buy a secondhand, portable Royal typewriter. It was then that Phil displayed his ability as a typist. He had gone to telegrapher's school in Salt Lake, only to find there were no job openings in the field at that time. I had not so much as set a finger to a typewriter key. I purchased a typewriter manual from the university bookstore and went to work.

Phil was still attempting to devise another principle for receiving the image beyond the usual cathode-ray tube. He contemplated using crystals whose optical properties could be altered instantly and electrically to perform a similar task. This led him to the study of conical refraction. In his 1926 journal, he describes this and its ability to produce color transmission. He invited his cousin, Arthur Crawford, now a specialist in crystallography, to come to San Francisco to do a research paper on the subject. Arthur did an excellent job on his assignment, and his work was ultimately bound in Phil's 1927 journal. Had Phil continued his work with crystals, the world might have had liquid-crystal technology some fifty years earlier. But Phil soon decided to modify and improve the cathode-ray tube to reconstruct the image at the receiver. This decision saved him much valuable time.

As precious time slipped by, Phil began to rely more on his hunches. One trick involved using a finely ruled grating over the photocathode in the Image Dissector, so that during scanning of the televised frame, high-frequency horizontal pulses would be generated automatically as the electrons were swept across the ruled lines. This process involved, besides acquiring an old German ruling apparatus designed for counting blood cells, some very painstaking and exacting procedures, usually performed by Cliff.

One day Mr. Cummings came to deliver a tube, and upon watching Cliff work a few minutes, he said, "Say, you've got enough patience to be a glassblower. Come on; I'll give you a lesson." Cliff proved to be a very apt student, taking to glassblowing like the proverbial duck to water. He learned the basics in one lesson, and soon he was taking over not only Mr. Cummings' work but also that of tube specialist Jimmy Lee. Cliff's skills increased, along with his knowledge of and feel for the various materials used in experimental tube work. Within a year he was making tubes other glassblowers had called impossible. But for the time being, Phil continued to form the photosurfaces and seal off the tubes from the pump.

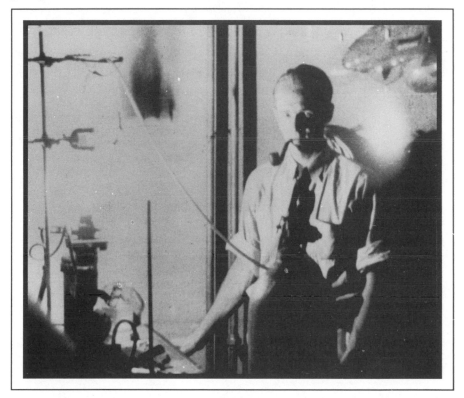

Cliff Gardner making television tubes at 202 Green Street.

Cliff also had the job of distilling potassium and sodium for forming photoelectric surfaces. These cantankerous metals were so reactive they decomposed when exposed to the water vapor of air. If placed in contact with water, they burned explosively. They came in small balls and little bars, both packed in oil. I often helped him with the tedious job of peeling off the discolored layer that formed on these materials. They were then sealed on a vacuum line and put through the purification process by distillation.

Probably because of the variety of tasks thrust upon him, rather than being accident-prone by nature, it seemed that Cliff had more than his share of accidents. One day he was distilling potassium under vacuum when the tube imploded. The molten potassium flew everywhere, including into Cliff's eyes, hands and face. In Cliff's words: "I was on the other side of the table from the sink. At that time we had a very long bench with a complicated pump system and everything on it. I had a technique: I'd been in trouble before, and I'd whistle as loud as I could, which was *loud*, to let people know I was in trouble. Well, I whistled, then ran around the table and met Carl Farnsworth, who had come to help, head-on. I had my eyes closed tight to keep the potassium out, and they really hurt. I had to knock Carl down to get at the sink. He thought I had gone crazy. I thought I was going blind. Fortunately, I was able to wash my eyes out fast enough to save my sight. I must not have had much in them, but I was burned pretty good."

Such was the nature of work in an experimental laboratory. The materials involved were often highly volatile and more than a little dangerous, but the challenge of the task at hand always outweighed the risks.

CHAPTER 9

A Picture

The human will, that force unseen
The offspring of a deathless soul,
Can hew a way to any goal,
Though wall of granite intervene.

James Allen

The main problem with the Image Dissector tube was its low sensitivity to light. Its very nature is to reflect the instantaneous light values falling on its light sensitive surface, and its performance was compromised by the primitive photoelectric materials available in 1927.

Phil started using a new trick that multiplied his usable output by a factor of ten. While the Dissector tube was on the vacuum pump, and after the light sensitive potassium had been deposited on the photocathode, he admitted a little pure hydrogen gas into the tube. The high voltages created a glowing discharge around the cathode, causing the highly reactive potassium surface to combine with the hydrogen. The resulting surface, potassium hydride, released many more electrons at a given light level.

Low output from the camera tube also made the signal quite susceptible to contamination from electrical "noise" from the hum of power lines and any other form of interference, such as the scanning currents used in the deflection coils. Shielding the Dissector from these stray signals became essential to further progress. Trial solutions took on many forms, some rather exotic, such as the iron coffin-like chamber with copper foil lining, which for a time was used as a case for the whole amplifier.

As Cliff became more proficient in tube work, he and Phil started to improve the cathode-ray tube which would ultimately serve as the receiver for the signal generated by the Image Dissector. At the beginning of 1927, the state of the art could be inferred from the fact that the best cathode-ray tube on the market was a gas-filled Western Electric tube used for early oscillographs. But the cathode-ray tubes Phil and Cliff were turning out were greatly improved for receiving television transmissions.

Seemingly endless varieties of electrode structures were tried to give the intense, sharp, small "spot" necessary for good definition and intensity in the receiver. As his technique improved, Cliff began coming up with innovative ideas of his own. At this time his ideas were chiefly concerned with better ways of putting things together, but later, as they became generic, they won him many patents.

George Everson and Les Gorrell were frequent visitors at the lab. Les would walk in jauntily and greet Phil breezily with, "Hi Phil! Got the damned thing to work yet?" This was always said in a joking manner, with a pat on the back. Les was more aware than anyone else outside the lab how much effort Phil was putting on the project to meet his deadline.

As the months slid by, we all felt the pressure to produce demonstrable results by the coming September. This tension was reflected in the rate at which the work increased to a fairly steady twelve hours a day, six days a week.

One night, going home on the ferry, Phil led me out on the deserted back deck. The sky was clear for San Francisco, and the stars were brilliant. Phil put an arm around me as shelter from the ever-present wind. Looking skyward, he asked if I thought there was life out there.

"I haven't thought much about it," I confessed.

"Don't you think it pretty egotistical to think that we, on this tiny planet we call Earth, are the only intelligent creatures in this immense universe?"

"Now that I think about it, I guess it is."

"I think there are beings out there who have far surpassed us in development, mentally and otherwise. I intend to take an expedition out there some day and find them."

"That sounds very ambitious to me."

"It *is* ambitious. We would need a carefully picked group of people, hopefully couples, each well trained in some phase of science or medicine. The spaceship would have to be large enough to be entirely self-sufficient. We would take animals for food and grow our own vegetables in hydroponic gardens, because we would be gone for a very long time. In fact, it might be up to our children or even our grandchildren to bring the ship back."

"You keep saying *we*; I hope you aren't expecting me to go along." (What would he come up with next?)

"I had hoped you would. I hate to think of going *anywhere* without you." I was glad he felt that way. Certainly, if he left this earth, I didn't want to be left behind.

"I get goose bumps just thinking about it, but when it comes right down to it, I'd rather die with you in space than live on earth without you."

"That's my girl. I knew I could count on you. Anyway, we have much to do before we could take on such a project—it may take longer than we think to get television to the commercial stage."

"Trust you to think big."

"Well, as my father said when I explained my television ideas to him, 'It's all right, son, to keep your head in the stars . . . as long as you keep your feet planted firmly on the ground.'"

"Your father was a very wise man. I know you loved him very much."

"Yes, I guess we were about as close as a father and son ever get." Then, after a short silence he said, "Pemmie, since you say you would go with me into space, how about a shorter distance? Do you still feel the same about living in San Francisco? We are now behind the schedule I had set for us, and I have begun to begrudge the two hours plus we spend on the ferry every day."

"Honey, I'm sorry to have been so selfish. I've enjoyed the cottage on Derby Street, but if we moved to the city, I could spend more time at the lab. I really enjoy being part of the action."

With the help of Les Gorrell, we found a flat on Vallejo Street on the west side of Telegraph Hill and within a week were moved in. Phil bought a secondhand Maxwell touring car to facilitate shopping for lab supplies and to act as all-around family camel. Although it was on its last legs, the boys wouldn't let the Maxwell die. It was fortunate that both Cliff and Phil were born tinkerers and very adept at impromptu repairs, because the Maxwell had more than its share of problems. Phil always carried a few spare parts so he could make repairs on the road if necessary.

The most embarrassing episode with the Maxwell happened on California Street in San Francisco. California Street is one of those long, steep hills that depend on the historic cable cars for transportation. The cars going uphill depend on underground cables and the downhill cars to pull them up, so they always have the right-of-way.

That's why one just does not stop cable cars in the middle of the block, but old Maxi seemed to have a mind of her own. She chose the middle of the block on California Street—in the middle of the cable track—to become temperamental. We could hear the clanging of the bell of a cable car coming up the hill behind us. Phil directed me to get behind the wheel, while he and Cliff jumped out and pushed the recalcitrant Maxi to the curb, barely ahead of the cable car. The passing brakeman was very upset and suggested we drive on some other street thereafter.

One Saturday night Phil and Cliff had been pumping a tube very late and discovered they were out of gas, with no service stations open. Almost without breaking stride, they marched back upstairs and mixed a cocktail from the chemical closet, mostly alcohol and ether, that had Maxi kicking up her heels all the way home.

Phil's sister Agnes graduated from high school that spring, and she and my thirteen-year-old sister Ruth came to stay with us. Soon after that, Phil's cousin Arthur Crawford wrote that a friend of his who had training in radio and electronic engineering was coming to the Bay area for some postgraduate work. He would be willing to work part-time at a reasonable wage to help defray expenses.

Phil's budget was already stretched to the limit, but he saw this as an opportunity to get some help on his amplifier problems. An arrangement was made whereby we would furnish board and room as part payment. Even though the flat was beginning to bulge, the arrangement worked to the advantage of all. Agnes went to work at the telephone company, Ruth helped at home to allow me more time at the lab, and Phil got some badly needed assistance.

The new engineer was Carl J. Christensen, a tall, angular man a few years Phil's senior, with a quiet dignity. Unfortunately, he was often inclined to view things with something of a negative attitude. Carl seemed to harbor grave doubts that Phil would ever achieve his goal of electronic television. Nevertheless, exposure to the day-to-day problems in the lab, along with Phil's solutions to them, did much to reassure him, and he became a very useful addition to the small work force, making many valuable contributions.

Paradoxically, Phil's central problem through most of 1927 was not experimental tubes at all but what is now usually considered a housekeeping item: amplifiers and amplification. Shielding the low-level, vulnerable Dissector output against stray interferences and losses was one thing; performing the actual enormous amplification of the signal over the broad range of frequencies necessary for even a low-definition picture was an accomplishment that not merely strained the state of the art in those days but far surpassed it.

Most amplification was then performed by the simple triodes of the day; these tubes offered small gains that got much worse as the range of frequencies to be amplified (the bandwidth) was increased. When enough triode tubes were used in series to give the needed amplification— in the order of millions—other problems arose. These included oscillation of the whole amplifier (motorboating) or sensitivity to mechanical vibration of the first few tubes (microphonics), as well as the basic problem of wide frequency range. It seemed each new trick they tried brought with it even more problems. This state of affairs continued through the summer. It is no exaggeration to say the transmission of a simple picture was being held up by a simple lack of amplification.

Both Phil and the tube industry made a decision at approximately the same time but separately and for different reasons. What was needed for the problem was a new variety of tube that employed an extra grid to isolate the input and output electrodes of an amplifying tube. That would give better gain and frequency response.

Because there were no shield-grid tubes on the market at the time, incredibly, Phil and Cliff started making their own. I do not mean they went out and bought existing tubes and modified them; they started from basic materials and *made their own*. It was a little like making one's own automobile tires.

The multi-layered elements necessary for these "tetrodes" presented an almost insuperable problem. The few people in the trade who were aware of what was going on at 202 Green Street found it hard to believe.

Phil taught me to use the precision spot-welder and do some of the component construction, which saved them much time. Later, Carl Christensen took over this operation, freeing me to do office work and to make Phil's drawings.

By the end of August, the men had worked out a reasonably useful design and had shaken it down to a working amplifier. The men were getting hot now, and things started to go together faster. That sort of energy and feeling can be quite contagious, and everyone was getting excited at what was coming up. Phil was now very anxious to make a successful transmission as soon as possible.

A young radio engineer named Robert Humphries was added to the staff. Bob Humphries had red curly hair and a happy disposition. That made a work force of five, counting me. I was still paid the fabulous sum of ten dollars a month for office work and filling in wherever an extra hand was needed. Phil put Bob

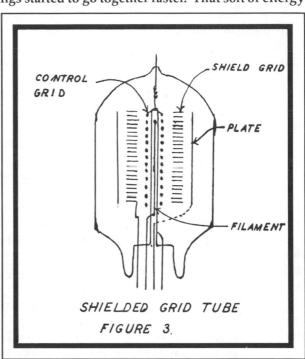

Shield-grid tube, from Phil's notes,
September 24th, 1927

to work on mountings for the latest tubes and deflection coils.

On Monday, Phil took a new Dissector off the pump, and on Tuesday, August 30th, he was ready to make a stab at his first crude transmission. The latest Dissector, a cathode-ray tube, and the improved amplifier chassis were hooked up, but with deflection only on the horizontal axis. This arrangement limited the display to a straight line.

Phil's journal entry August 30th, 1927:

"The Image Dissector tube was excited by the ten-cycle current only and was coupled to the receiving oscillograph in an attempt to obtain a line picture. Although lines appeared across the tube and the image would go bright and dark with changes in the illumination of the object, still I did not believe it to be a transmission, but only due to other currents on the input of the amplifier. This was experiment number 11."

Sensing he was getting near now, Phil had a Dissector made up embodying some final changes. Then he spent a week going through the entire apparatus, looking for anything that could be improved or made more dependable. Cliff worked on the high-voltage source, which consisted of a rotary static machine charging a large paper condenser; Humphries and Christensen worked on the focusing and deflection coils and the sine-wave generators that drove them.

On Monday, September 5th, Phil performed the hydride operations on the new Dissector and sealed it off from the vacuum pump. Once more it was mounted in the deflection "yoke" and preliminary adjustments made. Cliff put a new cathode-ray tube together, and last-minute changes were made in the ten-cycle-per-second sine-wave generator (more on this later).* On the next day, everything was connected and given a final check. Anticipation and tension were running high at this point.

The morning of September 7th, 1927, dawned with the high fog typical of San Francisco in autumn, but it had already begun to clear as we drove to the lab. With high expectations, we climbed the stairs. Phil said, "Pem, if you'll finish the drawings I left on my desk for you, I'll let you know as soon as we're ready to turn things on."

"OK, but don't you forget!" I didn't want to miss this one.

The drawings were finished and I had caught up on some typing before Phil finally appeared at the door. In the room where the receiver was set up, we waited as he took his place at the controls.

With everyone standing around the receiver, Phil called instructions to Cliff, who was in the next room with the Dissector setup.

"Put in the slide, Cliff," Phil called out.

"OK, it's in. Can you see it?" Cliff called back.

An unmistakable line appeared across the small bluish square of light on the end of the Oscillite tube. It was pretty fuzzy, but Phil adjusted the focusing coil, and the line became well defined.

"Turn the slide a quarter turn, Cliff," Phil instructed. Sure enough, the received line followed suit, turning 90 degrees.

"That's it, folks! We've done it! There you have electronic television," Phil announced, with a trace of a tremor in his voice. He hurried in to the transmitter to give Cliff a chance to see this historic transmission.

Everyone stood glued to the spot, the import of what we were seeing

---

"On Admittance Neutralization [from Phil's notebook].

"The uses of this idea are almost limitless. It may be used to neutralize the output capacity of the Image Dissector, thus giving 1,000 to 100,000 times more signal voltage. It may be used to neutralize the inner stage capacity of amplifiers, thereby making it possible to build amplifier systems covering broad bands of frequencies, and to amplify very high frequencies."

slowly sinking in. This was it, all right: there was a raster, with moving picture present. When Cliff saw it, his response was a characteristic, "Well, I'll be damned!"

"What do you know!" Carl Christensen commented dryly, "If I wasn't seeing it with my own two eyes, I wouldn't believe it."

I was jumping up and down in my youthful exuberance.

George Everson arrived about then. Seeing him, Phil and Cliff resumed their places.

"Stand here, George, where the light from the window won't reflect off the tube." Phil told him. Again he and Cliff went through their routine, and again the bright line obligingly turned on its side.

"What you're seeing, George, is the transmission of a single line. But this proves we can easily get a two- dimensional picture by adding the vertical scanning currents and magnetic deflecting coils," Phil explained.

As George took in the significance of the situation, he

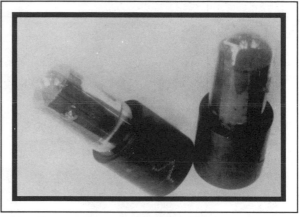

The Image Dissectors, 1927. The one on the left is the one used in the first all-electronic TV transmission.

became very jubilant, pumping Phil's hand and slapping him on the back at the same time.

"There's no doubt about it, Phil; you *have* got a picture. My faith in you all these months has been justified!" Then sobering, he added, "Of course you'll want more of a picture before you show it to the Crocker group."

Phil agreed. Then they decided to wire the news to Les Gorrell in Los Angeles. The wire read simply, "THE DAMNED THING WORKS!"

Top:
Carl J. Christensen
with camera.
Center:
Phil and Pem (l);
Robert Humphries (r).
Below: Cliff Gardner
with receiver
(from the Farnsworth
journal, 1927).
This crew produced the
first all-electronic
television picture
on September 7, 1927.

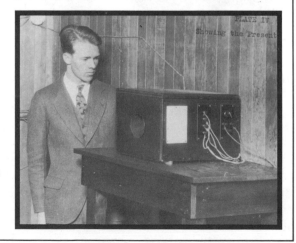

CHAPTER 10

Backer Talk

Early in 1928, word of what was happening at 202 Green Street began to be whispered about in San Francisco financial circles. Nothing made us more aware of that than a visit from Les Gorrell. Les brought around his friend Helen Bacigalupi, who sang soprano with the San Francisco Opera Company. Les announced that they had just been married. Helen's lovely olive complexion and long raven hair were beautifully framed by a full-length, luxurious ermine coat, a wedding present to Helen, which Les had just insured for ten thousand dollars. Then he called our attention to a sporty new Phaeton touring car out front, a two-seated convertible.

When the excitement had subsided, Les turned to Phil. "Phil, old man, we owe it all to you. I sold part of my television holdings to pay for this. There's a lot of interest in your work down at the stock exchange. You should cash in on it and live it up a little. Buy Pem a new fur coat; she deserves it." Phil said he would have to think it over. Les also told us he was buying a house in San Francisco so his parents could live with them.

Later, Phil asked me how I felt about a fur coat. I told him there were many things more important to me, but I did think we both needed some new clothes to be more presentable. Our two-hundred-dollar-per-month salary allowed only bargain-counter, sale clothes. The subject was left in abeyance while the work continued.

By this time, Phil and Agnes had succeeded in bringing the rest of their family to San Francisco. Phil hired his brother Carl and taught him to wind deflection coils. This was a continuing job, because new coils were needed every time there was a change in the Dissector tube or oscillight. Carl became very good at it. Phil had also hired my brother

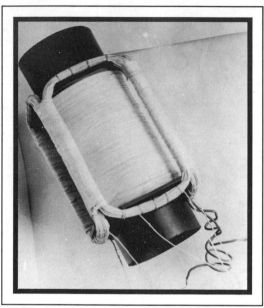

The magnetic deflecting coils used around the Image Dissector, 1928.

Art part-time to do odd jobs to give Carl Christensen and Bob Humphries time for more important work and was a big help to Phil.

One day Mr. Mann came to the lab with a message, supposedly from Mr. Bishop, that it looked bad for Phil to hire relatives. Phil found that quite upsetting. He was paying Carl and Art only half the amount he had paid Carl Christensen and Bob Humphries, who had been performing these jobs. He needed Christensen and Humphries for more important work. As for me, I was still being paid only ten dollars a month, and now I was serving as secretary, draftsman, and lab technician, having become quite proficient in fabricating tube elements on the precision spot-welder.

After dinner, Phil suggested we take a walk. There was little chance for a private conversation at the flat, outside of our bedroom. He told me about his visit from Mr. Mann.

"What are you going to do about it?"

"I'll have to let you all go, honey; I can't chance an upset at this stage of the game."

"I can type your letters and do your drawings at home, dear, but who will keep track of things at the office?"

"Well, I called George. He has a young man by the name of Jim Atkinson who has acted as his personal secretary. He thinks Jim can spend enough time at the lab to take care of the necessary work there."

"Oh, yes, I remember Jim. He was at our Christmas party last year, but what about Cliff, Carl, and Art?"

"I could never get along without Cliff, nor do I intend to try. They can see that. I'm sorry about Carl and Art; I'm afraid they'll have to find another job."

"Oh, they'll find a job. But you are the one who is losing out."

"Yes, I know."

We were now near the Alhambra Theater, so Phil suggested we go in to see a movie. That was probably what he had had in mind in the first place.

Hiring Carl, Phil's brother, along with Art, my brother, had made Phil's enterprise the focus of our families' lives. In addition to Phil's family, my older sister Verona's unhappy marriage had ended in divorce, and she had come to San Francisco with her two-year-old daughter Virginia. Verona was then working in an overall factory, cutting patterns. Since I was no longer allowed to work at the lab, I became bored with so little to do, so I also took a job there, sewing overalls. A short time later, Verona and I were hired in a lamp shade factory, trimming lamp shades at a higher wage.

One day Phil called me at work. Very excited, he told me to quit my job and meet him out front in one hour. Since he would not take no for an answer, I complied with his request. As I walked out the front door, there was Phil sitting in a new Chrysler Roadster with the top down, a broad happy smile on his face. My mind was racing as he opened the door for me. I knew he must have sold some of his television interest but demanded an explanation.

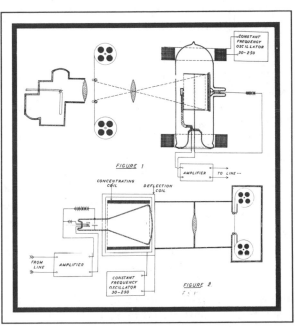

Pem's sketch, showing the first Farnsworth setup for transmitting movie film, 1928.

He said he had been thinking about how much he was at the mercy of his backers' whims and had sold one percent of his holdings for five thousand dollars. He felt we needed a dependable car and some new clothes, so he had come to take me shopping. We visited a ladies' shop and a men's store, but kept our purchases within reason. After paying some medical bills for Mother Farnsworth and for Verona, he put the remainder in savings.

That evening, we walked up to the top of Telegraph Hill. The last block was in steps, because of the steepness of the incline. The view of the city from the top was sensational. Phil pointed down the sheer face of the hill facing the Bay to the roof of our lab at 202 Green Street. That is at the northern end of what is called the Barbary Coast, from which tall-masted sailing vessels once set sail.

After a while, Phil talked of the things on his mind. · He told me about the image-analyzing tube he had designed. I had seen it demonstrated but had no idea of its importance. He said that its ability to magnify would allow doctors to study germs and find ways to control them and also to study body cells where trouble was suspected. In fact, it would be a wonderful tool for any phase of science. His concern was that he had neither the time nor the money to develop it.

He said he would do well if he were allowed even to take television to its commercial stage. The sale he had made today was only a small beginning of what would happen if he were able to achieve this goal.

"Oh, you will, Phil, you will!" I assured him. "Come on; I'll race you down the hill."

I was no match for him, so he waited, caught me in his arms, and whirled me around in the dance of exuberance I had come to know so well.

By May 1928, the Crocker group had become increasingly impatient, wanting to know when it was going to "see some dollars" in Phil's "gadget." Phil had set a standard of performance for each part of his television system, and he and his men were working long hours to reach his goal, but the system was still a long way from producing anything in the way of a meaningful return on the backers' investment.

One night Phil came home very late and told me he had carefully tested all parts of the apparatus and felt he was now ready to try for a two-dimensional picture. In fact, he planned to do this the next day and wanted me to see it. At the lab the next morning, I noted that the long cables running from the transmitter in the next room had been connected to the receiver. Phil had asked George Everson to be there at ten.

George arrived early, and there was an air of great expectation in the lab. Cliff was stationed at the transmitter. After making a few minor adjustments, Phil called to him.

"Cliff, is the arc light going OK?"

"Just fine, Phil," Cliff answered.

"Put in the slide!" Phil directed.

Almost at once, there appeared on the tiny bluish screen a fuzzy triangle.

"There it is, folks! A two-dimensional picture!" Phil's great pleasure and excitement were apparent in his voice despite his effort to remain calm. We all stood for a moment in stunned silence; then I gave him a very big, unbusinesslike hug. He made some fine adjustments, and the triangle became more clear but still a little vague in spots. He was explaining to George, "Those blurred places are due to the irregularities in the photosensitive surface. We've been having the devil's own time with this."

"But, Phil!" George said, clapping him on the shoulder, "that's some-thing you can work out! The important thing is that you actually have a two-dimensional picture!"

Phil was trying for a better focus. All eyes were still glued to this modern miracle, when suddenly the triangle disappeared and in its place was a cloudlike apparition flowing from bottom to top of the picture.

"What's that?" George called to Cliff. "We're getting something that looks like smoke!"

With visions of his precious baby all going up in smoke in his hour of triumph, Phil rushed to the transmitter. He was back in a trice with Cliff close behind. Seeing the broad grins on their faces, everyone breathed a sigh of relief.

"Tell them what it was, Cliff!"

"I was just trying something," Cliff explained, "First, I put my face in sideways, between the arc light and the camera, but I got no response, and it was too hot anyway. Then I blew a cloud of smoke from my cigarette so it would rise up past the viewing area."

"Stay here, Cliff; let me take your cigarette. I want you to see this," Phil told him.

When Cliff saw the smoke billowing up on the miniature screen, he gave a whistle and exclaimed, "Holy smoke! Just look at that!"

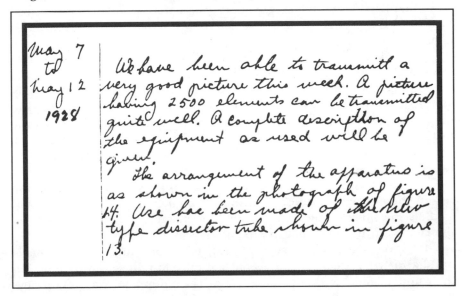

May 7 to May 12 1928

We have been able to transmitt a very good picture this week. A picture having 2500 elements can be transmitted quite well. A complete description of the equipment as used will be given.

The arrangement of the apparatus is as shown in the photograph of figure 14. Use has been made of the new type dissector tube shown in figure 13.

Excerpt from Phil's notes, May 1928

Phil came back in, and everyone was shaking hands and slapping backs. George was wringing Phil's hand, and they were congratulating each other. Then sobering, Phil said, "You realize of course, George, that our ability to see that smoke rising means we'll have no trouble transmitting moving objects, whether it's moving pictures, sporting events, or anything else that moves."

"This is all very encouraging, Phil," George told him, "but I think you should show this to our backers before you decide to make any more improvements. You know they're getting very impatient. Mr. Fagan asked me again yesterday if I could see any dollars in your gadget yet." George was also finding it difficult to be patient with Phil's "eternally fiddling around," as he expressed it.

To George's great relief, Phil agreed and suggested an appointment be made immediately with the backers. Nevertheless, he warned George that there was still much work to do before they could hope to generate any big interest and get anything like what this invention was really worth.

Despite Phil's reservations, an appointment was set up for eleven the next morning, and when the time arrived, the lab was all slicked up. A state of tension prevailed; everyone on hand was keenly aware of how much was at stake. By that night their jobs would either be more secure or nonexistent.

As the awaited steps were heard on the stairs, everyone went to his post, and Phil went to the door to greet his guests. George led the way, ushering in R. J. Hanna, vice-president of Standard Oil of California, W. H. Crocker and his son W. W. Crocker, James J. Fagan, and Roy N. Bishop. This occasion was the first time this distinguished group had been reassembled since that fateful afternoon more than a year before when they had agreed to give Phil a year and twenty-five thousand dollars to prove the worth of his ideas.

Phil turned the television receiver on as the assemblage gathered. They had all greeted Phil warmly and were in a jocular mood. As the equipment warmed up, Phil explained they would see at this time only simple geometric figures. Then he went in to check on the transmitter to make sure all was as it should be. After a few minutes, his guests began to fidget.

"When're we going to see some dollars in this thing, Farnsworth?" called Mr. Fagan.

That was just the cue Phil had been waiting for. Phil's showmanship seized the moment. "Here's something a banker will understand," Phil said, as the shimmering image of an unmistakable "$" sign appeared in the center of the small bluish screen.

"Well, that's your answer, Mr. Fagan," George told him. This made quite a hit with them all and served not only to relieve the tension, but their understandable skepticism as well. The equipment was put through its paces, including the smoke demonstration, which was at least an indication of what was to come. Then they all went in to Phil's office to talk it over.

Mr. Bishop started the discussion with congratulations to Phil for producing the promised television transmission, although it had cost forty thousand dollars to get to this point. He added that this was understandable because Phil really had had little idea of what he was up against when he had made his predictions. He also pointed out that they had fulfilled their part of the bargain as well. They thought it was time to decide what was to be done with their project. As bankers, they thought it would take a pile of money as high as San Francisco's tallest building to bring the idea to its commercial stage. Mr. Bishop suggested that the venture should be sold as quickly as possible to one of the big companies already in that field.

"That is all true, Mr. Bishop," Phil acknowledged, "but I was hoping I could finish my idea of a continuous film setup and a telephoto demonstration. Either one of these could bring us to the point of realizing a much greater profit than we would realize if we sell out now."

When asked how long this would take, Phil told them he thought he could do it in another month.

"I would be in favor of giving Phil another month," said young Mr. Crocker, who had made a habit of dropping in on Phil to watch the boys work. "Then we can reassess the situation and go from there." They all agreed with this proposition and wished Phil well; the meeting ended.

In telling his men of this decision, Phil warned them that a month was not very long, and they really had a job ahead of them. That evening after dinner, he asked me to grab a coat and walk with him down to the Alhambra to see a movie. This was his favorite way to clear his head of problems.

As we walked the now familiar route to the Alhambra, Phil expressed his apprehension to me about what had transpired that morning.

"I don't know how much longer I can count on this group to support our work, Pem."

"What are you going to do?"

"I know that I can perfect this invention and make it commercially viable, but it's going to take some time. And Mr. Bishop was probably right; it will also take quite a bit of money. But if I can persuade the backers not to sell out now, then once television does become commercial, we'll have all the money we could ever dream of. We'll be able to build and operate our own independent laboratory."

"And then what would you do?"

"I don't really know. But I do know that television is just the beginning. The point is, I want to be able to follow my imagination in whatever direction it takes me. To do that, I need to hang on to what we've already created and take it all the way to the marketplace. But I'm afraid these guys are just in it for the quick buck. I'm afraid that, sooner than later, they are going to force me to sell out."

With that he fell deep into his own thoughts, and we walked silently the few remaining blocks to the theater.

Returning to our flat after the movie, Phil wrote down a plan of action. After a briefing next morning, his men caught his enthusiasm and, thus motivated, went to work with a renewed vigor at their assigned tasks.

In June, Carl Christensen completed his postgraduate work and returned to Utah, leaving Phil badly in need of a circuit man. Donald K. Lippincott, who worked for the law firm now filing Phil's patents, recommended Robert E. "Tobe" Rutherford for the job. When Phil learned of Tobe's expertise in circuitry, he hired him, even though his salary was higher and he had to pay him personally. When Mr. Mann reported this action to the backers, word came back that in no way was Phil to add to his lab force. There was even talk of closing the lab. So, assuring Tobe he would be rehired at the earliest opportunity, Phil had to let him go.

Phil handled this disappointment, as he had previous ones, with a squaring of the jaw and bulldog determination to succeed no matter what the odds.

CHAPTER 11

Phil Meets the Press

The oscillograph tubes Phil used in his receiver were not much of a problem. Cliff could turn them out at the rate of two or three a day, with improvements. They also had the coil system, for magnetic focusing at both the receiver and the transmitter, down to a formula. The Image Dissector, vital to the telephoto demonstration, was another matter. Although significant progress had been made, the transmitted picture was still fuzzy.

From Phil's bound Journal number two dated week ending March 3rd, 1928:

"The first part of the week was spent in preparing for a demonstration of our telephoto apparatus, which was given Thursday. The rest of the week was spent in preparing for a demonstration of television . . . We demonstrated to Dr. L. F. Fuller (UC Berkeley) and Mr. James Cranston of General Electric Company."

Mr. Cranston was greatly impressed with Phil's image analyzer. He said whether or not Phil did anything with television, this device, with its tremendous magnification, would really be important. It was decided to make a disclosure of television to General Electric Labs.

During this period, young W. W. (his father called him Willie) Crocker continued dropping in occasionally to see how things were going. He would perch on a lab bench for long periods of time, asking questions and showing interest in the work. Thus, when the time came for the financing group to reassemble and reevaluate the situation, Phil, aware of the growing interest in his project, came to the meeting with more self-assurance, even though he had not achieved all the goals he had set.

The atmosphere of this meeting was subtly different from that of the previous one, in which his goals had been so clearly differentiated from those of his backers. Then, Phil had felt that his chances of continuing on with his work at the lab beyond the month given him were slim. Now, he was treated less like a boy wonder and more as a serious worker, someone not to be taken lightly. That change could have been due partly to the realization that television was fast becoming a salable commodity, thanks to some recent publicity and partly to the respect of the younger Mr. Crocker. Of course, Les Gorrell and George Everson were also frequent visitors to the lab. George, aside from his natural interest in the project, felt a big responsibility to the backing syndicate for bringing them in.

The original partnership (l to r):
Les Gorrell, Phil Farnsworth and George Everson

Although Phil never lost sight of his ultimate goal of taking television to the people, he had to content himself with achieving that a small step at a time. That he had lost none of the charisma that had enabled him to sell himself and his ideas was apparent.

This meeting resulted in the financing group agreeing to continue their support, provided the original three partners put up their share. This new arrangement obligated each participant to contribute funds commensurate with the size of his holdings. One other stipulation required that the work be confined to television per se, with no side trips into telephotography, electron microscopy, or any other application.

The singular purpose of this new accord was to concentrate on producing the best possible picture in order to attract a buyer. After all, as the backers frequently pointed out, they were bankers and had no wish to branch out into the television business.

Phil was satisfied with this setup, even though it meant that as the largest single shareholder, his assessment exceeded that of any of the others and would require him to sell off portions of his stock to raise his share of the funds. Although he recognized the temporary nature of this arrangement, he saw it as an interim step enroute to his goal, a means to an end. George and Les felt that it was an equitable arrangement, because the backers had invested more than twice the amount originally committed.

Despite the new structure, however, the bankers were still anxious to cash in and reap a handsome profit, so it was understood that every effort should be made to find a buyer.

Privately, Phil still continued to hope that he would somehow find a way to continue his work independently and avoid being gobbled up by a large company.

Phil with Image Dissector and camera
at the Crocker Lab

In his report, Phil tried to emphasize that he was handicapped by not having enough skilled help. They all agreed to absorb their share of the added expense entailed in additional hiring, at least for the time being, and Tobe Rutherford was rehired March 5th.

On March 15th, Harry Lubcke, a brilliant young electrical engineer soon to graduate from the University of California at Berkeley, joined the staff. An ambitious man, Harry was thorough in his investigations, very much "by the book," and made voluminous notes. He was also very interested in patents. Cliff and Tobe much preferred to perform the experiments than write about them. Phil immediately assigned Harry Lubcke to working out some of the theories in his admittance neutralization amplifier. This idea further improved his television picture, and gained him another patent.

Phil was always available to his men. Aside from frequent group meetings in his office, his routine always involved morning rounds. He would examine the work on all benches, answer any questions, make suggestions when they immediately came to him, or take the problem back to his desk for further consideration. He almost always came up with workable solutions, even though at times he found it necessary to approach the problem from another angle. When not thus occupied, he was helping wherever his help was required. As Tobe Rutherford liked to say, "You worked *with* Phil, not *for* him. He never asked us to do anything he couldn't or wouldn't do." His men held a great respect for this process and considered him something of a miracle worker.

Phil always encouraged his men to think for themselves. If they came up with an original idea that furthered the work, he helped them formulate it into patentable material and had it filed in their name. If he contributed materially to the idea, the patent was filed in both their names. He made inventors of those who exhibited an ability to extend themselves toward original thought. Cliff, on the crest of the wave when it came to building high-art vacuum tubes, came up with many ideas that resulted in patents.

It was the custom then, as now, for workers to assign any patents to the company for which they worked, and of course that practice included Phil's contributions. Each patent added to the value of the company. Usually, a worker's wages were supposed to cover his contributions to the company, whether or not his work was patentable. In Phil's case, because he was a part owner of the company, he benefited directly. Some companies now pay a bonus for each patent. During Phil's last few years at ITT, he was given fifty dollars per patent and a Christmas bonus ranging from four thousand dollars to eight thousand dollars, certainly a token amount, considering the sums they derived from many of his patents.

Phil had realized early his need for acquiring a great amount of knowledge and had set up a mental filing system for instant recall. One night, when he was struggling with a particularly difficult problem, he told me about it.

"Pem, I'm sure I have the answer to this in my head; I just can't seem to put it together."

"Well, you've told me when trying to remember something, not to force it. Go on about what you're doing, and it will come to you. I find it usually works. Have you tried that?"

"Yes, but tonight I'm going to try something a little different. I'll try to fall asleep thinking about it and see what happens."

In the early hours of the following morning, I was awakened by the sound of Phil's voice:

"Pem! Pem! It worked!"

Shocked out of a sound sleep, I shot bolt upright in bed. "Phil! What is it? What worked?" I was having trouble orienting myself to a state of wakefulness.

"My idea worked! Pem, I went to sleep thinking about that problem, and I was just awakened with the answer! Pem! It's wonderful!"

"That's just dandy! Now you can work twenty-four hours a day instead of sixteen!" Of course I was happy he had found his answer, but I feared that working his brain all night, added to his long hours at the lab, would be his undoing. I felt he really needed his rest.

"I'm sorry I startled you, sweetheart. Go back to sleep; it's only three o'clock. I have to go and put this in my notes."

It seemed hours before he came back to bed so I could tell him I understood. He continued to use this method whenever he had a problem that refused to budge, and I continued to worry that he was not getting adequate rest. He seemed to derive energy from his very creative process, however, and because his creativity was at its height, his energy seemed boundless. Many times, he ran into what appeared to be insurmountable obstacles, but his stream of consciousness, like a stream of water when blocked, made other channels and found a way around, through, or over the problem. Thus, the work at the lab progressed.

Until this time, the lab machining work had been done by the machine shop on the lower floor of our building. Now, as Phil's needs were greater and time was of the essence, he hired Thomas Lynch, a very capable machinist. He also hired Harry Lyman, an excellent radio man. Since Carl Christensen had gone back to Utah and Robert Humphries had left, Phil now had five men, all well trained in some phase of the work. With Phil's inspired leadership, Cliff's work on tubes, and the added help of Rutherford on circuitry, Lyman on broadcasting, Lubcke largely on the theoretical side, and Lynch on precision machining, they were a capable, close-knit, effective group. Then there was me. I was Phil's personal secretary/draftsman, friend, confidante, and lover.

I had been making up the monthly statements and payroll for Mr. Mann, who took them to Mr. Bishop, who made a check from which Mr. Mann paid the bills. That was fine for a time, until we began receiving letters from our creditors, saying they had not received payment.

Mr. Mann had made life difficult for Phil in many ways, but his meddling became even worse when his claim to be an acoustical engineer turned out to be a deception. As a representative of the Johns Manville Asbestos Company, Mr. Mann had landed a contract for acoustically treating the beautiful Grace Cathedral, San Francisco's largest and finest church. After spending many thousands of dollars, they were still experiencing reverberations from their organ.

When called upon for advice by Mr. Mann, Phil quickly spotted the problem. The legs of the church pews were set on heavy felt pads to avoid resonance with the organ. Mr. Mann had bolted them to the floor through the felt, making the padding useless. Because Phil considered this a rather obvious error, he may have communicated some of his feelings to Mr. Mann. That would have been unintentional, because it was Phil's nature to be tactful and considerate in his dealings with people. At any rate, from then on, Phil's problems with Mr. Mann increased.

As for the bills, Phil paid them from his personal account.

"Why don't you report this to Mr. Bishop?" I asked Phil when it happened the second time.

"Mr. Mann has the trust of the Crocker group or he wouldn't have this position, Pem. On the other hand, I'm on shaky ground as far as they are concerned, and at this point, I don't want to do anything that might rock the boat. If we give Bert Mann enough rope, he'll hang *himself*." Accordingly, Phil continued to pay the bills whenever Mr. Mann failed to do so.

Recorded in Phil's notes are frequent analyses of the problems standing in his way of getting a good picture. From the beginning, they had been plagued by interference from the 500-cycle scanning and synchronizing currents. These were provided by motor generators, because they needed DC current. The fluctuation in the currents due to the light and dark areas in the picture being transmitted caused a surging in the motors. This surging caused interference to be introduced into the picture signal going from the Image Dissector to the Oscillight at the receiver. It was a seeming impossibility to screen it out at the receiving end.

After trying everything they could think of, Phil hit upon the idea of producing a carrier wave by placing a 25-line opaque grating over the picture to be transmitted. This effectively cut out both the 500-cycle waves and their lower harmonics, eliminating much of the trouble.

At this point, although the men each had areas of expertise, television was beyond their experience. On the other hand, Phil had gone from a bare loft to a television transmission within one year, a fact that spoke for itself. Therefore, even though some of the ideas Phil tried were, to say the least, unorthodox, the "gang" followed him unquestioningly. As they became more familiar with the problems, they were able to carry more of the load.

Another persistent problem Phil had was a double or shadow image at the receiver, created by the return scan line. He solved this problem ingeniously, by using the grid to cut off the signal during one-half of the cycle (the return half), and this process was patented. This became known as his famous "Blacker than Black" case and was one of his most important patents. It survived eleven years of interference in the Patent Office.

Up to this time Phil had been frustrated in his attempts to get a Dissector tube with a flat, optically clear end, to cut out distortion. He had been told by all the glassblowers he consulted that this was not possible. The glass was not sufficiently strong to withstand the difference in pressure of inside a high-vacuum tube and the outside atmospherical pressure. Phil had instilled in his men the motto that nothing was impossible, but like the ram butting the dam, it took more effort. He and Cliff had discussed this flat-ended tube many times; now Phil again broached the subject. "Cliff, as I see it, we just have to have a Dissector with a flat lens end!"

Cliff's artistry with glass was by now growing by leaps and bounds. It is difficult to visualize, with modern automated tube-making techniques, what it was like to build a tube with a hand-held torch and an air tube in one's mouth.

"Well, I don't know, Phil, but I'll work on it and see what happens."

Some years later, Cliff described the techniques he developed: "It was tricky, because all the other glassblowers thought the tube would implode. I didn't know any better, so I went ahead. At first I had the devil of a time, because in those days we didn't have such things as glass lathes or multiple stationary fires that you could move your work around in.

"Finally, I got a turntable used to grind lenses and mounted a small furnace I had made on it. Then I clamped the tube inside in a vertical position and closed the furnace, bringing the temperature up to where I could work on it. Tobe had ground a piece of optically clear glass, used in furnace doors, to the required thickness and size, then polished it. This I laid on top of the tube. Once it was in place, it was fairly simple to heat it up and make the seal. I got so that by turning the work slowly, I could seal it in only one time around. I would let it cool down, then open the furnace and go on to finish the tube."

When asked whether any of his tubes actually imploded, he said, "Oh yes, every once in a while! The first one I remember well. I was standing there with the tube in my hands, and all at once, poof! It wasn't there anymore, and I had tiny slivers of glass in my eyes and face, as well as my hands. I was rushed to the hospital and got fixed up. Luckily there really wasn't much damage, but I had these little red dots all over my face."

That was an understatement. We were quite afraid for his eyes, and he was just plain lucky to get off without more serious damage.

Typical of Cliff, he went right on making tubes, but Phil held him up until he could work with the Corning Glass Company engineers to develop a glass with greater strength. At the same time, he arranged for special tube blanks from our own molds. That was advantageous, but there was still a continuing necessity to seal the optical flats in the ends of the Dissectors.

With the new Dissector, improvements in the amplifier, and Tobe's expertise in circuitry, they began to get better results.

From Phil's journal entry for May 7-12, 1928:

"We have been able to transmit a very good picture this week. A picture having 2500 elements can be transmitted quite well."

At this point, the backing syndicate decided the demonstration was good enough to impress any possible prospect, and with virtually no advance notice, it suspended funds and closed the lab. George Everson came to Phil's aid, convincing the backers that a continuously working demonstration was essential if they expected to find a buyer for the project.

There followed weeks of many demonstrations of the apparatus, interspersed with periods of downtime to allow for improvements Phil had thought up. From Phil's journal for the week of August 6-11:

"This week the pictures are infinitely better than had ever been possible with our apparatus before this time."

Cliff had worked hard to get extra tubes made. He now announced that he wanted to go to Baker, Oregon, to marry his girlfriend, Lola Buker, with whom he had been corresponding since coming to San Francisco. Phil loaned him our new Chrysler convertible, and he set off with our best wishes.

He was back in less than two weeks with his bride. Lola was a tall, willowy girl with large, expressive brown eyes and a pleasant disposition. They rented a small apartment. With Cliff moved out and my sister Ruth having returned to Provo when my father remarried, Phil and I were alone for the first time since we left Hollywood. We rented a small efficiency apartment with a wall bed which folded up into a closet during the day. Although we had enjoyed having Cliff and Ruth with us, it was heaven to be alone once again.

In late August, a much improved Dissector was completed, and to quote from Phil's notes, "The picture was improved (again) tenfold."

Phil had made an effort to keep quiet about what was happening at 202 Green Street, hoping to preserve his lead in electronic television. Now, however, to stir up enough interest to attract a buyer, the backers decided it was time to make a public announcement. Therefore, a press conference was called at the lab for September 1st, 1928.

On the day of the demonstration, Phil came home in high spirits but would say little about what had transpired that day. The next evening we took Cliff and Lola to a downtown movie at the new Fox Theater. Eddie Peabody, one of Phil's favorite performers, was appearing on stage with his banjo.

After the show, Phil drove us down Market Street. Stopping to buy a morning paper from a shouting newsboy, he handed it to me and told me to open it. There, on the front page of the second section, in glaring headlines, was the following article.

The excitement in the car was electric. I begged Phil to hurry and get us home so we could read more than the headlines. At our apartment,

San Francisco Chronicle

SAN FRANCISCO, CAL., MONDAY, SEPTEMBER 3, 1928

S. F. Man's Invention to Revolutionize Television

Young Genius and Part of His New Black Light Machine

NEW PLAN BANS ROTATING DISC IN BLACK LIGHT

W. W. Crocker, R. N. Bishop Head Local Capitalists Backing Genius

Two major advances in television were announced yesterday by a young inventor who has been quietly working away in his laboratory in San Francisco and has evolved a system of television basically different from any system yet placed in operation.

The inventor is Philo T. Farnsworth, and local capitalists, headed by W. W. Crocker and Roy N. Bishop, are financing the experiments and have aided him in obtaining basic patents on his system.

In any method of transmitting moving images at a distance, some means must be evolved of breaking the image into pin points of light.

These points are translated into electrical impulses, the electrical impulses are collected at the receiving end and translated back into light, and the image results.

NEW PRINCIPLE APPLIED

All television systems now in use employ a revolving disc, two feet in diameter, to break up or "scan" the receiving end, and the two discs must revolve at precisely the same instant and at precisely the same speed or blurred vision results.

Farnsworth's system employs no moving parts whatever. Instead of moving the machine, he varies the electric current that plays over the image and thus gets the necessary scanning.

The system is thus simple in the extreme, and one of the major mechanical obstacles to the perfection of television is thereby removed.

It was through this simplicity that he achieved his second great advance, the cutting in half of the wave band length necessary to prevent television broadcasts interfering with each other. The importance of this is manifest, inasmuch as it requires approximately four times the wave band length for television than ordinary sound broadcasting requires. Farnsworth has cut this television wave band in half and is hoping for still further reduction.

PERFECT MOTION RECORDS

His system sends twenty pictures per second, so motion is perfectly recorded, and there are 8000 elements, or pin points of light, in each picture to insure fine detail. The laboratory model he has built transmits the image on a screen one and one-quarter inches square. It is a queer looking little image in bluish light now, one that frequently smudges and blurs, but the basic principle is achieved and perfection is now a matter of engineering.

The sending tube which is the heart of Farnsworth's transmitting set is about the size of an ordinary quart jar that a housewife uses for preserving fruit, and the receiving tube containing the screen is even smaller. Farnsworth estimates the receiving apparatus could easily be attached to an ordinary radio set and can be manufactured to retail at $100 or less.

Farnsworth is a native of Provo, Utah, and conceived the idea for his television set while a student at Brigham Young University there. He was discovered by George Everson and Leslie Gorrell, who brought the set to the attention of research engineers at the California Institute of Technology. These experts pronounced it workable and helped Farnsworth obtain financial backing. The research laboratories are at 202 Green street.

Philo T. Farnsworth holding the sending and receiving tubes of his new television set.

True Electrical Scanning
Radical Television Step

Smooth, Clearly Defined Images Claimed for
Revolutionary San Francisco Invention

Perfection of electrical scanning is claimed for a new television system, which means that the inherent limitation of the mechanical scanning disk now used in television, an idea over ⅓ years old, is about to be cast aside. Motion pictures only require 16 "frames" a second to give clear images. The Farnsworth system can give 30 or more. The number of points which make up the ordinary television picture are very limited, giving rather crude images. The system outlined below claims 8000 points, with 12,000 as a possibility. Last but not least is the statement that this can be sold under $100, an essential requirement of any television instrument if it is to be popular. This appears as one of the most advanced developments of the last five years in radio.

SPECIAL TO THE CHRISTIAN SCIENCE MONITOR

SAN FRANCISCO—A television system which gives promise of revolutionizing the visual department of radio has been developed by a young San Francisco inventor after five years of patient research.

This new invention, the work of Philo T. Farnsworth, differs materially from the present type of television apparatus. Most radical of its features is a new type of "photo electric image dissecting tube," which pro̶ obviates the use of mechanical moving parts—one of the limitations of existing television sets. It is this tube, visualized by Mr. Farnsworth when still a student in Brigham Young University, Provo, Utah, that has taken years of experimenting and research to evolve.

The transmitter tube used by Mr. Farnsworth is about a foot long and three to four inches in diameter. It is a special photo electric cell which pro̶ an electric ' the

Left: The first Image Dissector tube to transmit two dimensions.
Right: An excerpt from the Christian Science Monitor.

I read the article aloud amid frequent outbursts of joy and consternation. Phil's beaming face suddenly clouded. "This leaves us wide open to our competition." That was a sobering thought. "Although we're now years ahead of the pack, our lack of adequate financing means we will be working under a severe handicap. We have proven in the past two years that we have something the big companies don't have, however. Our small size and method of operating allows us to maneuver like a speedboat alongside their juggernauts. But speedboats eventually run out of gas. We have our work cut out for us, that's for sure."

The press had been full of reports from the East Coast, mostly from Bell Labs, Westinghouse, and Jenkins Television Company in Baltimore. Baird Television in London was also frequently in the news. Baird was selling make-it-yourself disc television receiver kits and maintaining a limited broadcasting schedule. All these workers were using mechanical methods.

The Farnsworth story caught the fancy of the news media and, through them, the public. The news services picked it up and sent it around the world. They played up the story of how a young farm boy had come up with the answer to a method of practical television when so many large research groups with unlimited funds had been unable to do so. Utah and Idaho both claimed him as their own, and rightfully so; they had helped forge this remarkable being.

His dogged determination had brought Phil to a point of recognition, but his awareness that much remained to be done to bring television to the public was apparent when he called his men together the next day and told them simply,

"From here we can go further."

CHAPTER 12

Friction

With all the publicity after the press demonstration, the banking group decided the time had come to cash in on their investment, its efforts to find a buyer were therefore redoubled. Unfortunately, the likeliest candidates, the big companies that had pioneered in other areas of radio and electronics, had heavily invested in mechanical television systems and were not yet ready to accept the futility of their approach. One notable exception was Dr. Vladimir Zworykin, presently employed by the Westinghouse Corporation, who was working on ideas first expounded by his Russian professor, Boris Rosing. Because Dr. Zworykin had been unsuccessful in designing a workable electronic camera tube, he was still using mechanical scanning discs.

In this hard-pressed period, Phil would gladly have settled for a small flat fee for a license under his patents that he expected to be worth millions. Those who had witnessed his demonstrations seemed thrilled with the wonder of his accomplishments, although few were sufficiently interested to invest. They were entirely myopic as to the full revolutionary implications of the Farnsworth invention, for they still hoped that within their own companies they might develop something to justify the large sums already invested in spinning discs.

Phil was confident that his patents and his very real contributions—not only to television but to the burgeoning new field of electronics in general—were the only valid claims in this emerging new realm of communication. The professors of electrical engineering at Stanford and UC Berkeley to whom Phil had turned for advice considered his accomplishments of the past eighteen months nothing short of a miracle. That he had achieved so much almost singlehandedly, with the benefit of little formal education, now raised their estimates of him from an ambitious dreamer of impossible dreams to the rarefied category of genius.

The Farnsworth backers, however, were not dreamers. They were businessmen, with a leery eye always turned toward the bottom line. Late in 1928 the backers had decided that any further infusion of funds would only dilute their equity, and so voted to withdraw their support, effectively suspending the project while they continued their search for a buyer.

Phil, on the other hand, determined to keep things going until he could bring his work to a commercial conclusion, called his men together. He told them the situation was grave but not hopeless. He would try to raise enough money to carry them until something could be worked out. In the meantime, their pay was cut to a bare subsistence level.

"Well, it's finally happened, Pem," Phil told me that night. "The backers have given me notice that no more funds will be forthcoming. This time, I'm afraid it's final."

"Oh no! Can't they hang on at least until you can find a way to keep going?" I knew the specter of this happening was always on his shoulder to spur him on to some kind of a conclusion while he had an operating lab.

"I told the men I would try to raise enough money to carry us for a while, but they will have to take a bare living wage until we find a better answer. They all agreed to stay on. We talked it over and feel that with our combined capabilities we can take in odd jobs to help out. By the way, Mr. Linden dropped in this afternoon. He's having trouble with local radio stations—they're always straying off into someone else's frequency. He suggested we try to develop something to prevent that. Cliff and Tobe are already working on it."

"I remember Mr. Linden. He's our local representative of the Federal Radio Commission. He's the kind of friend we need. There are probably dozens of jobs you could pull in."

"Yes, with the boys behind me, I think we'll do all right. I'll make this up to them." They later opted to take company stock to make up their back pay.

The boys built up a small side business of making thermal units to keep radio stations on frequency. Cliff made the thermal control unit, including the tiny thermometer, and Tobe ground the crystals and honed them in. One of the stations needing frequent replacements was that of Father Devine, a self-styled evangelist with a setup somewhere in the Santa Cruz Mountains. He was under much criticism from the public and the local Federal Radio Commissioner because he used his station to recruit young women to his cause. He even attempted to sign up Phil's new secretary, Doris Haggerty, on one of his visits. Insulted, she hurled a well-aimed book, striking him squarely on the head.

Cliff also made photo cells for small, independent movie houses that were setting up for the first "talkies." Phil was called in by several theater managers to help them with their sound systems. These were exciting times. We looked forward with great anticipation to hearing as well as seeing our favorite movie people.

Harry Lubcke went to some of his old professors at UC Berkeley and obtained an order to build some special experimental equipment, which the "lab gang" was well able to handle. At this time, the personnel included Lubcke, Harry Lyman, Tobe Rutherford, Tommy Lynch, and of course, Phil and Cliff.

After a month of scraping along, George and Jess McCargar decided that a working television demonstration was imperative if they hoped to find a buyer, so they persuaded the other backers to make a monthly contribution to the operation. Although the reprieve was only temporary, Phil and his crew had now proven their ability to get by on their own, a real morale-builder for all of them.

Their schedule had been very demanding, so Phil and Cliff began to feel the need for some outdoor exercise. George suggested golf, his own favorite sport, but Phil said it was too expensive in both time and money for him. So Phil and I outfitted ourselves for tennis and set up a schedule to meet Cliff and Lola several mornings a week at a nearby tennis court— at six a.m. we could always find an empty court. This was good therapy for all of us. No matter how serious Phil's problems were, for one hour he gave himself wholeheartedly to the game.

One Sunday morning our game was interrupted by a policeman who carried some shattering news.

"Are you Farnsworth?" the policeman wanted to know.

"Yes, I am," Phil said, not knowing what to expect.

"Well, you might want to get down to your laboratory right way. The place is on fire."

With siren screaming, the policeman led the way to the lab. We were on the scene in a matter of minutes, but it seemed like an eternity. Phil was met by the fire chief, who said his men were completely spooked. Every time they shot water on the fire, the place exploded. They were on the verge of giving it up.

Phil explained that this was due to the vacuum tubes and chemicals, such as sodium and potassium, which violently react with water. Phil had experienced this trouble before. A wastebasket containing potassium and sodium peelings had once burst into flames. One of the men threw water on it, causing a not so minor explosion. Phil directed the fire chief on chemically controlling such lab fires, the chief directed his men, and Cliff, Lola and I stood helplessly by, watching what we feared was the final end of our beloved television project. Unfortunately, by the time the firemen had figured out how to combat it, the fire and the water had pretty well wrecked the contents of the lab.

The place was a shambles. The wax container holding hydrofluoric acid had melted, and the acid had eaten a hole in the wooden floor and was dripping down into the machine shop below. Phil was grateful to the intrepid San Francisco firemen for staying to help clean up the mess.

The fire was a devastating blow to Phil. Heartsick, he called George, who came immediately. His first question was, "What happened?" Phil told him he thought it must have been some kind of electrical trouble. He had left an Image Dissector on life test on a bench, but the heavy, fireproof bench top should have prevented a fire, even if a short had developed. Investigators later indicated it must have been electrical.

Mr. Guisti and Mr. Scattini, the owners of the building who operated the machine shop and carpenter shop on the first floor, arrived. They told Phil their insurance should cover most of the damage. Then George remembered that Mr. Mann was to have insured the contents of the lab. Somewhat reassured by this, and since there was nothing more to be done until morning, we went back to our apartment for a late, late Sunday morning brunch. Despite George's reassurance, a gloomy feeling of loss prevailed over the four of us. George was not aware of the problems we had been having with Mr. Mann. We felt it was entirely possible that the lab equipment had not been insured at all. Phil spent a restless night.

The next morning, meeting with the insurance adjustors, Phil and George were greatly relieved to find they were indeed well covered and would be out only the time it would take to put the lab back in shape. Phil took advantage of the situation to update his equipment, and within a month, they had a much-improved picture. Because he could leave most of the reconstruction to his men, he was able to spend time on his two newest ideas: admittance neutralization and slope-wave generator.* Also, during this time, he and Don Lippincott completed his ninth patent application of the year.

Copies of these nine applications were bound with his 1928 lab notes, along with a picture of him with his television apparatus from his first news release.

By the first of December, the men were back to work on their respective projects. Tobe was putting the finishing touches on the apparatus for transmitting motion picture film over television; Lubcke was assigned work on certain aspects of admittance neutralization; Lyman worked on the radio transmission of television over a distance; Cliff was proving to be a wizard on tubes, coming up with several innovative ideas that later

---

The sine-wave form Phil used first for scanning produced a double image. He determined that the best way to vary current through the deflection coils that move the electron beam from left to right and back in order to scan a picture was a steady increase in current up to a certain value, at which the current almost instantaneously decreases to zero and immediately repeats the cycle. This saw-tooth wave-form is still in use to scan television pictures, both vertically and horizontally. The bulky and inefficient magnetic deflection coils being used at that time to manipulate the video signal required substantial power. In order to drive the coils, Phil used a motor-driven variable resistor which delivered a saw-tooth pulse (and therefore a new frame) ten times a second for the vertical deflection (this occurs 60 times a second in modern television). The horizontal, faster, saw-tooth wave was produced by a different 500-cycle-per-second generator (in modern television this occurs about 15,000 times per second). Although this generator produced the desired saw-tooth wave, it also caused the most interference, and sometimes other problems.

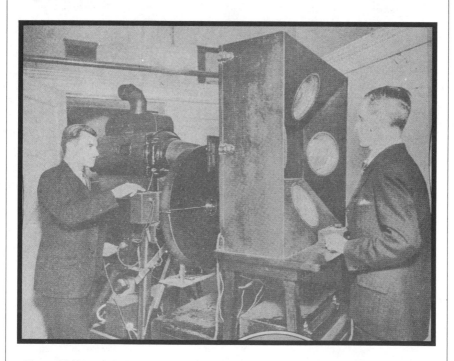

Top: Philo with his first television receiver. Bottom: Television in its latest form at the Radio Corporation of America Station, 411 Fifth Avenue. The person to be televised stands before the four "radio eyes." The images travel in the wave band between 142.8 and 149.9 meters daily, 7 to 9 p.m.

developed into patents. Phil was absorbed in an idea for narrowing the wave band requirements for television, since that appeared to be the next roadblock in the way of commercial television.

In January 1929, Tobe finished his film-transmitting setup. Now sports and movie shorts were easily transmitted over the television system. Lyman was making field tests to determine how far our television signal would carry and setting up to receive our television signal by radio broadcast at the Merchants Exchange Building, which was more distant than the Hobart Building where they had previously received wired transmissions.

Phil and Lubcke were still working on admittance neutralization, and Phil was designing a deltatron tube for building up the television signal by producing secondary electron emissions. Despite the specter of financial uncertainty hanging over them, they were all making good progress, thanks mostly to Phil's positive attitude. His strong faith in his ability to achieve his goal had already overcome more than a few obstacles. He would meet trouble head on and somehow find a way to keep going. Each success forged a new link in his armor.

Although Phil faithfully reported the events of each day and I was still making his drawings and writing a few letters, I had become essentially an onlooker. I felt somehow removed from the excitement. One day I told him I was going to find a job to keep me more occupied. I was rather surprised at his reply.

"I'm sorry you can't be more involved in my work, sweetheart. I've been thinking this may be a good time to start our family. How do you feel about it?"

"We don't even know whether we *can* have a baby."

"Don't you think it's about time we found out? We would have to decide where we want to live, because no child of mine is going to be raised in an apartment."

About a month later I greeted Phil at the door with, "It's time to start looking for a home, honey."

"Pemmie! You've heard from Dr. Keyes! Are we really going to have a baby?" Picking me up in his old exuberant fashion, he whirled me around several times; then, setting me back on my feet, he suggested we drive around and do some looking after dinner. The weight of his problems had begun to rob him of much of his old way, but for the moment he was the same lighthearted Phil I had met five years before in Provo.

After looking over all the new areas in that part of town, we settled on a home being built by Mr. St. George Holden at 3208 Lyon Street in the Marina District. This house, in its final stage of completion, had a third floor with one room and a large closet. They called this an "airplane" room, not only because of its many windows but for the door leading out onto the flat roof, excellent for viewing airplanes, which at that time were a rarity.

There was a nice, large fireplace in the spacious living room. Phil agreed to take the house, provided Mr. Holden build a corner fireplace in the airplane room. He wanted this room for his study. Mr. Holden agreed to that and several other small changes, and best of all, he agreed to take a percentage of Phil's television interest as a down payment, with low monthly payments to follow.

This was a rather typical San Francisco row house, with garage and utility room on the ground floor and living quarters above. Of the two bedrooms, I chose the one on the southeast corner of the house for the nursery, because of its sunny location. We were delighted with the idea of having our very own home. By the time the house was finished, we had carefully chosen all the furnishings and were ready to move in. A local department store had made and hung the living room and dining room drapes.

Mother Farnsworth had helped me make white organdy tie-back

curtains with deep ruffles for the nursery, which was all decorated in white and yellow. We purchased a wicker bassinet, which I trimmed with gathered rows of six-inch lace finished off with wide yellow satin ribbon. I bought a combination bathinet/dressing table and matching drawers for baby clothes and supplies. Phil said no nursery would be complete without a rocking chair, so he had one delivered. Phil had thoughtfully provided wood for

3208 Lyon Street in the Marina District, San Francisco

the fireplaces, so our first night in our new home was just plain heavenly for us. Sitting by the fire, we decided everything was perfect, except for one thing—no piano! Phil had a baby grand piano delivered the very next day. He had signed a contract for only fifteen dollars per month. Now everything was perfect—we had everything but the baby. My due date was not until mid September, and that seemed a long time to wait. I would not be idle, however, because I was busy crocheting and knitting little things for our baby.

CHAPTER 13

Television, Inc.

Phil was delighted to have his family living near us, and although he worked long hours at the lab during the week, we were often treated to Mother Farnsworth's home cooking on Sundays. Mother Farnsworth had been in need of medical attention, so Phil sold five percent of his television holdings to pay for operations for her and Lincoln, who had been left, after a case of osteomyolitus, with a shortened tendon in his heel. He also paid for an operation for my sister Verona.

Mother Farnsworth, Agnes, and Laura were soon happily involved in church activities. At that time, the Latter-day Saint Church unit consisted of a small group meeting in inadequate facilities. Bishop Claude Nalder, who led this small flock, soon recognized Mother Farnsworth's leadership potential and called her to be the president of the Relief Society, the women's auxiliary organization.

Later, Mother Farnsworth was made president of the stake Relief Society, which covered the East Bay area as well as San Francisco and South San Francisco. Agnes and Laura sang in the choir, and Laura formed a trio with two friends, who sang over the radio and at various functions in the area. As the church grew, both in numbers and scope, Bishop Nalder came to Phil and explained the need for a chapel. Phil promised to contribute to the building fund.

The LDS Church headquarters in Salt Lake City would pay half the cost if the local members raised the remainder. When the ward members had contributed half of their portion, Phil made up the difference. The members took great pride in their new chapel, as well they might; they had donated not only money but had given generously of their time and talents in its construction.

One of Mother Farnsworth's responsibilities was to visit the sick and the needy, and that was a full-time job. Agnes was working in the office of a local car dealer, Laura was a sales clerk in a variety store, and Carl was a drugstore delivery boy. Lincoln's responsibility was to build up the strength in his foot and ankle. Spending hours each day on his roller skates, he soon became very familiar with the city.

What happened soon after this would seem in retrospect to demonstrate Emerson's law of compensation. Early in March 1929, Jess McCargar decided to hook his wagon to Phil's star and cast his lot with television. In effect, Mr. McCargar took the reins of the enterprise from the other backers and so became a major influence in Phil's destiny. On March 27th, 1929, papers were signed, and a new company—Television, Inc.—came into being.

The officers of the new company were Jesse B. McCargar, president; Philo T. Farnsworth, vice president in charge of research; and George Everson, secretary/treasurer. Ten thousand shares of stock were issued to the company for the patents, and ten thousand shares to the backing syndicate and the original partnership of Everson, Farnsworth, and Gorrell. Each stockholder was to contribute one dollar for each share of stock he held to keep the lab going. Phil, still the largest single stockholder, was therefore expected to be the largest contributor.

Jesse B. McCargar,
first president of the
Farnsworth Television Company

Word of the new company was carried in the press, resulting in renewed interest from investors. George Everson sold a 1/40 share of his future profits in television to two friends for twenty-five hundred dollars, an action that considerably strengthened Phil's resolve to achieve his goal of commercial television.

In early May, the scanning current and 60-cycle interference had been neutralized, making a big improvement in the picture. At this point, Phil decided to incorporate his idea of an electron multiplier in the Image Dissector tube to build up the signal strength. He had described this secondary emission idea to Lippincott the previous year.

Up to this time, the largest Oscillight had only a four-inch viewing end. Phil's new design called for a seven-inch viewing end. An electron "gun" was built with tiny nickel compartments arranged vertically up its length. These were so angled as to deflect the electrons (current) from one compartment to the next. Each time an electron hit the wall of a box, a number of electrons would be knocked out of the metal. These would in turn knock out more electrons in the next box, until the original signal would be greatly magnified. The result was another big step in picture quality.

Phil now had two setups going: a small four-inch picture, using his new slope-wave generator, and a seven-inch one, with the electron multiplier. Hardly a day went by without interested people coming to see this new wonder of the world.

Phil with first motion picture film projector for TV (left)
and the spinning disc receiver used in other labs (right).

Among the people who came were representatives from the RKO Picture Company and the Fox Theater interests. They came to see what they feared was a very real threat to their business. As George Everson put it, "they were flabbergasted" and wanted to buy in. By this time, however, Television, Inc. was operating on a fairly sound basis, and McCargar agreed with Phil and George that they were close to the awaited dawn of commercial television. They saw no need to dilute their holdings by the amount these people wanted, which would have given them virtual control. The offer was refused.

By June the stock market was going crazy. Investors were buying stock on margin, with 10 percent down and the balance when they took their profits. That was fine unless the stock took a drop, in which case the investor sold quickly and took his losses.

Les Gorrell had been playing on this merry-go-round and doing very well for himself. He kept urging Phil to diversify and invest in stocks.

Phil finally gave in and took a flyer, only he insisted on buying outright rather than on margin. He invested four thousand dollars in what looked to be the most stable stocks. We found watching our stocks earn money a fascinating game. After several months of this, Phil had a strong feeling that the market had just about reached its peak and issued an order to sell. Within the month, his worst fears were realized. In October 1929, the stock market became too top-heavy and crashed with a bang that was felt around the world.*

Thousands who had been millionaires on paper one day awoke to the realization that they were paupers the next. Many men, not psychologically equipped to handle such a traumatic change in their lives, jumped from high buildings or took their lives by other means. A large number found their families disrupted; an air of deepest gloom pervaded Wall Street, the home of the glorious bubble, now burst and trampled.

Although repercussions of the financial crash were felt in San Francisco, it did little to disrupt the small world at 202 Green Street. Hardly a day passed without its quota of interested visitors. Some of the better known people who visited Phil's lab were Guglielmo Marconi, inventor of the wireless; Herbert Hoover Jr., eldest son of the president of the United States; Dr. Lee DeForest, inventor of the first amplifier tubes; Dr. Frederick E. Terman, professor of electrical engineering at Stanford University (later provost), and Dr. Leonard Fuller of UC Berkeley, the professors who had told him he was attempting the impossible; and a frequent visitor, Dr. Ernest O. Lawrence, who later built the Cyclotron and Bevatron at the Lawrence Radiation Laboratory at UC Berkeley.

Years later, when Dr. Lawrence was putting the Bevatron together, Phil was a consultant to the Lawrence Radiation Laboratory. Dr. Lawrence was describing to Phil and me in his office an idea for an improved television camera tube to produce color. Suddenly, he turned to me and said, "Do you know that I got my ideas for the cyclotron when I visited your husband's lab in San Francisco and saw his electron multiplier working? It was really a learning experience to visit his laboratory." This was not the first . . . or the last . . . such comment that was made to me.

In the early days of television, many young men came to ask Phil's advice and guidance on how to prepare for a career in the field opened up by television. He was never too busy to stop and chat with them. He well remembered the teachers who had put themselves out to help and encourage him. Quite a number of these young hopefuls came back years later to thank him for his advice. Several attained top-notch positions or were playing leading roles in research groups. Phil's inspirational effect

---

*Several years later, Phil had a letter from the man who had been his first investor. He had purchased one percent of Phil's holdings for five thousand dollars, back in 1928, before any stock was issued. He had lost everything he had in the collapse of the stock market with the exception of his Farnsworth stock, which had advanced so rapidly it had been split 100 to 1. This made it possible for him to start a new business. He told Phil he owed it all to him. That made us both very happy. It was a good feeling to know that our first investor had been so rewarded.

on many of these young people served as a catalyst leading to many and far-reaching innovations; like a pebble dropped in a lake, Phil's influence generated waves that reached to the farthest shores.

When Dr. Fuller and Dr. Terman saw what Phil had accomplished, Dr. Fuller was astounded, and Dr. Terman said, "This is unbelievable. I'll have to learn to recognize genius when I see it." They later became good friends.

Another frequent visitor was Bernard Linden, the local representative of the Federal Radio Commission. He was very impressed by Phil's work and lost no opportunity to sing his praises to the head office in Washington.

Phil was attempting to prove to the FRC that his television system had reached the stage where it presented real entertainment value to the public. He had acquired a number of short films, including Walt Disney's first Mickey Mouse film, *Steamboat Willie*, and a bootleg copy someone had brought in of the famous knockout sequence in the Dempsey-Tunney prize fight. He also had segments of Mary Pickford and Douglas Fairbanks in *The Taming of the Shrew*, parts of which he used for demonstrations. These came over television very well, proving his system's commercial viability beyond any shadow of a doubt.

Two engineers, Frank Miramontes and Nathan Clark, were hired to help in this phase of the work. In beaming their signal toward town and the Hobart Building, they found that much of the interference they were getting was from tall buildings in the way. So they aimed their signal east toward Berkeley and Oakland across the Bay and found they could deliver a signal free of any interference. To further prove that television was ready for public consumption, they designed and built a floor-model console receiver to sell for just under three hundred dollars.

Farnsworth receiver

One of Phil's favorite recreations was to drive to the airport to watch planes come and go. He was delighted when one of his television investors invited him to look up his pilot and take a ride in the plane he kept there. After his first flight, Phil arranged for his family to take turns going up for a sight-seeing flight at five dollars for fifteen minutes for two people. They were all enchanted with the flight except Phil's mother. She flatly refused to fly. I must confess I felt the same way about it; heights had always made me dizzy.

When Lola's mother and father came for a visit, we all went down

New Tube Makes Television 'Practical,'
Californian Tells Radio Commission

DEC 5   1930

SPECIAL FROM MONITOR BUREAU

WASHINGTON—Television as "immediately practical" due to a revolutionary new tube was the view presented Dec. 4 by Philo T. Farnsworth, California inventor, at a special conference with the Federal Radio Commission.

Two problems have confronted television workers. One was the limitations of mechanical "scanning," or rapid "sketching" of a view. The second was the requirement of the equivalent of 10 broadcast wavelengths for sending a single television showing. With the limited number of wavelengths available this has made television so far prohibitive.

Mr. Farnsworth uses electrical scanning, rather than mechanical. This eliminates moving parts, inertia effects and complicated mechanical parts permitting transmission of any desired amount of detail, including half-tone effects, at television speeds. Thus a 300-line picture is obtained, it is claimed, compared with 60-line pictures under the present systems, giving much greater detail.

In accomplishing this refinement, the inventor has found that the 100-kilocycle band, thought necessary for television broadcasting, is not needed and that good television may be accomplished in a band the same width as is necessary for voice transmission —10 kilocycles. In fact, he claims to have obtained a 300-line picture on a channel only six kilocycles wide.

Broadcasting of football events and other large spectacles have been the dream of television researchers for years, but the existing systems could not attempt to handle such events. Only very small fields of vision, about nine by nine feet, brilliantly lighted, could be sent with the present method, and even so the results have been crude.

This new invention makes direct "pick-up" of out-of-door events possible, according to Don K. Lippincott, noted West coast radio engineer.

Another issue before the commission is the rejection of the Columbia Broadcasting System's application for an experimental television station license by a commissioner examiner, and a subsequent protest by the Columbia system to the commission.

Elmer W. Pratt, examiner of the commission, recommended against immediate granting of a television license to the Atlantic Broadcasting Company, subsidiary of the Columbia concern, on the ground that the equipment and engineers from the R. C. A.-Victor Corporation, subsidiary of the National Broadcasting Company, were used for the Atlantic company's experiments, and that such experiments would be a duplication of those conducted by the N. B. C. In a rejoinder, the Columbia company charges that it may be forced to use "foreign" television equipment, if the application for the license is barred. It asserts that its television experiments will not duplicate those of other organizations.

Christian Science Monitor article and Left: W.C. Fields on television.

to the airport. When Phil asked Mrs. Buker if she would like to take a sight-seeing trip, she was overjoyed at the prospect. Not to be outdone, Mother Farnsworth said she would go along. She came back singing the praises of air travel. That left only me.

I agreed to go if Phil would tell the pilot we wanted a no-frills ride. I was nearing my delivery date, so I certainly didn't want to do anything that would jeopardize the baby.

Phil spoke to the pilot, but I learned all too soon what he had told him. The plane was a small, two-seater with open cockpit. The pilot put it into a steep climb, then stalled it so we fell over a thousand feet. I was furious with Phil, but it did no good to try to tell him. He would never hear me over the roar of the engine. He had an arm around me and was yelling in my ear to relax and enjoy it.

The pilot climbed high again and came down, literally spinning on a wing. Of course we were held tightly to our seats by the belts, but the force of gravity pressed us even harder into our seats. Then at Phil's insistence, I stole a glance downward. Between us and the ground there was nothing but . . . air! I jerked my gaze away and riveted my eyes on the back of that pilot's head, willing him to land. The thought crossed my mind that if we crashed we would at least all go together. When we went into another stall-and-fall routine, I screamed in Phil's ear, "If you don't make him land, I'll jump!" That did it. Phil tapped the pilot on the shoulder and motioned for him to take us down.

The next day Phil was soundly scolded by my doctor. She asked if he wanted his baby "airborn." Actually, it seemed as though the baby were reluctant to enter such a frightening world. Our nine-pound, ten-ounce son was born on September 23rd, 1929, two weeks late. We named him Philo Taylor Farnsworth for his father and great-grandfather. Phil was one proud papa.

In those days, it was customary to keep new mothers in the hospital for ten days to two weeks, but Phil could not wait to get us home. He had hired a registered nurse to attend me at the hospital, and by going home in an ambulance and keeping the nurse an extra week, we came home a week early. On the first night we were alone, he came in singing, "Just Pemmie and me, and baby makes three, we're happy in our blue heaven," from the song "My Blue Heaven." Since Phil went back to the lab most evenings, I scheduled our baby's last feeding and nightly oil rub for after he came home. That strategy worked wonders in getting his mind off his problems.

Early in 1930, Robert Fairbanks, business manager for the United Artists Film Company, called to ask if he could bring a group to San Francisco to see this television they had heard so much about. Phil was told to expect Mr. Douglas Fairbanks Sr., his wife, Mary Pickford (America's sweetheart), and producer Joseph Schenck. The other founder of their company, Charles Chaplin, was in Europe and would not be with them.

Phil decided that one last change should be made before the United Artists group came. It was a simple change that should have caused no problems. For some reason, however, after the change, he and Tobe were unable to get a picture. The demonstration was for ten the next morning, and things began to look pretty grim. About dinnertime, Phil called me.

"Pem, we're having trouble getting a picture. It appears to be a bad connection somewhere, but we've not yet been able to locate it. This demonstration is important. I'm going to take the boys out for a bite to eat, and we'll work all night if necessary to clear up the trouble."

"I'm sorry, Phil. What happened to the marvelous picture I saw yesterday?"

"Oh, you know me; I had to try to make it a little better. I don't see how the small change I made could have done this to me."

"I think you're trying too hard. Try relaxing. Go into your office, shut the door, and try to clear your mind. Let me know if there is anything I can do."

"Thank you, dear, but you had better not wait up for me. Save yourself for little Philo."

Around seven the next morning, Phil called to ask whether I could cook some bacon and eggs for the "gang." They had gone over the entire apparatus without being able to spot the problem. They were coming over to shave and freshen up before making another try at it. An hour later, somewhat revived, they were on their way back to the lab.

The visitors arrived on the Lark, and called Phil from the Mark Hopkins Hotel. Apologetically, Phil explained his situation. He told them he expected to have the trouble corrected soon and would call them.

At 3:00 p.m., Mr. Fairbanks called and asked if they could just come and see the setup, because they would have to catch the evening train for Los Angeles. Phil told them he would be happy to have them come. He would show them a picture of some kind. He just could not have these stellar bodies cooling their heels in a hotel room any longer.

They came and were shown through the lab, but the lab gang, already in a state of advanced fatigue, found it even more difficult to concentrate on their work with America's sweetheart perched on a lab bench watching them. At Phil's suggestion, Cliff demonstrated some of his glassblowing tricks. Imagine his embarrassment when Mr. Fairbanks told him they had imported several glassblowing artists from Vienna for a film last year. Phil finally turned on the equipment and was able to show them a rather fuzzy picture before they had to leave.

Miss Pickford was very gracious. Understanding Phil's embarrassment, she invited him to bring me for a visit to Pickfair, her palatial home in Hollywood. On the train that night she wrote him a thank-you note. She said that even though they might not have seen his best picture, she thought it was wonderful and felt they had been well repaid for their visit. They were probably comforted to see that television was no immediate threat to the movie industry.

Perhaps it was just as well for their peace of mind that they had to leave, for no sooner were they gone than Tobe found the trouble. A small, obscure wire that had completely evaded their searching eyes had

TELEVISION BRINGS 'EM HERE

Douglas Fairbanks and **Mary Pickford, here** today with movie executives to inspect sensational television of Philo Farnsworth, San Francisco inventor, found time to "phone" Maurice Chevalier, ill at a local hotel, and wish him a speedy recovery.

MARY, 'DOUG' HERE TO TEST TELEVISION

Douglas Fairbanks, Mary Pickford, President Joseph Schenk of United Artists, and technical experts are at Hotel Mark Hopkins today for a special demonstration of the Farnsworth television apparatus.

The demonstration is to determine the possibility of adapting the sensational television apparatus of the young San Francisco inventor for commercial broadcasting of movies and talkies.

The television demonstration follows a preliminary demonstration made to Fairbanks, which so impressed him that he phoned Schenk, then in London, and arranged for the investigation by Schenk and technical experts of the apparatus, with a view to radiocasting of movies.

Schenk and Theodore Reed, head of the United Artists' engineering department and chairman of the technical division of the Academy of Motion Picture Arts and Sciences today declared Farnsworth's television transmitting apparatus very remarkable, and already perfected about the stage of the old head-phone radio sets.

If United Artists exploit Farnsworth's television system, it will not be to the exclusion of other producers, Schenk says, all being permitted to radiocast their pictures with the new device.

Douglas Fairbanks and Mary Pickford created the United Artists Film Company with Charles Chaplin to make their own films. They feared television might replace movies.

become disconnected. When it was attached, they had the best picture they had seen to date. Of course, Phil came under much criticism from Jess and George for his "incessant changes." Such comments revealed early on that Jess and George had little patience for the experimental nature of Phil's work.

When Don Lippincott saw the improved picture, he prevailed upon Phil to speak before the next meeting of the Institute of Radio Engineers (IRE, now the Institute of Electrical and Electronic Engineers, IEEE).

Following the meeting, the group was invited to the lab to see, for the first time, electronic television! Phil was made an associate member of the Institute. All that was very gratifying to Phil. A few years later his status in the Institute was advanced to that of fellow.

The next Sunday Phil and Cliff went for a walk down to the Yacht Harbor while Lola and I prepared dinner. They had been gone for some time when the doorbell rang. Ordinarily, I asked for identification before activating the door release, but since I expected Phil and Cliff, I just released the lock. There in the doorway stood a tall, raw-boned man with ruddy face, bushy eyebrows, and wiry red hair that stood on end as though starched. I stifled a scream as Phil peeked around this apparition: The stranger's large frame had completely hidden Phil, who was directly behind him. Phil introduced his friend Russell Varian, whom the boys had found walking in the wind at the Yacht Harbor. A radio engineer, recently graduated from Stanford University, Russell had heard Phil's IRE talk and wanted to work with him. Phil saw in Russell a brilliant man and did hire him later.

After the Television, Inc. stock was issued and the company was on firmer ground, Phil transferred a block of stock to his mother, which made her financially independent for the rest of her life. He also gave shares to his brothers and sisters. Then he gave my father stock and one share each to my three brothers and five sisters. This stock was split one hundred to one and later fifty to one. Being able to share with our families made our own good fortune mean even more to us.

On January 15th, 1931, just fifteen months after Philo, Jr. arrived, our second son, Kenneth Gardner Farnsworth, was born. Once more we were brought home in an ambulance with the same nurse. This time they had covered my face on the stretcher because there was a heavy, wet fog in the air. I learned later that we had disrupted a home wedding next door. A wedding guest became excited when she saw what she thought was a corpse being brought in next door. The wedding party was disrupted when all the guests rushed to the window to see.

By this time, I was very tired of maternity clothes. Phil evidently felt the same way, because he arranged for the nurse to stay long enough to take me shopping at I. Magnin's, San Francisco's finest ladies-wear establishment. Phil said, "Don't spare the horses." We didn't. I came home with several outfits from skin to top coat. Phil was very pleased, He was indeed a proud daddy and husband. The time he spent with the boys and me chased away all cares for him.

One day when Philo was about nine months old, I left him on a blanket in the living room with his toys while I prepared dinner. When I peeked in to check on him, he was gone. I became frantic when I couldn't find him. Phil was up in his study, and I went to the stairs to call him. There, almost to the top, was my baby. Hearing me, he turned and, with a triumphant giggle, hurried to reach the top. Hearing the commotion, Phil appeared at the top of the stairs. I started up the stairs to the rescue, but Phil motioned me back.

"Don't spoil his achievement. He deserves to look around and spend some time with me after coming this far." He waited for little Philo to finish his climb; then with a sigh of relief, he caught his son up in a grateful hug. The look on little Philo's shining face as he waved to me was one of triumph. He knew he could do it!

CHAPTER 14

Enter RCA

In the February 1930 issue of the *California Engineer*, there appeared an article by Phil and Harry Lubcke, entitled, "The Transmission of Television Images." This article included a photographic reproduction of the image taken from the end of the Oscillight. This, I believe, is the first such picture ever published. I was (and am) proud to have been the subject of the photo.

Shortly after this, Russell Varian was hired, along with Archie Brolly, a Massachusetts Institute of Technology graduate in electrical engineering. Clark and Miramontes had finished the jobs for which they had been hired and had left the previous month. With the added experience and ingenuity of Arch and Russ, the work was making better progress. Russ was well trained in chemistry, and Phil put him to experimenting with fluorescent materials. At this point, the fluorescent screens in the receiving tubes were the weakest component in Phil's system.

Needing to know whether the trouble came from the coating they were using or the method used in forming the surfaces, Phil designed a special tube for Cliff to make, to be connected to a circuit as an electronic magnifier. With it he could watch the surfaces forming, molecule by molecule. He also used it to analyze the image on the end of the Oscillight.

In April, Mr. Mann told Phil to expect a visit from Dr. Vladimir Zworykin of Westinghouse. It was important that Dr. Zworykin receive every courtesy, since the backers hoped to interest Westinghouse through him. Phil was thinking in terms of a patent license deal, but he couldn't

12

Vol. VIII, No. 5
Feb 1930

The Transmission of Television Images

By PHILO T. FARNSWORTH and HARRY R. LUBCKE

Television Laboratories, Inc.

THE transmission of television images requires the transmission of a high order of intelligence. Information regarding the light intensity of a great number of elemental areas must be conveyed, reproduced in the same relative position as they occupied before transmission, and the process repeated with sufficient frequency to give the illusion of motion. In effect, the field of view transmitted must be dissected, an electrical intensity transmitted corresponding to the light intensity on each elemental area, the electrical intensities converted back to light intensities and placed in their proper relative position at the receiving terminal, this being accomplished by a system capable of presenting fifteen or more complete pictures to the eye each second.

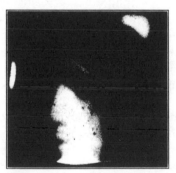

(Figure 1)

A television photograph. It is believed that this is the only photograph of a television image yet published. (Spots are due to photographic imperfections.)

Thus far man has evolved only one means of electrical communication. This system is a single dimensional time continuum. The commercial wireless, the telegraph, the telephone, and the radio transmit intelligence that is initially single dimensional, since a dot or dash or the modulations of voice or music are intensity variations occurring in time and time only. In television, however, information must be transmitted regarding space as well; that is, the placement of the various intensities in the area that make up the picture must be conveyed, all of which must be transmitted at a rapid rate if fifteen or more complete pictures are to be presented to the eye each second.

Since the nature of the transmission medium is the same for all cases it is obvious that as the amount of intelligence transmitted increases the portion of the medium used must also increase. In term of radio broadcasting, the sideband width must increase as the amount of information transmitted increases. Thus, a commercial code station requires only 200 cycles as a sideband, and the conventional broadcast station approximately 5,000 to 7,000 cycles.. Telephoto transmission, the sending of pictures or printed matter, requires 3,000 cycles in which system one picture is transmitted in approximately seven minutes. But for television a sideband of at least 50,000 cycles, and better 500,000 cycles or more is required, depending upon the detail desired.

A certain minimum amount of detail must be transmitted by a television system in order that the received image may be said to possess "entertainment value." The system must transmit a person's face, for example, with sufficient detail to make the features readily discernible and sufficiently clear to "entertain" the viewer if the person should talk and attempt to convey meanings by facial expressions. This minimum has been specified by some workers in the field as an image consisting of 2,500 elementary areas, or elements. The picture shown in Figure 1 is a photograph of a television image consisting of 20,000 elements. This image of a lady with her eyes closed was transmitted by the Farnsworth system of electrical scanning and is perhaps the first published photograph of an actual television image. The original image was approximately 3½ inches square. It can well be considered as having entertainment value. The reticence of those working with a 2,500 element picture to publish photographs of an image would seem to indicate that the 2,500 element limit was fixed more because of the limitations of the apparatus than because of true entertainment value.

Apparatus Available Shortly

It is felt that real entertainment in television will require an image eight inches square of some 60,000 elements. An image of this size containing 250 lines per side contains 62,500 elements and can well be defined as one of real entertainment value. Such an image would extend the quality of the image of Figure 1 to include semi-closeups and small full length groups. Apparatus for producing an image of this size and one approaching this quality is under construction and will be available shortly.

This 62,500 element picture requires a sideband width of 470,000 cycles if it is transmitted at a rate of fifteen pictures per second. Such a frequency spectrum places transmissions of this nature of necessity in the short wave region, and it is in this region that the ultimate television image will be transmitted.

If the short wave region is penetrated sufficiently this ordinarily considered impossible sideband becomes no greater in proportion to the carrier frequency than a 5,000 cycle sideband at broadcast frequencies. Considering an average broadcast carrier of 1,000 K.C. (or 300 meters) and a 10,000 cycle or 10 K.C. channel width as allocated by the Federal Radio Commission we find that the channel width is one per cent of the carrier frequency. At a frequency of 50,000 K.C. (or 6 meters) a channel 500,000 cycles or 500 K.C. wide is still only one per cent of the

(Continued on page 22)

be certain that something more serious, like an outright sale, wasn't in the minds of Jess and George.

The week of April 19th, 1930, an entry in Phil's journal stated:

"Dr. Zworykin spent three days in the laboratory. Demonstrations were given on moving-picture transmission, admittance-neutralized receiver, slope wave, deltatron, mutual conductance, etc. The demonstrations were all successful."

Dr. Zworykin was also very impressed when Phil demonstrated his electron magnifier, so much so that he later developed it into an electron microscope and wrote a book about it, though there was no mention of where he first saw the idea demonstrated.

Phil had talked to me about the endless possibilities of this tube and what a useful tool it would be for scientific and medical research. He lamented that he had neither the time nor the money to pursue it further. He was happy to see that it had been made available.

Utahn Finds Way To Make Germs Visible

Philo T. Farnsworth, native Utahn whose work in television and radio has astounded scientists the world over, today made known a new development that will make hitherto invisible disease germs visible to the human eye, according to an International News Service dispatch from Philadelphia.

Farnsworth's new disclosure involves the use of his special tube designed for transmitting radio pictures, and of ultra-violet rays. His process will make it to subir   ms t

Dr. Zworykin was also very intrigued with the Image Dissector, with its flat lens sealed in the end to prevent distortion. He told Cliff his men had told him this was impossible. "That's what they told us," Cliff told him, "but Phil wouldn't believe it." At Dr. Zworykin's insistence, he was allowed to watch Cliff build an Image Dissector. When shown the finished tube, Dr. Zworykin remarked, "This is a beautiful instrument. I wish I had invented it myself." To answer Doctor Zworykin's many questions about how his system worked, Phil let him read the article he had written for the Institute of Radio Engineers Journal.

A few years later, in the course of patent litigation with RCA, we learned that Dr. Zworykin had not visited our lab on behalf of Westinghouse. Just prior to his trip to San Francisco, he had been hired by David Sarnoff to work for RCA. Dr. Zworykin later said his visit was requested by the RCA patent attorneys. He did stop at Westinghouse enroute to the RCA Labs in Camden, New Jersey, but only long enough to have his former helpers build a copy of the Farnsworth Image Dissector, exactly as Phil and Cliff had shown him. Dr. Zworykin took the new tube and reported to RCA.

Mr. Sarnoff had hoped by hiring Dr. Zworykin he would be able to provide RCA with a firm foothold in the emerging new industry of television. Already, RCA dominated the radio industry to the point that it was not possible to manufacture any radio broadcasting or receiving equipment without paying patent royalties for the privilege to RCA. This point was forcefully driven home to dozens of small manufacturers who were drummed out of the business for failure to pay proper tribute to RCA. RCA's policy regarding patents, licenses, and royalties was very simple: the company was formed to *collect* patent royalties. It never *paid* them.*

David Sarnoff fully intended to extend this domination into the new field of television. He began by hiring Dr. Zworykin, who had applied in 1923 for a patent for an electronic television system based on the ideas he had learned from Boris Rosing, his professor in his native Russia, before emigrating to the U.S. There was no bonafide evidence that the device disclosed in 1923 was ever built or operated, but the existence of the application was all Sarnoff thought he would need to establish his territory in television. That was before he discovered what Farnsworth had already accomplished.

From Phil's notes for the week ending May 10th, 1930:

"Two demonstrations were given Friday. In the morning we demonstrated to Mr. Porter of RCA and W. W. Crocker. In the afternoon, we demonstrated to Lieut. Highleyman of the U. S. Navy Department, who had been sent to investigate our system."

These people were surprised and very complimentary to Phil regarding the quality of the picture. This was especially true of technically trained Lieutenant Highleyman, who later became a staunch Farnsworth advocate in Washington.

Not long after Mr. Porter's visit, Jess and Phil left for Washington, where Phil was to testify before Senator O'Mahoney's committee investigating monopolistic practices in the radio and television industries. Who should appear at the door of 202 Green Street but David Sarnoff himself. In Phil's absence, George Everson instructed the boys to demonstrate Phil's equipment. Mr. Sarnoff was particularly interested in the seven-inch picture and expressed a great deal of interest in what was going on around the lab. At the end of his visit, however, his tone changed abruptly, and as he left, he told George he didn't think he had seen anything that RCA would need to introduce television.

Despite insisting that Farnsworth had nothing that RCA would need, within a year Mr. Sarnoff offered to buy Farnsworth, both the company and the man, for one hundred thousand dollars. This seemed a paltry sum, even in those days, for what RCA would be getting. Besides, Farnsworth was not interested in selling his patents—he wanted to license them and collect royalties that would support his future work. Phil responded to Sarnoff's insulting offer with a flat refusal. He had no interest either in

---

*Corporations have always had a curiously ambivalent attitude toward inventors and the patent system. Although they regard patents as a huge bulwark when protecting their own monopolies, they see the patent system as a great nuisance when it upholds the rights of an individual. Both Major Howard Armstrong and Dr. Lee DeForest had battled (unsuccessfully) for their rights against RCA. Dr. DeForest died bankrupt and Major Armstrung donned his coat, hat, and gloves and walked out of the high window of his New York apartment rather than give in to them.

turning over his valuable patents to RCA or in going to work for David Sarnoff. He was determined to maintain his independence. And so the die was cast for one of the most protracted and important battles in the early history of television.

About this time, "Navy Day" was being celebrated in the San Francisco Bay. Many ships, including the new aircraft carrier *Saratoga* were in the Bay. Phil invited Secretary of the Navy Wilbur and his entourage to the lab to see television. The reports they had heard about television had not prepared them for what they saw. They were surprised and very impressed with the quality of the picture. The next day, at the invitation of Secretary Wilbur, Phil and I were given a VIP tour of the Saratoga, and were also taken aboard a captured World War I German U-Boat.

In June, the lab was visited by a representative from the Bell Labs

Pem Farnsworth, subject of 1931 received image.

in New York. By then the picture had been improved to the point where the individual features of groups of ten or twelve people were easily recognized, which put the new medium on a visual par with the movies. Phil was invited to visit the Bell Laboratories. By this time, Ray Olpin, one of Phil's BYU professors, and Carl Christensen, who had worked for us, were working for Bell Labs. Jess urged Phil and George to go, suggesting it might be an opportunity to sell AT&T a patent license.

Although Phil, as the largest stockholder, was still putting up the largest share of the money for lab expense, Jess and George had the job of selling the stock. That was not easy, because the country had fallen into a deep depression in the wake of the crash of '29. Even though Farnsworth was considered a "glamor" stock, it was still not easy to sell the shares required to raise the necessary operating funds.

Because of the difficulty he had encountered, Jess took aim at Varian and Brolly. After Phil and George left for the east coast, Jess went to the lab and fired all of the men, announcing that the lab would be closed indefinitely. Then he wired Phil and George to tell them what he had done.

Upon receiving the wire, Phil wired Cliff and told him to tell the men to hold tight until he could get there, and he took the next train to

San Francisco. Phil's carefully cultivated self-control usually worked for him, but this was a low blow that hit where it hurt—his men! It was just as well that this all occurred in the days before commercial passenger flight; the four days it took for Phil to cross the continent gave him time to simmer down and plan his strategy. George's advice, as usual, was to "approach the situation with a spirit of graciousness."

The Farnsworth company was not alone in experiencing financial troubles. Thousands were being laid off all over the country. In the Bay area, the Bell Telephone Company alone had just released two thousand men. Phil had strong feelings that he could turn this situation around by launching a new industry and thereby creating new jobs. He was not inclined to let Jess McCargar interfere with his plans.

Of course, to do that, television needed to be further refined so it could be commercialized and generate enough money to keep people employed. Phil was painfully aware of the monumental task before him to keep ahead of the well-heeled and technically advanced herd.

Upon arriving home, Phil was still fuming. After allowing him to blow off steam, and with George as a mediator, Jess agreed to open the lab, provided Phil dispensed with the help of Varian and Brolly. For the "good of the cause," Phil agreed.

Within a short time, George was able to sell enough stock to keep the operation going, and the efforts to get on the air continued. Harry Lyman was now receiving the signal at the Merchant's Exchange Building. That is believed to be the first all-electronic television transmission via radio.

Adding to this encouraging success was the issuance on May 13th, 1930, of the first Farnsworth Patent. This was patent number 1,758,359, "Electric Oscillator System." Then on August 26th, 1930, Phil's "Television System," patent number 1,773,980 and "Television Receiving System," patent number 1,773,981 were issued.

The issuance of these patents was a cause for great rejoicing in the Farnsworth camp. Phil's first patents had run into interference with several others besides those of Dr. Zworykin. That his patents were finally issued was good news, indeed, to all of us.

In the meantime, the number of radio broadcasters had mushroomed to the point where the responsibility for deciding which ones were working in the public interest was an impossible task.

Donald K. Lippincott, the patent attorney who filed most of the Farnsworth patents.

The Federal Radio Commissioners were wringing their collective hands. Since policing stations in the field was out of the question, the yearly license renewal was based on information provided by station managers who usually traveled to Washington.

In this chaotic situation, the government decided it was time to catch up to technology and replace the old Federal Radio Commission with a body more able to cope with the problems. The new Federal Communications Commission was given much broader powers. This body was faced with the responsibility of finding spectrum space for television. Extensive lobbying in Washington against television involved radio broadcasters, Western Union Telegraph, the facsimile people, radio amateurs, and others who feared the broad bands thought to be required by television would crowd them out of the sky.

The new FCC called a hearing for December 4th, 1930, in Washington to decide how it was going to divide up the air waves. It seemed that everyone wanted a piece of the "pie in the sky." Phil was invited to testify for the cause of television, and he invited Don Lippincott to accompany him.

The airmail service had begun to carry a limited number of passengers to help defray their expenses. Phil leaped at the chance for a transcontinental flight. Over my and Don's wife Ruth's objections, he booked passage for himself and Don. Three days later, they called from Washington. Ruth and I had been frantic with worry. Bad weather had forced them down. They had been obliged to stay the night in Kansas City, Missouri, where they dispatched a telegram (which never did arrive) to Ruth and me. Then they were downed again in St Louis, Missouri, took the night train to Indianapolis, and were flown from there to Washington. The total time saved was one day over the four days by train. Such was the plane service in 1930.

According to Don and the press writeups on the meeting, Phil gave a good account of himself in stating his case. By this time, he was good copy, and his every move was well covered by the press.

On their return trip, they were favored by good weather and were able to fly all the way, although they narrowly escaped disaster when their plane blew a tire on takeoff in Detroit. Luckily, the only problem was the time it took to replace the tire. Phil and Don, well pleased with the meeting, returned with high hopes that television would at last be given its place in the spectrum. Television publicity, however, was hurting radio sales, and radio manufacturers were fighting mad.

CHAPTER 15

First Licensee

By the spring of 1931, Philco Radio Corporation was the largest manufacturer of radio sets in the country, its sales exceeding even those of RCA, whose patents Philco licensed. Officials at Philco noticed that every time there was a flurry of publicity about television, their radio sales dropped, and so decided it was time to launch their own participation into this new medium.

Walter Holland, Philco's vice-president in charge of engineering, came to San Francisco to see what Farnsworth had to offer. Much impressed, he stayed to put together a preliminary agreement to present to his board of directors. Farnsworth executives were invited to come to Philadelphia for further negotiations.

Another deal was also in the offing for Farnsworth. A fast-talking promoter by the name of Cox was attempting to put together a large conglomerate including Farnsworth and several other leaders in the television, radio, and movie industries. Jess McCargar and Phil went to New York City to talk to the Cox group before visiting Philco in Philadelphia.

Upon reaching New York, they found that Cox had so overstated the deal that several of the participants had backed out. Then, when a closer scrutiny of Mr. Cox's background and character revealed some dealings of a decidedly questionable nature, the top blew off the whole deal, and everything fell apart.

The fast-thinking Mr. Cox was not finished, however. He filed suit, naming all of the principals involved—and some who were not. Jess and Phil were served with a court order restraining them from leaving the city. No particulars were given as to the charges. Un-American as it was, this was allowed, at least in New York City at that time.

UTAH YOUTH INVENTS NEW TELEVISION SET

Philo T. Farnsworth, Former B. Y. U. Student, Goes East to Build Production Model

Born 1906 aug 19

By CARLE H. BENNETTE   *1931*
(United Press Staff Correspondent)

SAN FRANCISCO, July 11—Philo T. Farnsworth, 24-year-old Utah inventor, tonight told executives of the Crocker First National bank at San Francisco, who have backed him for five years, that radio television by electricity was an accomplished fact and ready for commercial production.

Jess called Bart Crumm, their San Francisco attorney, to come and extricate them. At this time, the Cox group claimed breach of contract, which was reaching for the moon. While Mr. Crumm labored to cut the red tape holding them there, Jess and Phil did their best to carry on their business by mail and telephone.

At the end of the third week, Phil was so homesick he called me in San Francisco. Our fifth wedding anniversary was just a week away. Since he was unable to come home, he invited me to join him in New York.

As luck would have it, my Aunt Rhae Barton was with me. When Aunt Rhae heard me tell Phil I had no one to whom I would trust our young sons, this lovely lady, who was in San Francisco for cancer treatment, insisted she be allowed to stay and care for them. My concern that it would be too much strain for her was allayed when my sister Verona offered to help on the weekends and after work.

Grateful for the opportunity, I was on the train the next day, headed for New York and Phil. By the time I arrived, four days later, Phil had a busy schedule planned. For our anniversary, he wanted to take me to the elegant St. Regis Hotel to dance to the music of the Vincent Lopez Orchestra.

In preparation he took me shopping at Lord & Taylor, a leading fashion establishment of the day, for evening clothes. Phil found it difficult to explain to the saleslady what he had in mind, but the first six or eight gowns were not it. When I came from the dressing room in a flowing, pale blue silk chiffon creation, his eyes lit up, and he said, "That's it!" This gown was cut in a flattering princess style, flared from waist to hem, making it very full and swirling at the bottom. A matching velvet wrap with blond baby fox trim, silver slippers, and matching evening bag completed the picture for him.

I felt like Cinderella. I had never dreamed my very first formal evening gown would be so elegant. Phil had outfitted himself with a dinner jacket and all that went with it in preparation for our big night out.

As we were dressing for the evening of May 27th, Phil hit a snag. Try as he would, he was unable to produce a passable bow with his black tie. I could do no better, but I had an idea. I went downstairs to the haberdashery shop in the lobby and bought a black tie, then asked the salesman to demonstrate how it should be tied. This was one of the many ways I had of fussing over Phil—and he loved it.

We made a handsome pair as we hailed a cab, but as the cab pulled into traffic, the problems began. We were caught in the eight o'clock theater crush. Cars were bumper-to-bumper, and often at a standstill. It was a very hot evening for May, and since air-conditioned cars were a thing of the future, the cab windows were rolled down to catch any possible wayward breeze. The blaring of horns by impatient drivers and the stench of exhaust fumes assailed us. Our driver, sensing a generous tip, outdid himself in maneuvering us through the jam at every opportunity.

We found ourselves stopped beside a freight wagon pulled by a team of dray horses, the only horses then allowed on New York City streets besides those of the elegant white-gloved mounted police. The near horse's head was just outside my window. Suddenly, his huge head turned and sneezed, sending a fine spray of spittle at my new chiffon gown and velvet wrap. The shock of this sudden insult quickly turned to anger, and I furiously cranked the window closed to avoid a recurrence. Then I ordered the driver to turn at the first opportunity and take us back to the hotel. Phil turned on the dome light to assess the damage.

"I can't see anything on your dress or wrap, Pem."

"Neither can I," I acknowledged, "but I know it's there, and I want to go back to the hotel." I was not to be dissuaded. It took so long to reach a turning point, however, that Phil was able to make me see the humor of the situation. We went on to have a memorable evening, made more so by its ignominious beginning.

The next day, Jess took us to the Yankee Stadium to see a baseball game between the New York Yankees and the Boston Red Sox. Babe Ruth, the "Sultan of Swat," outdid himself that day, hitting two home runs in one inning. This exciting experience was enhanced for Phil and me as Jess entered wholeheartedly into the spirit of the game. This was a facet of Jess's personality heretofore unknown to us. He was indeed an avid baseball fan.

On Sunday Jess took us to dinner at a highly recommended Italian restaurant in Greenwich Village; then we took a cab to Battery Park at the very tip of Manhattan Island, where I had my first view of the Statue of Liberty and Staten Island. Phil delighted in sharing these sights with me and in seeing my wide-eyed wonder at places I had previously seen only in magazines and movies.

We returned by way of a strangely silent and empty Wall Street. Even the towering office buildings on either side had an eerie, vacant look. It was hard to visualize the teeming swarms of people who scurried to and fro in this area during the week, like bees storing a hoard of honey for the hive.

The next day Phil took me to the top of the newly completed Empire State Building which at the time was called the Smith building, for Al Smith, a political figure of the day credited with some responsibility in its erection. From this vantage point we could see all of the seven boroughs and beyond, with their connecting bridges. We took many pictures with the baby Graflex camera Phil had given me to keep a photo record of our babies. I was especially intrigued with the beauty of the Chrysler Building and the docked ships from many lands.

Within a short time the attorneys were able to liberate Phil and Jess. The Farnsworth Company, along with most of the other principals, agreed to a cash settlement to rid itself of the Cox group. The Farnsworth group felt it could not afford to jeopardize the Philco deal by further delay.

We took the train to Philadelphia and checked in at the historic old Benjamin Franklin Hotel. While Phil was busy at Philco, I explored the historical sites that marked the beginning of our wonderful country, later sharing this tour with Phil. It was inspiring to stand in the presence of the ghosts of many seasons past, who had given birth to our Constitution. In the Betsy Ross home I could envision this remarkable lady as she sat in her rocker and fashioned our Stars and Stripes.

In due time, an agreement was reached with Philco, who would carry the expense of the Farnsworth lab in San Francisco and the salaries of Phil and five of his engineers while they came to Philco to set up a television research laboratory and experimental broadcasting station. Phil estimated the time to accomplish that would be from six months to a year. He felt he was getting the short end of the deal, but it was becoming increasingly difficult to raise operating funds, so he agreed. At least he was getting some recognition from the big boys in the East.

Philco, chafing under the stranglehold of RCA on the radio industry, was hoping to use Farnsworth's strong patent position to prevent RCA from spreading its control to television. Of course, the deal was predicated on a license to use the Farnsworth patents, and the whole arrangement was kept strictly confidential in order to avoid raising any eyebrows across the Delaware at the headquarters of RCA.

In mid July, Phil chartered a Pullman car to move his group and their families to Philadelphia, including Tobe and Emily Rutherford and their son Robert, Jr.; Harry and Lucy Lyman and their son; Russell Varian; and newly hired mathematician Wesley Carnahan and his wife Vina. Cliff elected to drive Lola and their little daughter Jean in his new Plymouth Roadster. They wanted to visit family and friends in Utah on the way. Phil and I, with our two boys, left a day early to spend a day with my family and to meet Carl's bride, the former Valdis Fowler. Phil gave them our Chrysler Roadster as a wedding present, not wishing to make the long drive East.

At the time, the entire country was suffering under a severe heat wave. The train was so hot that the thermometer in the dining car reached 140 degrees and exploded—or so we were told by our porter. We kept the children stripped to their skivvies, and we adults only wished we could do the same. Six-month-old Kenny broke out in a terrible heat rash. We occupied the drawing room, so I had the porter leave the beds down so little Philo and Kenny would be more comfortable.

As we were rolling through the oppressive heat of the Kansas plains, the irrepressible Emily Rutherford walked up the aisle and, raising her eyes and arms heavenward, pleaded, "Dear God, please send us just one little breath of San Francisco fog!" To that there was a fervent chorus of amens!" Phil bribed the porter to make sure there were plenty of cold drinks in the adjacent club car and extra ice to be brought to our car for making ice packs from Pullman towels.

Left: Cliff and Lola with Jean, Pat and Gayle
Right: Bob, Emily, Tobe and Tish Rutherford

We found no relief in Philadelphia. The added humidity turned the atmosphere into an all-encompassing steam bath. Were it not for the total commitment of the group to Phil and his project, our people would all have beaten a rapid retreat back to the cool sea breezes of San Francisco.

Our train was met by a Mr. Mortimer, who had been assigned the responsibility of helping us get situated. At his suggestion, we all rented apartments in a large old apartment building in the downtown area, while looking for more suitable living quarters. This also simplified Mr. Mortimer's job of taking the men to work, because there was not a car among us. Cliff had planned well. By driving his car, he was able to find a place in the country where his family were more comfortable.

Philco had chosen the top floor of the old Philadelphia Storage Battery Plant for the location of its television department. It planned to erect a television broadcast tower on the roof as part of the project. The PSB was the parent company of Philco Radio Corporation. This facility also housed its radio-manufacturing operations. The entire Farnsworth operation was treated with the utmost secrecy; only three of the top Philco executives were given access to that floor.

The flat asphalt-covered roof trapped and radiated the intense heat to the floor below. Phil requested exhaust fans—the only cooling method available at the time—to be installed in all the rooms. This request was either ignored or lost in the shuffle of getting started. In any event, no fans were installed.

William Grimditch, the new director of Philco's research department, was in charge of Phil's division. Phil had developed an easy and friendly manner of directing his men and had given each of them stock in his company. So they were really a part of this operation and were behind Phil one hundred percent. Mr. Grimditch, on the other hand, was something of a martinet and at times very difficult to deal with.

Philadelphians, like their cousins in Boston, had retained many of their Victorian English customs. Not even this heat wave could deter them from wearing long-sleeved shirts, coats, vests, ties, and yes, hats. Although Phil had set a similar pattern in San Francisco, here he was one of the boys. They wore ties to lunch, but no coats or vests. They even rolled up their sleeves!

One day as they were leaving for lunch, they were stopped by Mr. Grimditch, who told them they were undermining the high standards of Philco ethics. He suggested they go back upstairs and get their coats. Russell Varian, who seemed to pride himself in his rugged individualism, happened to be in the lead. Suffering from a painful boil on the back of his neck, he had even left his tie behind.

Towering over Mr. Grimditch, he said, "Do you think we're crazy? We'll be lucky as it is to avoid heat stroke!" and strode on past him. Phil stepped forward and informed Mr. Grimditch that under the circumstances, this was and would continue to be their mode of dress until the heat abated to a reasonable level. They were allowed to proceed, but among the Philco executives they were thereafter referred to as "those mavericks from the West."

That afternoon the heat in Cliff's tube room reached a new high. Mr. Grimditch came to check on their progress and found Cliff and his assistant stripped to the waist. The heat of torches, added to the already suffocating heat, had made a furnace of the place. Mr. G. blew his top. Calling them animals, he ordered them to put on their shirts. To this time, Phil's repeated requests for exhaust fans had not produced any results. Cliff had had it! Taking a stance akin to that of John Wayne about to challenge an outlaw in the movies, he said, "Mr. Grimditch! Not only will we not put on our shirts, if we don't get exhaust fans within the hour, I quit!" His tone left no room for doubt. They got their fans.

Perhaps as a safety valve to the tension of working such long hours, there was a certain amount of shenanigans among the men. Each, with the exception of Phil, took his turn as the butt of practical jokes. Russ Varian was no exception. His habit of concentrating on a problem, often ignoring his surroundings, along with other idiosyncracies, caused the other men to regard him as something of an oddball.

The first thing Russ did each morning when he arrived for work was plug in his Tesla coil, a very potent electrical device used to test vacuum. One morning, Joe Knouse, Russ's fun-loving young assistant, came in early and wrapped a thread of hair-thin wire from the tip to the handle of Russ's Tesla coil, then busied himself with his work at another bench. When Russ came in and started through his routine, he picked up the Tesla coil and got a tingle. He laid it down and examined it. Seeing nothing, he confidently picked it up again. This time he got quite a shock.

Russ matter-of-factly laid the instrument down on the bench and looked around the room until he spied Joe, who could not suppress his giggles. Russ calmly walked over to Joe and put him over his knee and spanked him! Then he picked Joe up, set him atop a tall supply cabinet and, without saying a word, returned to work. Poor Joe was stranded, as there was no way he could get down without endangering the special equipment in the cabinet.

Some of the men who knew of Joe's intentions came by to see how things were going. Seeing that Russ had the situation well in hand, they also went back to work. About an hour later, Russ, still not saying a word, lifted Joe down and calmly went about his work as if nothing had happened. Quietly, Russ had made his point. He was immune to pranks thereafter.

During July and August, we wives had our own problems. The small, musty apartments were oppressive to all, but to me, weakened by two babies arriving within fifteen months of each other, it was really bad news. I developed a severe case of asthma. Even with medication, I had trouble breathing. I was able to sleep only in snatches, while sitting up in a chair. The only daytime relief was to walk eight blocks in the blistering heat to a shady park with a small, cool stream trickling through it. The only wheels I had were those on my baby carriage. Emily Rutherford and I took our children there every afternoon.

The children had their own adjustments to make. One evening the adults decided to take in a movie. When the recommended babysitter arrived, they found her to be a jolly black lady. The children just stood and looked at her. Finally, Bobby Rutherford, the eldest of the group, said, "Gee, you're dirty. Why don't you go wash?" The lady must have had something like that happen before, because she laughingly told him this was her natural color. She soon had them playing games, and they forgot all about her color.

By the last of August, Phil had his lab work well organized. With things running smoothly, he could put his mind more on the comfort of his family. By this time, I had hay fever along with the asthma. We rented a nicely furnished house in Chestnut Hill, a better suburb in the North Philadelphia area. I had immediate relief; I must have been allergic to that musty apartment.

The other people in our group rented houses in our general area, and everyone was much more content. Phil bought a secondhand car so he could take the men to work and also go on a Sunday drive in the lush green rolling hills of the countryside. There we found many flowering shrubs and other scenic beauty. We most enjoyed our visit up into the land of the Amish people, which reminded us of our horse-and-buggy childhoods. We admired them for their strict adherence to their simple way of life. Although the country was still in a deep depression, these people seemed immune to the ills of the world surrounding them. Their serenity seemed never to be ruffled.

Phil wrote a letter to his mother, enclosing a check for three hundred dollars to be deposited to his account at the Crocker Bank, and said, "Ten banks have failed since we came here. I am enclosing a check to you which will pay a few bills for you. I'm so glad you like our home. Are you able to keep the house comfortably warm without too much expense? We are getting along very nicely—our work is progressing splendidly and we're very comfortable."

Shortly after this letter was written, our next door neighbor, the wife of a Western Union official, came to our door in a high state of anxiety. Her husband had called her, saying she was to hurry to their bank, which also happened to be our bank, and draw out everything they had on deposit there. She felt duty bound to let us know. Although Phil had just deposited nine hundred dollars from a stock sale, he told her, "You do whatever you think best. As for me, I will not contribute to a run on the bank."

We had the bad news before Phil went to work the next morning. Our bank, the Franklin Trust, would not be opening. There had been a run on the bank the previous day. Investigations later disclosed that the president and vice-president of the bank had been helping themselves to depositors' money. It took months to settle the affair in the courts. We felt lucky to get fifteen cents on the dollar.

After the bank failed, we discovered that we had only one dollar and fifty-seven cents between us. As Phil kissed me good-bye to leave and pick up his men for work, he said, "Don't you worry, honey; everything will be all right. I'll call you from the lab." I was not so sure. It was toward the end of the month, and I had little food in the house. I busied myself with my household chores and tried to put it out of my mind. After all, Phil had said everything would be all right, and he had not let me down yet. Where was my faith?

He called me later that morning.

"Guess what! I got a check in the mail from the west coast office!"

"How did they know about the bank closing?"

"They didn't. Do you remember those times I had to cover our lab bills because Mr. Mann had failed to do so? Well, Albert B. Mann has been indicted for that and a criminal count for mishandling his dying wife's estate. My reimbursement came to over seven hundred dollars. How about that for timing?"

"Nothing short of miraculous. Someone must be looking out for us. By the way, what made you so sure this morning that everything would be okay?"

"You looked so worried, and I knew I could borrow enough from Mr. Holland to pull us through if necessary."

To avoid that kind of problem again, we opened accounts in two banks, one at the Chestnut Hill Bank and another, a household budget account, in the National Bank of Germantown. To provide me with more time for myself, Phil insisted that I hire a maid, but although he occasionally splurged when he could afford it, Phil was basically a frugal person.

The work at the Philco plant was progressing nicely. The broadcast tower on the roof was in operation, and the boys were now broadcasting a test pattern. They were still working three nights a week to meet the schedule set for them, but they were taking it in stride.

Then in March 1932, a profound tragedy struck our happy little family. Our sweet little Kenny of the blond curly hair, large blue eyes, and laughing disposition, developed a serious streptococcus infection in his throat. This was before the discovery of sulpha drugs, penicillin, and streptomycin. At that time all medical science could do was to perform a tracheotomy, in an effort to prevent the infection from going down into the lungs. This operation, recently developed by Dr. Chevalier Jackson of the Pennsylvania University Medical Center in Philadelphia, entailed cutting into the trachea and inserting a breathing tube.

The operation rendered our sweet little Kenny speechless. It tore at our hearts to see him so sick and so frightened at being unable to make a sound. Several times, when the breathing tube clogged up, our pediatrician, Dr. Chapple, sprinted with him down the hall to the operating room to clear it. He stayed with us until Kenny seemed to be out of immediate danger. At about 11:00 p.m., Dr. Chapple left an intern in charge. Finding an empty room for us down the hall, he suggested we try to rest a while and left for the night. He had been with us since early morning.

Since Kenny was sleeping and I had been up most of the previous night with him, we took Dr. Chapple's advice. Completely drained, I fell asleep. Phil, however, found it impossible to relax. After about an hour, he went to check on Kenny. He found the intern asleep in his chair and Kenny blue for lack of oxygen. Alerting the intern, he ran down the hall for me. We returned to see our precious baby near death. We had to stand helplessly by and watch his precious life slip away. Phil vowed to Kenny on his deathbed that he would find a cure for this deadly malady. No more children would die this way if he could help it. Suddenly, unbelievably, our darling son was gone. This moment would stay with us the rest of our lives—so profound is the trauma of losing a helpless baby.

As tragic and unbearable as was the loss itself, the insensitivity we encountered from the brass at Philco only compounded our grief. We could not stand the thought of little Kenny being buried in Philadelphia, so we decided to take him back to Provo, where Phil's father and my mother were interred. Philco said they could not possibly spare Phil for the time the trip would take. Phil almost split company with them then and there, but George and Jess made him see the importance of completing his contract with them. That left it all up to me. I arranged for my part-time maid to come in full time to take care of young Philo, cook for them, and care for the house.

It is hard to relate the agonizing loneliness and grief I suffered during those four seemingly endless days crossing the continent, knowing my baby lay cold and alone in a coffin in the baggage car ahead. In Provo, my father and family took over and made arrangements for the funeral and burial. Dr. Carl Eyring, Phil's favorite BYU professor, graciously complied with Phil's wish that he speak at the funeral.

Back in Philadelphia, Phil set about fulfilling his vow to Kenny. Since he could not take the necessary time off, he went to the University of Pennsylvania Medical College and arranged for a team to carry out his ideas on a serum, under his direction. They succeeded in producing an effective serum, that was used for a short time and did save a number of lives. Then the so-called miracle drugs became available. The penicillin, streptomycin, and sulpha drugs were so effective over a broad spectrum that they took over all similar problems.

The subject of Kenny was so painful to both Phil and me that we just could not seem to talk about it. Time is supposed to heal all wounds, but the passing weeks seemed only to intensify my own feelings of anguish and guilt. I tortured myself, mentally replaying Kenny's illness and thinking that there must have been something I could have done to prevent it, but of course, it was too late. Phil never talked about it, so I came to the conclusion that he also blamed me. In our inability to express and share our grief, a wall went up between us. We both lavished our love and attention upon our one remaining little chick, Philo, but we seemed to have little left for each other.

Despite our lingering grief and the cold silence that divided us,

Left: Pem Farnsworth with son Kenny at one year, 1932
Right: Pem with son Philo, also 1932.

life went on. At Christmas, Phil bought a Lionel train set for Philo. Phil had a great time setting it up on Christmas Eve after Philo was asleep. On Christmas morning, Philo was very much impressed with all of his toys. The train kept his interest as long as his father was operating it. When he was left alone, however, his interest centered on the transformer. That was something he could plug in. Much like his father before him, he was intrigued with anything electric. Some time before, he had experienced firsthand the power of electricity when he received a shock as he plugged in our waffle iron. From then on waffles were "shock toast."

Meantime, Phil was getting more pressure from Philco to complete its installation. After a time, the long hours caused some dissension for his men at home. To keep the wives happy, I organized a regular schedule of playing bridge with them. To relieve the pressure further and also give the men some relaxation, Phil organized Saturday night parties. They usually included dancing, one of his favorite ways to pass an evening. These activities relieved tensions and made the work run more smoothly.

While the transmitter and tower were being constructed, Phil and Mr. Holland went to Washington to apply for an experimental broadcast license. They found many factions lined up to protest their being allowed on the air. Among these were RCA, Bell Labs, Jenkins Television, Western Union, and the fast-growing Radio Amateurs Association. These people were fearful that the broad bands they thought would be needed for television would crowd them out. But because RCA, Jenkins, and Bell Labs (AT&T) had already been issued experimental licenses, the commissioners could hardly refuse Philco. It was issued the call letters W3XE.

When the tower was finished and experimental broadcasting began, Philco received some unexpected results. Calls began coming in with odd complaints. One lady said she was receiving the sound of the test signal on her electric range. A man said he received it in the metal filling of his tooth.

There were also complaints of a more serious nature. Phil had been clandestinely tapping into RCA's TV signal from their labs just across the Delaware River in Camden, but when RCA began picking up the Philco/Farnsworth transmissions, there were immediate repercussions. An ultimatum was delivered to Philco: either it dumped the Farnsworth Company forthwith, or its license to use RCA's radio patents would not be renewed.

That hit Philco below the belt. Its radio sales were its chief source of income. It left the company with no recourse but to terminate its agreement with Farnsworth. Although Phil was unaware of RCA's ultimatum, he sensed something was going on that vitally concerned him. Since he had completed his contract with Philco, he suspected Jess McCargar was negotiating to sell Television, Inc. to Philco.

To forestall any such move, Phil and his men packed up the gear they had brought east and put it in storage. He decided he was leaving Philco, but he was not leaving the east coast. The necessity of being on the front of the push for television was clear to Phil. That front was now on the eastern side of the continent. He needed to be near enough to keep a constant finger on its pulse, if he were to compete with the larger firms.

When they were all safely away from Philco, Phil called Jess and told him what they had done and why. As usual, Jess started to lay down the law to Phil. He ordered Phil to bring the men and equipment back to the San Francisco lab. Phil told Jess he was sorry he and George saw the problem in a different light, but he thought it was paramount to their survival to stay in the east. If Jess and George could not agree, it was time Phil parted company with them. He would go it alone.

Jess and George took the next train to Philadelphia. After seeing Phil's determination and not wishing to part company, they agreed to establish a subsidiary in Philadelphia, with the parent company remaining in San Francisco. Phil was put in charge of the eastern division, but to begin with, the crew had to be cut to Cliff Gardner, Tobe Rutherford, and Phil. They would have to keep operating costs to a minimum.

Reluctantly, Phil agreed. It was hard for him to hand walking papers to those loyal men who had seen him through such rough times. Harry and Lucy Lyman, Wesley and Vina Carnahan (each with a son), and Russell Varian returned to San Francisco. Russell Varian, with his brother Sigerd and Dr. William Hansen of Stanford University, later formed Varian Associates and built it into a top-rated engineering firm with several subsidiaries of its own.

Phil resented Jess for his shortsightedness but figured that a reduced staff was better than no staff at all. So Phil set about building a new lab to continue the struggle to perfect television and deliver it to the public.

CHAPTER 16

Troubles in Paradise

With the decision to stay in Philadelphia, I had to give up my dream of returning to our little love nest in San Francisco. Phil's family was living there and helping with the payments, but now Agnes was married, ready to move out. Phil said he would try to carry it as long as he could, but I knew there was little likelihood we would ever live there again.

The barrier between Phil and me grew daily as we bottled up our emotions following Kenny's death. We no longer confided in each other nor shared the events of the day. We lived together almost as strangers. Though our relationship seemed to be deteriorating, we continued to go through the motions of running a household. Now on a very reduced salary, we found an unfurnished house; the lack of any creature comfort seemed somehow symbolic of the condition of our marriage. We moved in with only beds and two chairs. Fortunately, we had a built-in breakfast nook and a kitchen with stove and refrigerator.

One day Phil called me to say he had a visitor from Japan, Dr. Karawada from the University of Tokyo, who had come to see television. He wanted to see a typical American home. Phil was asking if he could bring his visitor home for dinner.

"Phil! We simply cannot entertain *anyone* in this unfurnished house. Take him out to dinner."

"But Pem, they all sit on the floor in Japan. Besides, you know how I dislike taking business people out to eat."

"No, Phil, I can't have him going home with this as his idea of a typical American home. Anyway, all I have in the house for food is some leftover rice, lamb chops, and lettuce, and I have no way of getting to the store. I had intended making a peach upside-down cake for our dessert."

"That's great, Pem. Make some fried rice cakes, and you know your upside-down peach cake is my favorite dessert. Dr. Karawada is a very interesting gentleman. I want you to meet him. He doesn't speak English, but we've managed to get on quite well. Don't worry about the house."

How could he have so little concern for my feelings? I was uncomfortable enough having Phil in the house; I certainly did not want company. Nevertheless, I felt I should keep up appearances.

It proved to be a very interesting evening. Dr. Karawada seemed to enjoy himself and the food, although he let us know it was the first time he had eaten with anything but chopsticks. I doubt if I was very successful in explaining to him that ours was not at all representative of the typical American home. He taught us to say, "Good morning; how are you?" in Japanese.*

Phil, Cliff, and Tobe set up a lab in the Chestnut Hill section of Philadelphia, at 127 East Mermaid Lane. The building was an office/apartment complex at the rear of the home of Mr. O'Neal, the builder. George Everson took up residence at the elegant Plaza Hotel in New York City. Through his connections there, he found little difficulty selling Farnsworth stock. At this time the entire industry was beginning to make the shift from mechanical to electronic television. Those who were unable to make this change found it necessary to bow out of the race.

Because of Phil's apparent coldness, I was giving all my love and attention to little Philo. Regardless of what was happening at home, Phil's work continued. With the help of George's fundraising in New York, the boys soon had a well operating lab and an excellent demonstration. 127 East Mermaid Lane began to attract many important visitors. Once more Phil was able to enlarge his crew to a working unit. He rehired Tobe's brother Romilly (Rom) Rutherford, who had worked with them at Philco. Cliff needed help in the tube department, and Phil left it up to him to do the hiring. Cliff put an ad in the New York Times for a specialized glassblower. From the dozen or so applicants, he chose Albert Buttino. Al, a capable tube man, was of great assistance to Cliff.

Phil was now very much in need of a secretary. His first applicant was Miss Mable Bernstein, who demonstrated her office managing ability

---

*The Japanese television people thought highly of Phil's achievements. We had quite a number of visitors from Japan over the years. Often those visitors sent favorable clippings from Japanese newspapers. Some time after Phil's death, a young man at KBYU Radio Station in Provo, Utah, told me that while he was on an LDS mission to Hokkaido, the north island of Japan (this was about ten years prior to Phil's death), he and his companion had gone to the local radio station to sing. To their surprise, they found there a statue with the caption, "Philo T. Farnsworth, Father of Television." It has taken years for the United States to begin to recognize his many contributions.

by offering to take over the job of interviewing the rest of the applicants. She was hired, along with a capable engineer, Carl Smith, and an old world Italian, Joseph Spallone. Joe could fashion almost anything out of almost anything. His carpentry was flawless, and his molds and metal castings were a delight to Phil.

One day Joe came to Phil with a problem. His four-year-old daughter, born with mental deficiencies, had become such a problem that Joe's wife was close to a nervous breakdown. Phil looked into the situation and then arranged and paid for the child to be placed in a specialized school equipped to provide the kind of care that would give her any possible chance for an education. From then on, Joe would have done anything for Phil.

On December 13th, 1933 Phil wrote one of his infrequent letters to his mother.

Dear Mother,

Here's just a note to let you know that I do think of you sometimes. We have been demonstrating our apparatus today—the picture is very good. It is much better than we have had previously. Our visitors are always much impressed. I'm enclosing a small check for your Christmas—sorry that it has to be small. I hope that by next year our financial condition will be sufficiently improved to allow us to do some of the things we want to do, such as a visit by you to Philadelphia. We would surely love to see you and have you see Philo. He gets cuter every day, but he's growing up. Tell Carl and Agnes that I'm sorry to have neglected them so badly. I'll write to both before long. I'm glad Agnes is so happy, and I'm anxious to meet Claude.

It has turned cold as blixen here. We have a little snow and prospects of some good skating. I'm working on some new "gadgets" which I'm sure Carl and Lincoln will be interested in. I wish I could have a chance to tell them about them. I've just been looking at a "Mickey Mouse" cartoon. It is awfully good and has perfect sound along with the picture. These cartoons are going to be very popular over television—they are so easy to transmit that they come over perfectly and are most entertaining.

I have invented a new tube for short wave work that I want to describe to Carl. It has no filament or other thermionic emitter and at the same time is a high-vacuum tube. I hope to send him one to play with as soon as we can spare one. Well I hope you will have a very merry Christmas, dear. I wish that we could be there with the rest of your children.

Sincerely,

Phil

Though we continued to live in the same house, the fact remained that Phil and I were growing ever further apart. For instance, at our Saturday night dances, a new couple, Hank and Kay, had joined our circle of friends. When Phil began dancing with Kay quite frequently, I was very hurt. At this time Phil and I danced only one or two dances together, a tacit agreement to keep up appearances. So when Hank asked me to dance, I accepted. Hank was a tall, flamboyantly handsome blond fellow, an excellent dancer.

I decided to show Phil that two could play this game. It went on for weeks, with Phil outwardly unconcerned whether I went or stayed. Weeks passed since we had danced together. Our attitude toward each other by now might be called coldly civil, and I was actually thinking about running off to Reno for a divorce so I could marry Hank. Then good friend Don Lippincott came to town. Since he arrived on Saturday, Phil invited him to go with the crowd to the dance.

About the fifth dance, the orchestra began to play "Always." Suddenly, Phil was standing before me, saying through a forced smile, "I think this is our dance." In a daze, I allowed him to lead me onto the floor. At first it was like dancing with a stranger, because I was not at all sure we still loved each other. Then he held me close and whispered in my ear, "What's the matter with us? We must be crazy! You know I meant it when I told your mother I was going to take care of you. Let's get out of here. We need to talk."

We went home and talked the whole night through. It took that long to talk out all the hurt and resentment we had been harboring. I felt that since I had blamed myself for not being able to prevent Kenny's death, Phil had also blamed me. It turned out that all this time, he was blaming himself. Since the subject was just too painful to discuss, we drew within our innermost selves, and there the matter grew out of all proportion. When communications begin to break down between two people, what starts as a thin veil builds up until it becomes an almost impenetrable wall of stone. With us, breaking this wall down, stone by stone, was a very painful process. We really bared our souls to each other. From that night, we gradually rebuilt our relationship, this time with such a close bond that nothing ever again threatened us. The next day, we took Don with the Gardners and the Rutherfords on a canoe trip. It was then that the mending of all the soulsearing hurt began. I suspected Don's presence had something to do with our reconciliation.

Soon after this, an announcement came of Phil's sister Laura's impending marriage. Both she and Agnes were married in our home in San Francisco. We were happy they had been able to have our nice home in which to entertain their friends. Laura's marriage left only Mother Farnsworth and Lincoln. Phil suggested we rent a larger house in Philadelphia and invite them to live with us, which was fine with me. The cost of shipping our furniture was prohibitive, so we let it go with the house. We rented a three-story house on Durham Street in Mt. Airy, a suburb of Philadelphia, and furnished it from secondhand stores.

Mother and Lincoln arrived in late July. We loved having them with us. I learned how to make passable hot rolls but never could equal her excellence. I hoped that with her helping with the cooking, Phil might put on some weight, but that was just wishful thinking. He ate heartily but used the energy all up in his work.

Not long after the arrival of Mother and Lincoln, Phil brought home a dinner guest, Seymour Turner. Skee, as he liked to be called, and his father, Frank Turner, the proprietor of a San Francisco men's clothing store, had invested fairly heavily in Farnsworth stock. Skee had become very interested in the operation and came east to see what he could do to help. He seemed to have some very good ideas about how to get television to the commercial stage. Phil told him his budget would not stretch to include a salary for him, but if he would like to take over our third floor bedroom, he was welcome to do so. Skee seized upon this opportunity. Phil had become so busy it was not always easy to get his ear at the lab.

About this time, Lieutenant William Crawford Eddy came to town. Bill had followed generations of Eddys who were high-ranking Naval officers, but was mustered out of the Navy after losing his hearing in a submarine accident. Returning to civilian duty, Bill began looking around to see what up-and-coming industry he should enter and discovered television. He offered to work for Phil for nothing if Phil would train him in some branch of the business; Phil wouldn't let him work for nothing but offered to pay him a minimal salary.

*Bill Eddy
and children*

Bill was tall, thin almost to the point of emaciation, with a marvelous sense of humor. His cartoons had adorned the Honeywell Company's calendars for years, even when he was in the service. Bill couldn't decide which department he wanted to work in, so he made himself some funny little hats, one for each department, to identify where he was working at that particular time.

Phil continued to build up his lab crew, who were fast acquiring all the capabilities he felt he needed to run an efficient lab. By this time, Phil had filed twenty-five patents, and he was pleased that his men had filed around ten patents among them. He used to tell me he was building men, not gadgets, and his attitude toward his men was reflected in their loyalty to him.

Besides the dangers inherent in the explosive chemical compounds and high vacuums always present in the lab, television research involved extremely high, potentially lethal voltages as well. Over the years, the Farnsworth lab was the only one that had never experienced a fatality due to accidental electrocution, but there were some close calls.

To avoid the likelihood of deadly contact with high voltages, Phil implemented some strict procedures. One was the practice of turning on a red warning light whenever the high voltage supplies were in use. Cliff was especially careful to do that because he had already suffered more than his share of shocks. He wired a red bulb in series with his power supply so that it would automatically go on whenever the high power was on.

One day a young, newly hired Englishman by the name of Jan Forman needed a red light bulb for some experiment. Finding none on the supply shelf, he just helped himself to Cliff's warning light. Cliff was unable to identify the culprit, so he got another red bulb—only this time, to make an unequivocal statement, he firmly soldered the bulb into its socket.

Some time later, Jan needed another red light and knew just where he could find one. He discovered that Cliff's bulb was soldered in place, but it never occurred to him that this might have been deliberate: he just assumed the bulb had overheated and soldered itself in, so he got a soldering iron, unsoldered the bulb, and removed it.

Cliff came back, turned on his power, and went to work on a tube. Somehow, without his warning light, he made a wrong move and took a terrific jolt—right through the heart. He fell, hitting the floor cold. Fortunately, others nearby heard his fall and rushed to his side. His life hung in the balance, and it was only some fast thinking first aid that got his heart beating again.

This traumatic event taught all the lab crew an unforgettable lesson. Jan was fired, and Phil made another strict rule that no one was to work alone. Had Cliff not received immediate treatment, he would have died.

CHAPTER 17

Patents

P hil's concept of using electrons to eliminate all moving parts from both the transmitter and receiver in his television system was a brilliant display of his genius: by intuitive thinking, logic, and hard work, he combined seemingly unrelated elements into new instruments of amazing effectiveness.

The Farnsworth ideas have since become the most enduring concepts in all of television. With great sophistication, economy, and cunning, his simple concepts met all of television's basic needs. Even as the medium has evolved over the years, with the advent of color, videotape, and digital encoding, Phil's inventions still form the basic foundation of all video technology. His work has left an incalculable legacy, but the fundamental nature of his contributions remains a fact that history has been slow to accept.

The big guns in the east refused to consider the farm-bred boy from the west a serious threat. They were committed, if for no other reason than time and money expended, to the tried and not-so-true method of spinning discs. Nevertheless, as the industry became aware of the tremendous stride forward taken by Farnsworth, they were forced to sit up, take notice, and admit they were on a dead end road.

Not only had Farnsworth eliminated all moving parts, but his system was elegant in its simplicity. As so often happens once a new theory is proven, this simplicity has prompted remarks such as, "Why, that's simple; anybody could have done it." But the fact remains, "anybody" didn't do it. Philo T. Farnsworth did.

Nevertheless, sixty years later, the precise record of who invented what and when remains confused, at best. But a careful, objective inspection of the various patent interferences filed during the 1930s with regard to electronic television will reveal that what frequently passes for historical record is often far from the actual truth.

Farnsworth received patent number 1,773,980 for his electronic television system in August 1930. This particular patent covered all the fundamental operating principles of television as we now know it and formed the cornerstone of the Farnsworth patent portfolio. Farnsworth expected that, as his electronic approach became the norm, those companies wishing to participate in the industry would have to license his patents and pay him handsome royalties for the privilege.

Unfortunately, Farnsworth was not the only practitioner in the field who expected to reap the rich rewards of an electronic television patent. RCA, who already dominated radio with its virtually impenetrable patent structure, considered television part of its territorial imperative and fully expected to extend its domination into the new field. To that end, RCA President David Sarnoff hired Vladimir Zworykin in 1930, expecting Zworykin to spearhead RCA's effort to control the new art.

Zworykin was by no means new to the concept of television. As a student of physics in his native Russia, he was introduced to the theories of Professor Boris Rosing, who postulated that cathode-ray tubes could be used to send and receive a visual image. Zworykin brought these ideas with him when he immigrated to the United States, and while employed at Westinghouse in the early 1920s, he attempted to develop a working system.

In 1923, Zworykin applied for a patent for his system. He is reputed to have built at least one experimental model that was demonstrated to his superiors at Westinghouse. But there is little or no evidence that such a demonstration ever took place or that the equipment involved produced any encouraging results; to the contrary, Zworykin himself always stated that his superiors greeted these experiments with the suggestion that he turn his efforts toward "something more useful."

There was still no patent issued for Zworykin's 1923 application when he left Westinghouse for RCA—and stopped at Farnsworth's lab along the way. Nevertheless, Sarnoff was confident that Zworykin would be able to blaze a trail through the new field of television and lock up the controlling patents.

At the time, Zworykin was still experimenting with scanning discs on the transmitting end, though he was having some success with cathode-ray tubes for the receiver. In other words, he had figured out how to turn an electrical signal back into a light image, but he had still not found a way to convert a light image into an electrical signal by any means other than mechanical discs. Only Farnsworth had figured out that critical side of the equation. Zworykin's work was permanently hampered by this failure, because it was impossible to produce any more resolution on the receiving end than was produced by the transmitter. It is no wonder then that the first thing Zworykin did after visiting the Farnsworth lab was build his own operating replica of the Farnsworth Image Dissector.

By early 1931, Farnsworth was much in the news. While RCA was being very secretive about the details of its television system, Farnsworth had revealed his system in an article in the *California Engineer* in 1930. He had also given many interviews, resulting in articles in England, Germany, and the United States. There was an article in *Fernsehen* in Germany in February 1931, two by Dinsdale in *Wireless World* in March 1931, and another in Hugo Gernsback's *Science and Invention* in May 1931. There were at least two articles in *Radio News*, and in May 1931 an article appeared in the *Journal of the Royal Society of Arts*. In praising Farnsworth, the author stated, "He is about the only important worker making use of strictly electrical methods of transmission."

There were many reasons Farnsworth wanted as much publicity as possible for his system. Not the least of these was the continuing desire of his backers to find a buyer for their costly venture. Short of outright sale, Farnsworth and his backers continued to search for licensees for the patents, as they had found in their arrangement with Philco.

Although Farnsworth held actual patents controlling all of the basic elements of electronic television, RCA repeatedly claimed Dr. Zworykin to be its originator, by virtue of his 1923 patent application. Thus it became imperative to settle this question before Farnsworth could negotiate any more license agreements. It was also essential to clarify the matter before any more investors would buy stock in the Farnsworth venture.

Thus the battle lines were drawn for the patent litigation which was to follow. Or, as more graphically stated in *Television, a Struggle for Power*, by Frank Waldrop and Joseph Barkin (Morrow, 1938):

"How the Gods must have laughed that day when they set the impecunious ex-soldier of the Czar and a child in knee pants at each other . . . Philo Farnsworth and Vladimir Zworykin are the symbols of power, predicated upon invention, of fortune waiting upon the word of government. As between these two eventually must be decided basic rights under letters patent from the United States Government, rights of vital importance to the exploiter and user of television."

The issue of priority was taken before the Patent Examiners for a decision. Claim 15 of Farnsworth patent number 1,773,980 (filed January 7th, 1927, issued August 26th, 1930), was chosen as exemplifying and controlling the issue. This claim reads:

"An apparatus for television which comprises a means for forming an electrical image, and means for producing a train of electrical energy in accordance with the intensity of the elementary area of the electrical image being scanned."

This simple paragraph embodies the essence of the Farnsworth invention, and as such truly established and controlled the art and science of electronic television. It was therefore an entirely appropriate point on which to defend the Farnsworth position. The claim is indeed the first declaration of the ability to produce a television signal by wholly electronic means and constitutes a pivotal moment in the evolution of man.

In taking on the Radio Corporation of America, the Farnsworth organization was challenging one of the largest and most firmly entrenched institutions on the corporate landscape. This was truly a David and Goliath confrontation.

In its brief on behalf of Zworykin, RCA contended that no boy of fifteen with a background such as Phil's would be capable of conceiving such a technically advanced art as required for electronic television. When questioned by Don Lippincott about his early disclosures, Phil told him about his chemistry teacher, Justin Tolman. The only other person in whom he had confided at the time was his father, who was now dead.

Mr. Tolman was finally located in Salt Lake City, Utah, where he had been teaching. Arrangements were made for Samuel Smith, the attorney for RCA, and Don to travel to Salt Lake for Mr. Tolman's deposition. In Salt Lake, Don located Mr. Tolman in his rose garden, where the following conversation took place:

Lippincott: "Are you Justin Tolman?"

Mr. Tolman: "Yes, I am."

Lippincott: "Do you remember a student in Rigby, Idaho, by the name of Philo Farnsworth?"

Mr. Tolman: "I surely do; brightest student I ever had."

Lippincott: "My name is Don Lippincott, and I'm a patent attorney representing Mr. Farnsworth. His camera tube, the Image Dissector, is in interference in the Patent Office. Do you remember him discussing it with you?"

Mr. Tolman: "Yes, I do."

Don:" Will you come to this address at ten in the morning and testify to that effect?"

Mr. Tolman: "I'd be glad to."

So Don gave him his card with the address on the back and departed. He refrained from further conversation to avoid being accused of "priming the witness." Don had a restless night. His mind was filled with misgivings. Would Mr. Tolman, after twelve years, remember enough to satisfy the Patent Examiners? He arrived at the appointed place the next morning with a definite feeling of uneasiness.

His worries were needless, however, because Mr. Tolman did indeed remember Phil and very well. As a matter of fact, he had acquainted all of his subsequent classes with this unforgettable student. He told them all he remembered about the drawings Phil had made on the blackboard, then took from his pocket a well-worn sheet torn from a small pocket notebook whereon Phil had sketched his Image Dissector tube, saying, "This was made for me by Philo early in 1922."

With this testimony, Mr. Smith agreed that Phil's date of conception was substantiated. They interrogated several witnesses in San Francisco, then returned to Philadelphia.

After weeks of testimony in Washington, the Patent Examiners, in a forty-seven-page ruling number 64,027, gave priority to Farnsworth on the grounds that Zworykin's 1923 tube was inoperable. On page six it states, "In view of this testimony it is now considered that the Zworykin apparatus does not inherently operate to produce the 'electrical image' called for in the count."

"REMEMBER THE DAYS"—Justin Tolman, Salt Lake City teacher, talks over the past with Philo T. Farnsworth, whose inventions made possible modern television. Mr. Tolman's notes figured in a patent suit won by Mr. Farnsworth.

Philo T. Farnsworth to Be Banquet

Utahns to Honor

Tuesday night, Utah will honor publicly for the first time a native son whose genius brought television into millions of American homes.

He is Philo T. Farnsworth, a native of Beaver, Utah. Mr. Farnsworth is credited with having more than a half-dozen basic patents in every television receiver in existence.

He will be guest of honor at the annual banquet of the Utah Broadcasters Assn. Tuesday night in the Hotel Utah.

Born on Indian Creek near Beaver on Aug. 19, 1906, Mr. Farnsworth lived on ranches at Beaver and Vernal, Utah, before the family moved to a ranch near Rigby, ID. Even then he determined to be an inventor.

In 1922, when he was 15 years old he began the work which brings him world-wide acclaim. He had entered the chemistry classes of Justin Tolman at the Rigby High School. Tolman encouraged the youth and lent him books.

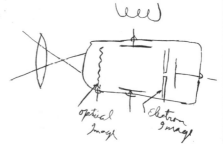

Justin Tolman, teacher, talks over the past with Philo T. Farnsworth, whose inventions made possible modern television. On right is sketch Philo drew for Mr. Tolman in 1922 which helped win patent suit.

In the course of this interference, Dr. Zworykin had ample opportunity to present evidence that he had built and operated the tube disclosed in his 1923 application. But no such evidence was produced. Despite the massive resources at his disposal over a period of more than eleven years, Dr. Zworykin was unable to produce a model of his tube, or even any notes to show he had actually built one. If ever there was a time when such evidence should have been produced, this was it. But it was not until many decades later that any such evidence appeared.

During the period when this interference was being heard, Zworykin was demonstrating a new camera tube, called the Iconoscope, which worked on something called "the storage principle." Where the Image Dissector employed a continuous photosensitive surface, the Iconoscope featured a photocathode composed of discrete elements, each capable of storing its electrical charge. While this produced a stronger signal, it did so at the expense of the instantaneous values which were produced by the Image Dissector.

While the Iconscope is most frequently attributed to Dr. Zworykin, its actual origins have never been clearly established. The storage principal has been traced to the work of a Hungarian scientist, Dr. Kalman Tihanyi who filed a patent on a similar storage-type tube in 1926. In 1928, this patent was filed in Germany, England, and France. In Europe, Dr. Tihanyi is given credit for this invention. In fact, four of the original claims in Zworykin's Iconoscope patent were taken out and given to Tihanyi.

Regardless of Tihanyi's contribution, Dr. Zworykin and his large laboratory force are given credit for the development of the Iconoscope. But the error that is most frequently cited in discussion of this tube traces its origins back to Zworykin's 1923 patent application—when in fact there is no direct connection between the two. So often, we read that Zworykin invented the Iconoscope in 1923, when nothing could be further from the truth. Regardless of what Zworykin may or may not have built and may or may not have demonstrated in 1923, it was NOT the Iconoscope that appeared in the mid 1930s. The Iconoscope appears in patent number 2,021,907, filed in November 1931 and granted in November 1935—more than five years *after* Farnsworth's patents were granted. Nevertheless, that is the basis upon which Dr. Zworykin is oft cited as the "Father of Television." Historians are now beginning to see Zworykin's "dubious chronology" in its true light and have begun to give Farnsworth the credit to which he is entitled.

While the 1934 interference was central in establishing Farnsworth's priority in the art of electronic television, it was by no means the only case that came into contention. Despite losing the 1934 case, RCA continued to challenge other components of the Farnsworth patent portfolio. Throughout the 1930s, Phil found his time divided between defending his patents, continuing to refine his system, and haggling with his own backers for adequate funding. No doubt RCA knew that the small firm's resources were stretched to the limit and continued its attack, expecting the weaker opponent eventually to fold under the strain. Although its assessment of Farnsworth's resources may have been accurate, the one factor it did not take into account was the sheer determination of Philo T. Farnsworth.

CHAPTER 18

TV Goes Public: Recognition Abroad

About the time the patent examiners were handing down their favorable ruling on the 1934 interference with RCA, Phil received word that Mary Pickford was appearing on stage in New York. Hoping to vindicate himself after the fiasco in San Francisco, he invited her down to Philadelphia to see a picture at the present state of the art. She had only the following Sunday afternoon free, so Phil asked Cliff and Tobe to come in and help with the demonstration.

At the appointed time, Miss Pickford and friend arrived in her chauffeured limousine. Phil was pleased when she stopped to talk to some of the neighborhood children who had crowded around as she emerged from the car. He introduced her, and she shook each grimy hand, to their everlasting joy.

The demonstration included several film loops of Miss Pickford in *The Taming of the Shrew*, notably one showing her combing her beautiful long hair. These clips had been used endlessly for test material. She was delighted and amazed at the quality of the picture and was probably wondering whether this was a medium to which she would have to adapt. She accepted the offer to be "televised," but after a few minutes under the kleig lights, she exclaimed, "Whew!, this is hotter than color!"

New work was proceeding at a good clip at the lab now. Representatives of competitive companies and other dignitaries were coming from around the world to investigate. There was also constant pressure on Phil to write articles give lectures about his work. Phil resisted these requests, protesting that he could not spare the time, but when an invitation came to speak before the Franklin Institute, he finally gave in.

I accompanied Phil to the lecture and to the formal dinner preceding it. I suffered with him through those first agonizing minutes of stage fright, then swelled with pride as he warmed to his subject. He was breaking new territory and opening up new technical fields of endeavor. He took considerable pleasure in sharing the results of his research with the scientific community represented by the Institute.

The concise description of his electronic television system included the first public disclosure of his new dissector-multiplier tube, which demonstrated his method of obtaining the electron power buildup. Also for the first time, he announced his Electron Multiplier tubes of the constant-potential type, a radio frequency type, and a photo-cell making use of this principle. By using pure nickle cathodes in the photo-cell, he reported obtaining a magnification greater than 50,000,000 times. This was all new art, and his paper was carried in the October 1934 issue of the *Journal of the Franklin Institute*.

Not long after Phil's talk at the Institute, one of the directors asked if it would be possible for him to put on a week-long live television demonstration at the Institute. They had recently opened their new automated museum and wanted something spectacular to draw the public's attention. The magic response of the public to anything connected with television indicated that this would be just what they needed.

Fortunately the Farnsworth group had just completed what was then a state-of-the-art television camera and monitor for the Century of Progress Exposition in Chicago, although not in time to be demonstrated there. This seemed to be a way to salvage some of the publicity value, thereby justifying the expenditure of time and money to build this, so they took advantage of the opportunity.

Farnsworth was now using Oscillite receiving tubes with a twelve-by-thirteen-inch viewing area that gave very good definition. Because of the high vacuum in these tubes, however, the danger of their imploding was ever present, and this risk was magnified when the blanks Cliff obtained from Corning Glass arrived with a 27 pound capability instead of the 45 pound capability he had specified in his order. Phil wanted replacement tubes to back him up at the Franklin Institute in case a tube gave him trouble. There was no time to wait for more glass, so Cliff went ahead and made the tubes from the thinner glass. Actually, one of these tubes did implode at the Institute. Luckily it was a spare, still in its box, and it happened at night when no one was around. Thereafter, they used thicker glass, and Cliff supplied them with two spare tubes in case of trouble. Fortunately, they had no further incident with them.

In demonstrations such as this, just keeping the equipment together was usually enough to worry about. Phil had failed to even consider another problem that still plagues modern broadcasters: where to get the talent and material to fill the insatiable appetite of television.

While Phil and his men set up the equipment at the Institute, Skee Turner scurried around trying to line up interesting people to be televised. The mayor and other local dignitaries were invited to open the show. Skee, a tennis buff, had joined the prestigious Philadelphia Cricket Club and through this connection was able to get sports personalities to appear. He also went to booking agents with the suggestion that their clients might well benefit from the publicity and experience that went along with this new medium. Before it was all over, he had tried everything he could think of to fill the schedule.

At the opening of the exhibit, Phil set up the mobile monitor and a camera trained on the entrance. As people entered, they were thus greeted by their own televised image, much to their delight and that of their friends.

We had trained dogs, monkeys, and even bears. A famous puppet show appeared and was very well received. The one act that went over better than any other was a ventriloquist. But the act that should have taken the prize featured Phil's brother, Lincoln, and me using my car to transport a rhesus monkey, which was on loan from a pet shop. We lost the monkey when the cage broke, then chased the rascal through the busy downtown Philadelphia traffic on foot. As we chased the monkey, the police chased us and the monkey, much to the entertainment of the gathering crowd, as the monkey continued to elude its pursuers. We managed to apprehend the errant beast, but I narrowly averted a major traffic accident when the monkey, now loose in the back seat, landed on the back of my neck. Only Lincoln's swift action in coming to my aid saved the situation.

On the first day of the exhibit, Skee brought in some chorus girls from the theater district. When they came on screen, an entire row of newsmen invited to see the demonstration arose and filed out. They wanted to see this act in the flesh. Then Dr. Swan, a physicist from Swarthmore College who also had a connection with the Franklin Institute, brought his cello and offered to play for us. As he was building up to a crescendo, a string broke. Undaunted, he went on playing. Then another string broke; still he continued to play, but when he saw the varnish of his cello begin to blister from the heat of the lights, he came to an impromptu finish, and Phil, who had watched sympathetically, asked me to bring some ice water for Dr. Swan and put the next act before the camera.

On bright days, the camera would be taken either to the little stage set up on the roof or outside on the lawn, where boys recruited from the crowd were encouraged to spar a few rounds in an improvised ring in return for free admission. They even had football scrimmages. From the roof of the institute, Phil would aim the camera down on the street traffic or familiar buildings in the area. The statue of William Penn on top of City Hall a block away came over clearly.

One evening when the moon was full, Phil caused quite a stir when he televised the man in the moon. The next day in a New York press interview, Phil told them about this. The story, carried in the next morning newspapers and relayed to San Francisco read:

"First recorded use of television in astronomy was announced yesterday in Philadelphia by Philo T. Farnsworth, young San Francisco scientist.

And it was the man in the moon that posed for his first radio snapshot.

Reproduction of the moon's likeness is just another sensational achievement by the young inventor who has been working on his television apparatus

SCIENTISTS SEE
NEW TELEVISION

Aug 24, 1934

Principle Discovered by Boy of 13 Acclaimed 15 Years Later at Franklin Museum

CALLED MOST SENSITIVE

(Illustrated on Picture Page)

A scientific principle struck upon 15 years ago by the inventive mind of a 13-year-old Idaho farm boy made its debut today in the Franklin Institue in the form of the latest system of television.

Scientists who witnessed the demonstration asserted it is the most sensitive apparatus yet developed.

The farmer boy was Philo T. Farnsworth, now, at the age of 28, head of the Television Laboratories, Ltd., a California corporation, at 127 E. Mermaid Lane, Chestnut Hill.

While Mr. Farnsworth, Mayor Moore, President Nathan Hayward of the Franklin Institute, Dr. James Barnes, head of the physics section of the Institute and others, including several of the Davis Cup tennis players, talked before the magic eye of the television camera or pickup in one room, a gathering of 200 scientists and laymen sat in an adjoining auditorium and saw and heard the speakers just as though they were watching a talkie news reel.

The speakers' images were seen on a greenish fluorescent screen about a foot square, to which the original image was brought by wire (it can also be transmitted over radio) from the camera.

Frank Shields, of New York, and Lester Stoefen, of Los Angeles, Davis Cup players participating in the doubles matches at the Germantown Cricket Club, were introduced by F. S. Turner, of San Francisco, an associate of Mr. Farnsworth.

They talked, swung tennis rackets and demonstrated their favorite grips, all of which was clearly seen by the audience on the other side of the wall. William Herrmann, Jr., star of the Olympic tumbling team, entertained with some flip-flops.

The instrument is capable of broadcasting not only closeup views but entire tennis matches, foot ball and base ball games as well as news shots directly from the scene.

Because it is sensitive to the unseen infra-red rays it is expected to be of great value in penetrating fog, etc. Its military possibilities are also great, it was pointed out.

Cloudy weather prevented the program originally scheduled, which was to have had the performers outdoor in the sunlight, while the audience saw them inside. The sunlight makes possible much better images, it was explained, than artificial lighting.

Both outdoor and indoor demonstrations will be made at the Franklin Institute every day for ten days, including the televising of the moon. The hours will be from 2 to 10 P. M. and from 10 A. M. to 10 P. M. on Saturday. At the conclusion of this demonstration the apparatus will be taken to the World's Fair in Chicago.

One principle of Mr. Farnsworth's system is the electron multiplication phenomenon in which one electron can reproduce six times in a hundred-millionth of a second, making possible the operation of the cold cathode tube.

With the exception of a large amplifier the televisor transmitting mechanism is enclosed in a camera-like box scarcely larger than an ordinary news photographer's camera.

A large photograhic lens focuses the image of the subject on a photosensitive surface at the front end of the Farnsworth cathode tube, a vacuum tube. At this point the visual image is transformed into an electron image, in reality millions of streams of electrons emanating from the photosensitive surface.

At the rear end of the tube is a small nickel sleeve or tube, a photoelectric cell, the opening of which is only a twelve thousandths of an inch in diameter. This picks up the electron image.

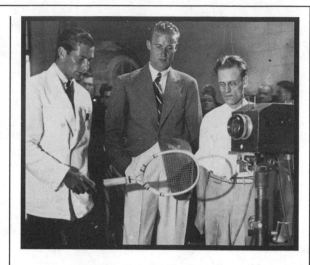

TELEVISION SET CALLED EPOCHAL

New Device, Shown at Franklin Institute, Hailed as Most Sensitive Devised

A new television system hailed by scientists as epochal made its debut today at the Franklin Institute, Twentieth Street and the Parkway, when about 100 scientific and civic leaders viewed a demonstration in which Mayor Moore and Lester Stoefen and Frank Shields, Davis Cup stars, participated.

The system, invented by a 28-year-old scientist, Phil T. Farnsworth, in his laboratory at 127 East Mermaid Lane, Chestnut Hill, centers around a cold cathode tube so sensitive that it can "televise" the moon and thin puffs of cigarette smoke.

While its ultimate potentialities can only be estimated now, it is thought that it will bring nearer the day when a person may sit in his home and see a movie or enjoy a sports contest. The system is so devised that its receiving set could easily be placed in a convenient-sized cabinet suitable for any home.

EPOCHAL TELEVISION SET INVENTED HERE

Top (page 162): (l. to r.) Bill Schneider and Bud Shields, tennis champs preparing to be televised by Philo T. Farnsworth at Franklin Institute. Center: Philo Farnsworth with his new mobile television camera on the lawn of the Franklin Institute, 1934; Bottom: Philo T. Farnsworth (left) with his television monitor and Seymour Turner (right) with mobile camera, 1934. Top (page 163): (l. to r.) Philo T. Farnsworth, inventor; Richard Schneider; Mrs. Nathan Hayward, Mr. Hayward, president of the Franklin Institute; and Dr. Barnes, of the physics department of the Institute. Bottom: Philo Farnsworth with electron multiplier tube, 1935

since the age of 15. And a 'return performance'—open to the public—is promised by Farnsworth for the benefit of all doubters. This 'show' will take place on the 'first clear night.'"

The picture of the moon, according to Associated Press dispatches, provided the ultimate test of the supersensitivity of Farnsworth's television invention.

After this, the lines waiting to see the television show were even longer. Since this exhibit was staged during the height of the tourist season, people from all over the country, in Philadelphia to visit the birthplace of the nation, found themselves waiting in line to see television. In order to accommodate the crowds, programs were staged in fifteen-minute intervals. We had no trouble keeping the fifty-seat auditorium filled.

Since the Institute charged seventy-five cents extra for admission to the television exhibit, I suppose this could be considered the first true instance of commercial television. Phil saw it only as a chance to get reaction of the public to his creation.

At the urging of Dr. Barnes, head curator, and Dr. Howard McClellan, secretary of the Institute, Phil agreed to stay for another week. Toward the end of the engagement, Skee Turner arranged for the entire floor show of a local night club to come and perform.

As they were setting up that afternoon, Dr. McClellan happened to come in. Shaking his head, he said, "I never thought the staid old Franklin Institute would ever come to this. It will never be the same." Dr. Barnes, who was standing with him objected. "But Howard, we've taken in more money this past two weeks than in the last two years." This sank in a moment, and the realization dawned on them that something more than just television had been demonstrated here; they were witnessing the *power* of television.

On our last night, the astronomer who operated the observatory on the roof invited us up after the show to see an unusually bright image of a distant galaxy. We became so enthralled that we lost track of time. As we left, we found the stairs only dimly lighted and the main floor in utter darkness. We groped our way to the main exit, only to find it locked. Phil told Cliff, Tobe, and me to wait there while he and Skee tried to find a way out. When they returned, they led the way to the other door. Phil, guiding me by the arm, reached the door first, and as he opened it, a cavernous, disembodied voice boomed throughout the empty building, "GOOD EVENING! I HOPE YOU ENJOYED YOUR VISIT." I choked off an impulse to scream, as I realized I had been set up for this little surprise. We had tripped the invisible ray which activated a giant robot programmed as a greeter.

The Franklin Institute exhibit caused quite a stir in our own back yard, but we had little idea of its repercussions around the world. Wrapped up as we were in our own little world, it was easy to lose track of the rapid development of television elsewhere around the globe.

In the mid thirties, the race for position in the emerging new industry was heating up, not only in the United States but in Europe as well. Here at home, the big guns, like RCA, AT&T/Bell Labs, Westinghouse, GE, and relative newcomers like Allen B. Dumont, were all jockeying for position and advantage.

And ironically, the battle lines in Europe were dividing along similar lines.

In Great Britain, the government assumed control of this new medium, as it had radio a few years before. The agency assigned to establish policy with regard to television was the British Broadcasting Company (BBC), which operated under the direction of the British Post Office Department. It was apparent that universal standards would have to be established before manufacturers and broadcasters would be willing to make the requisite investments in tooling and equipment. So the BBC's immediate task was to sort through the existing technology and derive broadcasting standards from it. The standards would include the number of lines per frame, the number of frames per second, and bandwidth requirements.

The principal competitors in Great Britain at this time were Baird Television (now a subsidiary of the conglomerate British Gaumont), and Marconi/EMI. The EMI people were presently conducting tests with an electronic camera tube they dubbed the Emitron, which they claimed to have developed independently. The Emitron bore a striking resemblance in both its mode of operation and its physical configuration to another tube being tested in the United States—the Iconoscope. The simultaneous appearance of the same device on both sides of the Atlantic has created further doubt about the tube's actual origins. In any event, EMI enjoyed a cross license with RCA, making the British corporation a power equal in many ways to its American counterpart.*

Despite the commanding position of EMI in the radio and recording industries, the British public was much more familiar with the work of John Logie Baird in television. A clever, if not exactly ingenious, Scotsman, Baird first achieved notoriety in 1926 when he employed a scanning disc system to send some semblance of the head of a dummy from one room to another. By the mid 1930s, the Baird Company was conducting a regular nightly schedule of experimental telecasts using Baird's mechanical system and a couple of spare BBC radio channels, and had managed to sell build-your-own receiver kits in some quantity to the public.

However, once EMI began testing its electronic system, the limitations of Baird's mechanical system became painfully apparent, and Baird's superiors at British Gaumont held little hope of competing successfully. In order to achieve the picture quality that would impress the BBC, the folks at British Gaumont decided they would have to find an all-electronic television system of their own.

In the wake of the Franklin Institute exhibit, word of Farnsworth's achievements spread around the world, and it was not long before emissaries from the Baird organization were dispatched to the United States to get a firsthand look. After seeing his system, British Gaumont invited Phil to bring

---

*Actually, the relationship between RCA and EMI was much closer than of simple cross-licensees. In the late 20s, two English record companies, the H. M. V. Gramophone and the Colombia Gramophone Company decided to merge in order to cut expenses. The new company was called the Electric and Musical Industries, Ltd. (EMI). Since RCA held a substantial interest in the Gramophone Company, this interest now transferred to the EMI Company. Therefore, David Sarnoff took his seat on the EMI board of directors in April 1931. RCA also had an alliance with the Telefunken Company in Germany. With its connections in other parts of the world, it now was a formidable world power.

his mobile equipment to London to demonstrate its capabilities to Baird and the British Post Office Department, who were organizing the BBC. Smelling a potential patent licensee, Phil quickly accepted the invitation.

Making a trip to Europe represented quite a gamble in both time and money for the already financially pressed Farnsworth organization. Because of the ongoing patent litigation with RCA, George and Jess were having a very difficult time selling enough stock to finance day-to-day operations. But it was equally obvious to Phil that until the patent problems were resolved, there was little likelihood of obtaining any more licensees in America. To Phil, it seemed there was no alternative to pursuing the possibility of a licensee in Europe.

Since the Baird people had only a short time to come up with an impressive demonstration for the BBC, they were anxious to see the Farnsworth picture immediately. Passage was booked on the next sailing, aboard the SS *Bremen*, for Phil, Skee Turner, Tobe Rutherford, and Arch Brolly. But the Bremen carried no freight. An enterprising shipping agent obtained permission to ship the considerable amount of equipment required for the demonstration, but it had to go as personal baggage, a detail that was to give them trouble later.

The *SS Bremen* was a luxuriously appointed seagoing hotel, well equipped to pamper the whims of wealthy globetrotters. The Farnsworth party took full advantage of this, not having had a moment of vacation for eight years, and the respite gave Phil and Skee time to review their objectives and plan their strategy. On deck in the sea air, they caught their breath and recharged their energies.

On the fifth day out (a fast passage in those days), a ship's officer sought them out to say they were approaching Southampton. Because the *Bremen* did not dock at Southampton, passengers and luggage had to be off-loaded onto a British boat at sea. A radiogram had been received, indicating that the Farnsworth entourage and effects would be taken ashore by a private launch sent by British Gaumont.

As the group came on deck, ready for their rendezvous with the launch, Phil took one look at the turbulent sea and started to worry for the safety of his precious cargo. The Gaumont launch came along side, and the four passengers were transferred safely aboard. Then the *Bremen*'s large loading crane began to lower the "luggage." Last to be lowered down were the crates containing the television equipment. As they were lowered down to the smaller craft, a huge wave tossed the waiting deck up to meet the cargo, and they collided with a sickening crash. Phil and companions stood rooted to the spot in utter dismay, wondering with dread what had happened inside those crates.

"It may not be as bad as we think," Phil ventured, being the first to regain some semblance of composure. "That equipment was packed very carefully."

"Yeah," Tobe agreed, showing no enthusiasm for even thinking about it. Adding insult to injury, the launch was met at the Southampton dock by her Majesty's customs officials, who flatly refused to allow the equipment to come on British shores as personal luggage. It would have to be impounded!

Leaving Tobe to guard the crates, the others went in search of help from the Baird people. After several hours, they returned with a British Gaumont representative who had miraculously cut through the red tape to get the equipment released. The crates were loaded onto a waiting lorry and driven to the Crystal Palace, an enormous, improbable structure of glass and steel that had been constructed for a world exposition during the reign of Queen Victoria. Among other things, this imposing edifice now housed the Baird Television Studios.

Baird engineers crowded around to see the much-heralded Farnsworth equipment unpacked, but as the first crate was opened, they saw the jumble of chassis broken off their supports and lying in a heap at the bottom. They shrugged and went back to work, obviously not expecting much help from that direction.

As soon as they were alone and before a severe depression could set in, Phil's group discovered, to their amazement and joy, that most of the real damage was superficial and mechanical. All the tubes had come through unbroken, and most of the electronic components were also in fine shape. This was really fantastic, considering how heavy, but delicate, such gear and components were in those days.

In a remarkably short time, they had things back together and a clear picture on the monitor. Apparently one of the Baird men had passed by the door and gotten a glimpse of the test picture, because very soon the room was filled with Baird personnel, all trying to get a look at the electronic picture.

Phil went off in search of Mr. Baird, to show him the happy results before something else went wrong. All the way back to the studio Mr. Baird was busily extolling the virtues of his mechanical system over Farnsworth's. As they came to the door, Mr. Baird, still in his argument, caught sight of the picture on the monitor and became silent. He advanced slowly, as if hypnotized, until he was standing directly before it. He stood there for a time; then breaking the spell with a visible effort, he turned without a word and left. With great empathy, Phil watched him go, aware Mr. Baird had seen the death knell of his beloved spinning disc.

The Farnsworth group was driven to London and settled at the luxurious Grosvenor House Hotel for what turned out to be a somewhat extended stay. The accommodations, ultimately paid for by their British hosts, were quite comfortable and even featured a lower-level squash court, often employed by Phil and Skee for exercise.

Baird executives, usually including one or more board members, took Phil and Skee on a round of sightseeing trips, wined and dined them, and in general entertained them socially for almost two weeks. This process of "getting to know each other better" was pursued with determination by their British hosts. Sir Harry Greer, a member of the British Parliament, was chairman of the Baird board of directors and also a member of the board of British Gaumont. He saw that Phil and Skee were made members of the prestigious English Speaking Union, as well as taking them out on the town several times.

Sir Harry, along with several other Baird board members, decided that an adequate demonstration of the Farnsworth transmission to the BBC should involve broadcasting over some distance and across a metropolitan area. An appropriately situated inn with pub was selected, about twenty-five miles out of London, and receiving equipment was set up there.

The demonstration was formally made before a committee appointed by the Postmaster General, authorized by Parliament to oversee the technical aspects of the BBC charter. The demonstration was generally regarded as a big success. The British press carried the story extensively and relayed it to the continent and the United States. This greatly elated the Baird people, who realized this put them in a good position to win government approval and thus to supply the BBC with with their initial television equipment.

Negotiations now began, with Phil and Skee Turner meeting with a group from Baird several times a week. Preliminary and background conditions having been established, it became time to confront the Baird board of directors in formal session to finalize a patent license. This of course involved numbers and some inevitable haggling. The board included some of the top men of British industry, who knew their way around the business world, and these two Americans appeared to them as easy targets when they entered the room.

Sir Harry started the meeting by observing that while Farnsworth had been receiving a lot of attention lately, the Baird organization had at its disposal two hundred engineers and extensive facilities. Baird would naturally be making significant contributions in the field over the next few years.

"You may have the advantage at the moment, but who knows? Next year it may be us," Sir Harry told them. He felt that, in view of the small Farnsworth operation, a simple cross-licensing agreement would be most appropriate . . . without royalties.

Phil bridled at this, knowing full well that they needed his patents even to stay in the race, and he was not at all sure he would ever need theirs. Also, both he and Skee were well aware how badly they needed cash back home. Skee then voiced their thoughts, stating they would not be interested in that sort of an arrangement. Farnsworth would require a substantial amount of cash on the line, as well as royalties based on future sales. Somewhere about here Skee mentioned the figure of fifty thousand dollars. Sir Harry told them in ominous tones that he feared Mr. Osterer, Chairman of the Board of British Gaumont, would cancel the whole deal irrevocably when he learned of their demands. And so it went for a time, with Baird objecting to every argument Phil and Skee advanced.

Finally, Skee asked if he might consult with Phil alone for a moment. They excused themselves and went into an adjacent office. As soon as they shut the door, still with no idea of how to break this deadlock, Skee spied a bottle of Scotch whiskey and a glass sitting on top of a filing cabinet just inside the room. Now, at this time, neither one of them drank alcoholic beverages, but they were losing the battle in the other room. Without a word, Skee poured a stiff drink and handed it to Phil, who gulped it down. Then he poured one for himself. Their eyes met, and they both knew what they were going to do.

Seated again at the conference table, Skee squared his shoulders and said, "Gentlemen, we want fifty thousand dollars or no deal!" Sir Harry again voiced his misgivings that Mr. Osterer would never go along with this, but the American's determination was quite clear, so the meeting was adjourned.

The next day Baird capitulated and agreed to arrange for the transfer of funds. Phil cabled the good news to George, and they set sail for home. It had been almost two months since they had arrived in Southampton. For the next five days they basked in the luxury of the *HMS Majestic,* their victory over the British Gaumont people, and in the comforting conviction that they were at last on their way to commercial television.

As they sailed home, Phil and Skee resumed their discussion of how to get television out of the lab and into commercial operations at home. With fifty thousand dollars in their pocket, they decided it was time to build a full-scale experimental broadcasting studio that would prove the viability of their system on a day-to-day basis. They agreed that such a facility would be easy to convert into a paying operation once the FCC got around to granting commercial broadcast licenses. Now, all they had to do was convince Jess.

CHAPTER 19

W3XPF on the Air

No sooner had Phil and Skee disembarked from their voyage home than their big plan to build a broadcast studio and transmitter were rudely trampled; Jess McCargar jumped on it with both feet, declaring that the windfall from Baird was going to be used to carry the company for at least the next year. Not only was it a challenge to find buyers, but Jess said he was sick and tired of constantly giving up more of his stock to fund operations. Of course his contribution was small according to Phil's assessment.

The dashed dream for a broadcast facility was very discouraging for Phil and Skee. Phil was starting to fear that he was losing the race, despite the big lead he had taken with his first all-electronic transmission. That had been nearly seven years ago, and the intervening years had given the competition more than ample time to catch up.

In 1935 Phil was invited to give a talk before the national convention of the Institute of Radio Engineers in New York City. His one-tube transmitter using his electron-multiplier tube caused considerable excitement. He later gave the same talk before the Franklin Institute.

Skee was still living with us. One night at dinner, he made an announcement.

"Phil, you're going to get your experimental broadcast station after all. I called my father in San Francisco today; he and I are going to put up the money for it. I'll need Bill Eddy to help me design it and draw up the plans. I talked to a fellow this afternoon who is starting out in the prefabricated building business. He said as soon as we can get him the plans, he will give us an estimate. From the way he talked, I don't think it's going to be all that expensive."

"That sounds great, Skee, but are you sure you want to do this?"

"You bet I do. Don't worry about the expense; it will pay for itself. Just wait and see."

"It most certainly will help our situation, Skee. I'll tell Bill to report to you in the morning for as long as you need him."

The design was drawn up and the foundation laid within two weeks. In another week the building components were ready. Within a few days

Farnsworth's one tube transmitter demonstrated at IRE New York 1935. The tube is an electron multiplier.

after the huge trucks rolled up carrying large wall sections, the outer building was complete. The utility services had been laid with the foundation, so shortly thereafter we were in business. It was unbelievable.

The new studio was located on Mermaid Lane, in the Wyndmoor township, a suburb of Philadelphia. We had moved into a leased home on Cresheim Valley Road in Wyndmoor on the first of October the previous year. Four days later, October 5th, 1935, I gave birth to our third son, Russell Seymour. A beautiful, healthy, happy child, he brought much joy into our home. The hair above his forehead had a spot which grew in a swirl. Despite all my efforts, it insisted upon standing straight up. Phil nicknamed him "Skeezix" after a small comic-strip character with the same problem. This was later shortened to "Skee" and has stayed with him.

Phil found our home located half way between the lab and the studio, to be very convenient. In fact, it was a little too convenient. I had even more luncheon guests, sometimes

Phil and baby Russell (Skee)

on rather short notice. He said he was sorry about that, but he wanted me to meet these people, and this was the most graceful way to do it. I was fortunate to have an obliging cook. To keep her that way, I hired a maid to help her.

Phil gave Bill Eddy, who had had some experience staging shows in the Navy, charge of the studio operations. Bill hired Nick Ross and his orchestra, with Nat Ragone on the piano and Kay Allen, vocalist, and then depended upon performers to come in just for the experience. Our "Little Miss Television" was eleven-year-old "Smiles" Blum. A little trooper, she sang and was ready to perform whenever she was needed. Later, Bill found Baby Dolores, a talented four-year-old who sang and tap-danced.

There were several amusing incidents. In preparation for a newsreel crew, Bill Eddy had rounded up two welterweight boxers. They were out on the lawn in a makeshift boxing ring, sparring a few rounds to prepare for televising. The bright red trunks of one boxer were not visible on the monitor; he seemed to be boxing in the nude. Fortunately he was able to change before the news crew arrived.

Cesium was the photosensitive surface then used in both the Farnsworth Image Dissector and Zworykin's Iconoscope. Since cesium is very sensitive to the infrared portion of the spectrum, red televises white instead of black as it does in still photography. We had not yet become aware of this problem.

There was a similar incident when a professional ballet dancer came to perform for a special group, only this time, the problem was that the material from which her costume was made was invisible to the camera. Another phenomenon of television was the way the camera brought out men's beards. Men with heavy beards, such as Phil, had to use powder or makeup even after a close shave, or they appeared unshaven.

George Everson arranged for Max Factor's representative, Mr. Cramer, to come from Hollywood to work with us to learn the art of makeup for television. Finding the problems to be quite different from those of the movies, he welcomed this challenge.

Phil asked his sister, Laura, to take over the makeup department. She and her husband, Lynden Player, had been invited to come and participate in the Electronic Equipment Company, which Skee, Phil, and his brother Carl had organized to fill the orders for tubes and equipment Farnsworth Television was not equipped to handle.

Laura spent a week or ten days with Mr. Cramer. They found the makeup problems of television to be quite different from those of moviedom, even though both were then in black and white. Laura enjoyed being part of the action and became very proficient at applying makeup. Then word came from Lindy's mother that his only brother, Wallace, was desperately ill. Lindy left immediately for San Francisco to be with his family. Laura, pregnant with their first child, followed by plane. Wallace died not long after this, and Lindy stayed in California to be near his parents. Before Laura left, she and I, since I had been privy to some of Mr. Cramer's expertise, gave Bonnie Kruthers, one of the company secretaries, the benefit of what

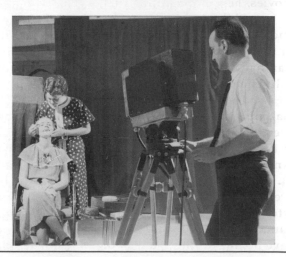

*Top to bottom:
Wyndmoor Television
studio and
broadcast facilities;
Smiles Blum, Baby
Delores in studio;
Ms. Laura Player
applying make-up*

we knew and turned it over to her.

Carl's long-time friend, Bill Twitchell, came to take Lindy's place in the Electronic Tube Company. Phil was a principal stockholder and advisor, but as president and director of the eastern division of Farnsworth Television Inc., he had little time for the new venture.

One day, Phil had a visit from Dr. Charles C. Chapple, our good friend and pediatrician. Dr. Chapple had a problem. As Phil related it to me, their conversation went something like this:

"Phil, we're losing too many 'preemies.' I want your help in doing something about it."

"Well, Charlie, you know I'll be glad to help in any way I can. What do you have in mind?"

"I believe we can build a small crib-sized unit that duplicates the atmosphere of the mother's womb. It will have to be a sterile unit to protect the tiny patient, and Phil, if it can be done, you're the guy that can do it."

They decided to have built-in, elbow-length gloves to minimize the chance of transferring germs through handling. The unit would have a sterilizer so nothing unsterile would be used around the infant. The top section of the unit would be transparent, with special lock-type entry ports to allow tubes for oxygen, intravenous feeding, etc. When they were satisfied that they had covered everything, Phil had a unit made for Charlie to test at the Pennsylvania University Hospital. The design was so successful that they built seven more units. These were flown all over the country to cover emergencies until a facility for turning them out in quantity could be built. Phil had frequent and glowing reports from Charlie about the premature babies he was saving. Reports from friends and acquaintances still come in attributing the Isolette with saving a child of their own. Having lost little Kenny, Phil was happy that he had been instrumental in saving at least a few other parents from such anguish.

One afternoon, Phil came home looking pale and distraught. When I asked what on earth was wrong, he told me.

"I just had to make the hardest decision of my life." He checked the apprehensive thoughts racing through my head with, "Lincoln was using an electric screwdriver under a television chassis trying to remove a stubborn screw. The screwdriver slipped and rammed into his eye. We rushed him to the hospital, but the eye was damaged beyond repair. The surgeon told me that if the injured eyeball were left in place, it might cost him the sight of the other eye. However, they could not perform the operation without the consent of the family. Since he said there was a small chance this would not happen, it was a very hard decision to make, but when he suggested that an artificial eye would be more cosmetic than a sightless, injured one, I had to decide that was the best thing to do."

"Oh! Not Lincoln!" Why does everything have to happen to him? When can I see him?" We went back to the hospital, to be there when he regained consciousness. While it was a devastating shock for Lincoln to realize he had only one eye, he let everyone know he wanted no sympathy from anyone. It was his problem, and he would handle it. In the months to come, he demonstrated tremendous courage and determination in making the many adjustments necessary to go on with his life. To keep him involved with the work at the lab, Phil put him in charge of public relations. In this capacity he spent many weeks helping author George Eckhardt with information on the Farnsworth Company for his book *Electronic Television*, published in 1936. The first volume was presented to Phil, with the signatures of the author and the officers and engineers of Farnsworth Television.

On Saturday, June 27th, 1936, Lincoln and Iris Fowler (sister to Carl's wife Valdis) were married in our home in Wyndmoor.   Donald B. Colton, president of the Latter-day Saint Eastern Mission, graciously came from New York to perform the ceremony. Both Phil's mother and my father had known President Colton for many years and held him in high esteem. All of the lab gang and their wives were there to join in the festivities, and see the newlyweds off on their honeymoon to the wilds of Canada.

Lincoln before his marriage to Iris Fowler

Not long after the broadcast tower was completed and Farnsworth was given the call letters W3XPF, a bustle of activity ensued at the broadcast studio. Bill Eddy constructed cleverly arranged miniature stage settings which greatly enhanced his programs. For although Farnsworth still broadcast movies at the lab, the programs at the studio were live. For the very special guests, when there was time to plan, talent was brought from New York. Bill found Bonnie Cruthers to be quite photogenic, so he coached her in the art of announcing. She would sign off with "This is WX3PF, Farnsworth Television, pioneer of the air—I'll be seeing you."

The men took turns at the monitors in the transmitter shack. The chill of an early winter was in the air, and since the company was still operating on a very stringent budget, Bill's request for heaters had gone unheeded. So when Jess McCargar came to New York for a director's meeting, and Bill learned that Jess and George were bringing some very important guests down for a demonstration, he waited for them in the transmitter shack. He had broken up a wooden stool, the only seat in the place, fashioning the pieces in a pile for a fire. When he saw them coming, he lit the fire, and when they came in he was warming his hands. He got his heater. Life was anything but humdrum when Bill was around.

Sometimes Bill got the short end of the stick. Some of the boys at the lab enjoyed an occasional ball game and usually stopped on the way home for a few beers. Bill would go with them, but always declined the beer. When Phil was scheduled to give a talk before the Institute of Radio Engineers in New York, he asked Bill to take two men and go up the day before to set up the multipactor exhibit he needed. All went well, in fact so well, Bill and his helpers decided to celebrate. They stopped in at a bar and had a few drinks. Bill was evidently feeling pretty good, because he turned his back to the bar and in a loud voice announced to the room,

"I can lick any gol-darned Irishman in the room!"

Unfortunately for Bill, this bar was located in an Irish neighborhood! At least a half dozen men came at him. Bill's men came to his aid, but these engineers were no match for those burly Irishmen. The Farnsworth men took quite a beating before the fight was quelled. It was a chastened and sober group that returned to their hotel. They stopped on the way to buy several beef steaks to apply to their black eyes and bruises. Before Phil and I arrived the next day, Bill had acquired some makeup and done a fair job of covering up their wounds. Consequently, we knew nothing about the previous evening until someone told us about it later.

Bill was given a free hand in running the broadcasting studio, and his very creative mind produced many ingenious ideas to keep everything running smoothly.

Nineteen thirty-six was a very productive year for Phil. He filed on twenty-two inventions, each of which resulted in patents. Nine of these were on new electron-multiplier tubes and methods of operation thereof. Others included Means and Method for Synchronizing Pulses in Television, Scanning Current Generator, Radiation Frequency Convertor, Secondary Emission Electrode, Beam Scanning Dissector, and Cold Cathode Electron Discharge Tube. Other patents covered improvements in the Image Dissector and receiving Oscillight.

Probably the most significant invention Phil produced during this period was his electron-multiplier tube, which he called the "Multipactor." This was a cold cathode device with amazing powers of amplification.

The Multipactor tube created considerable excitement among his fellow engineers. In effect a one-tube radio transmitter, it appeared to pull power out of thin air. Phil had sent an early multipactor to his friend Ralph Heintz in San Francisco. Ralph set one up at his plant (Heintz & Kaufman) and invited a group of technical men and university professors in for a demonstration before he even bothered to test the setup. He said if Phil Farnsworth said it would work, that was good enough for him.

When they turned the equipment on, the tube seemed cold and lifeless, but when Ralph taped a light bulb to a yard stick and held it near the tube, it lit up at full brightness. Ralph used the setup to transmit a message to Phil: "To Phil Farnsworth Greetings! This is the first message transmitted by your Electron Multiplier power tube." According to reports received later, this simple message was relayed from San Francisco by a Dollar Steamship in the south seas to Australia, on to several European stations and an Arctic outpost, reaching us in Philadelphia in the wee hours of the morning. This was so exciting, we didn't even try to go back to sleep. We sat up and talked the rest of the night.

Feeling the hot breath of his well-funded competitors closing in on him, Phil continued to push himself unmercifully. He had built his lab force up to the highest efficiency he had yet been able to achieve, but it had been a fight with Jess all the way. The strain of his long hours and the constant clashes over funding began to take a toll, and he began to seek relief in a cocktail before dinner, frequently followed by one or two more during the evening before he could calm down enough to go to bed. This change in his routine began to cause me some real concern.

Deal Advances Television in Homes of S. F.

Firm Granted Rights Here to Manufacture New Small Sets

By EARLE ENNIS

Commercial television came to San Francisco yesterday.

An announcement from Television Laboratories, Ltd., that Heintz & Kaufman, Ltd., radio manufacturers, has been granted a license to manufacture television transmitters under the Filo T. Farnsworth patents caused widespread interest in radio circles.

At the same time came an announcement from the Heintz & Kaufman crowd that an exchange of license had been effected between their concern and the Westinghouse Electric and Manufacturing Company whereby each can sell and manufacture communications equipment under the patents of the other.

DOLLAR STEAMSHIP LINK

The Heintz & Kaufman group are affiliates of the Dollar Steamship Company and manufacture all the wireless equipment for the Globe Wireless, Ltd., another Dollar affiliate. Under the television license the Heintz & Kaufman group will manufacture television apparatus under the Farnsworth patents, opening the way for the first time on the Coast to a commercialized form of what has been but a laboratory demonstration.

Similarly, a large Eastern radio manufacturing concern has been licensed to manufacture and sell receiving equipment under the Farnsworth patents, which are basic and which recently won a signal victory against contesting elements in a hard fought court action. The licensing of the local group brings to San Francisco a new industry whose financial rating is as yet unestimated.

BATTLE OF INVENTOR

The issuance of transmitting licenses to Heintz & Kaufman represents a hard battle by a young inventor with a revolutionary idea to win recognition in the scientific world. It was only when Farnsworth, by means of a variation of an ordinary cathode ray tube, was able to demonstrate an electrical eye that saw with visionary accuracy and rapid clarity that scientific skeptics began to believe in him.

Then followed a long battle for patent protection. At every turn he was blanketed with claims of infringment, most of which had no merit and were used as stumbling blocks to prevent competition. Through the maze of this obstruction, battling his way with legal counsel and his own knowledge, Farnsworth finally received Government protection. At the present nearly 100 patents protect his device against the world.

Phil rejected my pleas to take time off, saying there would be no relief from the stress he was under in going away. He felt his only answer was for Washington to relent and grant him a commercial broadcast license. This would relieve the tension between Jess and him, which was at the root of his troubles.

CHAPTER 20

S.O.S from Baird

There is little question that Phil's singlehanded crusade to launch commercial television was beginning to drain his vitality. The energy he had derived from the creative process was being overshadowed by the years of constant struggle with Jess to keep his lab operational.

Phil and his men kept improving his equipment and filing more patents to keep the company's patent structure in a leading position. The fact that several of Phil's patents were tied up in the Patent Office for up to eleven years, extending the life of these particular patents into the mid fifties was also to our benefit. Phil was acutely aware that the clock was inexorably ticking away on the life of his patents. His earliest and therefore most controlling patents had been issued in 1930 and would pass into the public domain in 1947. All RCA had to do was sit tight and "wait it out" until they expired—they still had plenty of revenue to count on from their radio-related and other business.

These were financially chaotic times, as the market was still trying to recover from the 1929 crash and the country was only beginning to show signs of recovering from the Great Depression. Although George, in New York, had now taken over the greater task of selling stock to cover expenses, Jess was the one who complained. Being on the west coast, he missed the excitement of the activity in the east, and was unwilling, or unable, to see Phil's problems in maintaining his position in the fledgling television industry. Neither could he acknowledge the reason for so doing. The strain was beginning to show on Jess as well as Phil, and George was finding it more and more difficult to keep peace between the two. Phil found this kind of pressure increasingly unbearable, and since doctors had no solutions for him, he relied on alcohol for relief.

Unable to make any headway in getting Washington to move on commercial television, Phil took every opportunity to announce to the press that television was indeed ready for the public. RCA did its utmost to counter Phil's statements with an article stating that television was nowhere near ready for commercialization. Of course this was true as far as RCA was concerned. David Sarnoff, determined that he, and only he, would be the one to launch commercial television, had enough influence in Washington to make it so.

It was some consolation to Phil that Farnsworth licensees, Baird in London and Fernseh in Berlin, were now earning much acclaim by using Farnsworth equipment in their commercial broadcasting.

In the summer of 1936, Fernseh A.G. broadcast the International Olympic Games from its mobile television unit in Berlin, using Farnsworth equipment. News of this was carried all over Europe and the United States.

George Everson had started his career in New York, and now ensconced in the Plaza Hotel, he began looking up old contacts. As executive secretary of the Committee on Criminal Courts in New York City, he hired Hugh Knowlton who, as a recent graduate from Columbia Law School, had become his protege. They had been out of communication with each other for years. George was happy to find that Hugh had become a lawyer in New York and was now a partner in the prestigious Wall Street investment house of Kuhn, Loeb & Company.

George told Hugh about his latest find, Philo T. Farnsworth, who was making a name for himself in television. Hugh Knowlton was very interested and George brought him to Philadelphia to see for himself. He went away very much impressed by what he saw there. When he heard of the problems George was having keeping the lab funded, he suggested that his firm might be interested in helping out. Eventually, a deal was made wherein Kuhn, Loeb & Co. would offer its assistance, at a modest compensation for services and an option on a limited block of Farnsworth stock at the present market price.*

This was of great assistance to the Farnsworth Company. Hugh Knowlton and Louis Strauss, both Kuhn, Loeb partners, were very helpful to the Farnsworth Company.

There was a constant flow of visitors to the Farnsworth lab and broadcast studio in Philadelphia, some of whom George brought down from New York as prospective investors. Jess, George, and the other Farnsworth directors were glad to have the broadcasting studio and transmitter at these

---

*Later, when it was most needed, Kuhn, Loeb exercised its option. By this time, due to the favorable press regarding the reorganization of the Farnsworth Company and plans for the future, the stock had almost doubled in price, partly due to the participation of Kuhn, Loeb.

America Takes World Television Control I S. F. Invention

Famed Tube Recognized By Germans

Philo Farnsworth, Local Genius, Signs Pact Involving Seven Countries

As a result of contracts signed this week at Philadelphia with representatives of the Hitler government, and involving Germany, Austria, Hungary, Czechoslovakia, Poland and Switzerland, America steps into control of world television through the genius of a young San Francisco inventor.

The agreements made are between Dr. Paul Goerz, director of television and broadcasting for the German government and directive factor of the Fernseh Company of Berlin, and Philo Farnsworth, San Francisco inventor and central figure of Farnsworth Television, Inc.

Recognition of the Farnsworth invention, the famous cold cathode tube, by the German interests, according to radio men, means that these inventions will dominate in television throughout the world.

SIX WEEKS' SURVEY

The signup by the Hitler representatives for television on a big scale followed a six weeks' investigation in this country of all television systems, and a previous survey by the German interests of all that Europe had to offer.

Under licenses granted Germany by young Farnsworth the German licenses will use the cold cathode dissector tube in all television work in the countries named.

Dr. Goerz indicated that an extensive series of public demonstration of television have been planned in Germany for this summer, at which the Farnsworth tube, which completely supplants the early type of disk scanner will be used. The tube functions both for transmitting and receiving and represents nine years of laboratory work in this country to bring it to commercial perfection.

HOME RECEPTION

The German interests plan the immediate building of transmitting and receiving sets for television reception, paralleling television introductions which have been planned in England by British interests this fall. Specially erected stations and the compilation of apparatus for theater and home reception will be among the first steps of the new licensed group.

New high-powered ultra-short wave equipment has been installed on Brocken mountain in the Harz and will be completed next month. There broadcasting will be shortly started, it is understood, using the new Farnsworth cold cathode televisor, which does away entirely with mechanical scanning.

times, but they all complained about the cost of keeping it going.

Jess McCargar seemed to have little understanding of, or sympathy for, Phil's problems in holding his lead in the television race. He never missed an opportunity to make things difficult for Phil. In one of his long string of mindless insults, Jess sent his newly acquired son-in-law, George Sleeper, to Philadelphia to "help keep things in line." This young man proved a very disruptive force, even to the point of spreading suspicious rumors among the men, not only about Phil but about each other.

In the midst of this turmoil, in mid November 1936, I got an unexpected call from Phil at the laboratory.

"Pem, dear, how would you like to have a real bang-up honeymoon, after all these years?"

"Sounds great! But what about the boys?" Philo was now seven, and our other beautiful boy, Russell, was just a little over a year old.

"I'll call Mother. I think she'll be glad to take care of them. Of course she'll have to fly, because we would have to sail on Friday for Europe."

"Friday! Europe! But this is already Tuesday, and you know how your mother feels about flying!" It had taken Phil weeks to talk her into even a short sightseeing flight when we were in San Francisco.

"Leave that to me, but can you be ready to leave Friday? You know we're members of the English Speaking Union now. When I was over there, the Prince of Wales presided over those gatherings. Also, you'll be expected to dress for dinner every night. I want you to have a really nice wardrobe, one you can be proud of."

"Wow! You're talking about big money now, Phil. At least a thousand dollars."

"That's fine. We're celebrating ten years of marriage, and I want it to be really special. The Baird people have sent me an S.O.S. They have a deadline for a crucial BBC demonstration, and they want me to come over. I really don't feel up to it, and I should not leave the lab just now, but I told Captain West (director of research for the Baird Company) my conditions for coming are a slow cruise ship and you with me. This should allow me to rest up a little on the way."

That sounded marvelous to me. I was relieved that Phil was taking some time away from the lab. The situation there was costing him both sleep and appetite. But how was I ever going to get a wardrobe together in time to leave Friday? Even after I found the right clothes, which I didn't expect would be easy, fittings and alterations would be necessary—and time-consuming.

Phil came home with the news that his mother would be happy to come, even though it meant flying. She disliked trains even more than planes. Lincoln and his bride Iris arrived to see what they could do to help us. Phil gave Lincoln the job of buying a large steamer wardrobe trunk for me and the few things he needed. He had outfitted himself with dress clothes while in England two years before. He would need every minute to get work lined up for the lab while he was away.

Iris offered to help. By making a list of everything I would need and starting early the next morning, we were able, with the help of Bonwit Teller's better dress salon, to purchase everything that would need alterations on the first day. By the next afternoon we had completed our list, and had even bought consolation toys for our boys.

It was closing time before the alterations were ready. Then Iris, in checking over our list, found we had still to buy gloves and hose. Our saleslady called the first floor and asked that they keep someone in that department to wait on us. As we came out of the elevator, the only lights still on were those guiding us to the glove department. As our package was being wrapped, a gentleman came up and introduced himself as the manager of the store. He asked if we had found everything we needed. Evidently word had spread about my shopping spree. I told him we had and that we could never have done it without the excellent service we had enjoyed. He said he was glad to hear that, because he had had the pleasure of visiting my husband's laboratory and studio a short time ago, and he hoped he had in some small way been able to repay the kindness he had been shown there. We gratefully accepted his offer to help us carry our many packages to my car.

Mother Farnsworth arrived on Thursday, singing the praises of air travel. Lincoln procured a terrific wardrobe trunk, which Iris helped me pack before Phil came home. I wanted to surprise him later. Mabel managed to have me added to Phil's passport, although Cliff had to swear that he knew where and when I had been born, since there was no time to get a birth certificate. Phil came home pleased with the way Lincoln had handled his responsibilities and delighted that I had done so well, even though I had gone over my thousand dollar estimate by another three hundred.

Friday, to make leaving the boys a little easier, we took them, Mother Farnsworth, and Gertrude Gaskins, our household majordomo, on the train as far as Trenton, New Jersey, where they were to catch the next train back. This was Skeezix's first ride on a train, and Phil had reserved drawing room "A" for our group. (In those days, each sleeping car was partitioned off into berths by curtains, except for two private compartments "A" and "B.") Lincoln and Iris continued on with us to New York to wish us bon voyage. Philo explored all the conveniences of the compartment, and Skeezix thought the pretty little pink bar of soap smelled very good, but he found it tasted terrible.

When we were safely on board the German Cruise ship, *SS Hansa*, and the good-byes and showers of confetti had dwindled behind us, we sought the peace and quiet of our stateroom.

During the night, I found that I was not a good sailor. It was the second day before I made it back up to the main deck. Phil helped me get my "sea legs" by walking me briskly around the deck. When I was stable enough to play him a game of ping-pong, I knew I had it made.

That afternoon at poolside, we made shipboard friends, whose company we enjoyed for the remainder of the voyage. The first night we entered into the festivities of this nine-day cruise, we were toasted as the bride and groom. We did not deny it.

In London, Phil was at once involved with Baird's problems at the Crystal Palace. We were staying at the Grosvenor House Hotel, and each morning he left early, taking a cab to Piccadilly Circus, where he met the Baird group and the commuter train for Hyde Park. He would return about seven, so tired he had to rest a while before even thinking of dinner. About half the time, we ordered dinner sent to our room.

I took a cab and saw some of the things Phil had talked about, but it wasn't much fun all by myself. I was grateful when an English couple we had met on the boat offered to show me around. Then I had a call from Diana Hewett, the owner of a smart Parisienne hat salon in London, whom Skee Turner and Phil had met on their previous trip. I had been delighted with the hat she had designed for me and sent home with Phil.

Diana invited me to go the next day to the Lord Mayor's parade, a yearly event of great importance to the English. It did much to keep alive their historical "pomp and circumstance" heritage, and everyone turned out to see it. The Lord Mayor was an all-powerful symbol in London. As a matter of tradition, even the Queen and King were required to obtain his permission to enter the city.

This impressive parade seemed straight out of the legends of King Arthur. There were knights in shining armour, mounted on prancing, armour-clad war horses in all their fine trappings, and lords and ladies in their ringleted wigs, plumed hats, velvet cloaks, and bustled gowns, all riding in antique carriages with footmen and prancing horses. Then of course there was the Lord Mayor himself, in all his splendid array.

All this was reminiscent of the early tempestuous history of English royalty. Even at this time, the royal family was having its problems. Edward VIII, made king at the death of his father, King George V, had assumed the throne reluctantly, then dropped a bombshell on the royal family. He demanded to be allowed to marry the lady of his choice, an American divorcee, Wallis Simpson. Queen Mary, the Queen Mother, adamantly refused her consent, as did the British House of Lords and the all-powerful Church of England. But while we were there, Edward abdicated and his brother became King George VI. The British people were very much stirred up over the scandal, and it was considered very poor taste even to mention the name of Wallis Simpson in polite society.

Toward the end of the second week, the problems began clearing up at Baird, and the engineers were able to relax somewhat. We were invited to dinner at Captain West's home and to a show later with him and his wife. He apologized that they had neglected me. He and his assistant Marmaduke Lance (whom they called Lance) had spent several weeks in Philadelphia being trained in electronic television. I told him I was familiar with emergency situations. I understood and sympathized with their difficulties; I only hoped Phil had been able to help them overcome them. He assured me that was indeed the case.

That weekend Phil took me dancing at the Hotel Savoy, the "Waldorf" of London. I wore my wine-colored Spanish lace gown that I had been saving as a surprise for him. Reminiscent of the late 1800s, it was form-fitting in front with full bustlelike gathering in the back, ending in a small train with a loop at the bottom to be worn on the little finger when dancing. This pulled the fullness to the side and up in a rather saucy and fetching fashion. Phil was enchanted with it. He always enjoyed showing me off, and I often catered to his whim. He was wearing his top hat and tails, and looking very Fred Astair-ish. He was determined that I should have one grand night to remember from this trip.

We found the dancing at the Savoy to be very sedate and proper. Young couples were inevitably chaperoned by the girl's mother, who claimed the escort's first dance. We were fascinated by one couple. The lady was tall, gray haired, and inclined to be buxom, but very elegant. From her high-coiffed head to her well-corseted torso, which made her lovely gown fit like a glove, to the silver slippers on her shapely feet, she was regal, and she danced as though she had been a professional dancer all of her life. Her escort, a tall, dark, good looking young man, also danced like a professional. They were a pleasure to watch, and they danced every dance. Their table was near our own, and I marveled that this lady was never short of breath, although some of their numbers were quite intricate.

We danced several times, but the music, although mostly originating from the States, was too slow to suit Phil. Suddenly, he broke into a fast doubletime step of his own creation. Of course, I was familiar with his variations. We danced in and out among the other couples, taking no notice of the disdainful, down-the-nose looks coming our way. We did have the grace to leave after that.

The next weekend, John Baird and his sister gave a dinner in our honor at their home in the countryside. There we met the Baird board of directors and their wives. This included Sir Harry, Chairman of the Board, and Lady Greer. I found them to be a charming couple. There was a distinct contrast between the graciousness of Lady Greer and the rather chilly reserve of the other wives. It was my experience that only those who had attained the higher rungs of the social ladder could afford to fraternize with those whose status was yet unclear.

By the time Phil had Baird's demonstration in shape, he was exhausted again. He told me he simply had to get away somewhere and get some sun and a rest. To add to his problems, Cliff wrote that Jess McCargar had been causing problems again. He had sent Russ Pond, a former stockbroker, to take charge of the lab, and the situation was grave. Phil realized that a showdown with Jess was inevitable, but he had no stomach for it at this point. Something first had to be done to improve his own situation.

We talked it over. Since it was now December, to go home would probably mean a trip to Florida or to California, if we even managed that. Phil suggested the French Riviera. However, this would present a problem, since we had only a few French phrases between us. We called Diana Hewett to see if she had any suggestions.

Diana, used to managing her own and, I suspect, others' lives, took over. If Phil could pay some of her bills at the shop, she would leave her mother in charge and go with us. She had spent half her life in Paris with her grandmother and spoke French like a native. Also, as was soon demonstrated, she was very adept at making arrangements and causing things to go smoothly.

With this problem solved, Phil wrote Cliff asking that he represent him (Phil) in management until he returned. He knew that Cliff would stand up to Russ Pond or even Jess and George to protect the standards Phil had worked so hard to achieve. Cliff had been his right hand from the early days in San Francisco. The men had learned to go to Cliff with their problems whenever Phil was not around.

The next day we found ourselves on the channel boat to Le Havre, being jolted to the very core of our beings. Phil, as usual, was as stable as a sailor, but I joined the crowd of other distressed passengers in the ladies' lounge. It was a great relief to be escorted to our "wagon-lit" (sleeping car) on the famous Blue Train bound for the Riviera.

Dining on the Blue Train was an interesting experience. Dinner was served family style, each dish being passed from table to table. This created a friendly atmosphere, which accelerated considerably after Diana introduced us. Uncomfortable being the center of a lively conversation of which we hardly understood a word, we excused ourselves as soon as we gracefully could and retired to our wagon-lit.

During the night, we were awakened by excited voices arguing in the corridor outside our compartment. The next morning we learned there had been a murder committed in the car next to ours. The argument we heard in the night had taken place at Monte Carlo, the first stop after the murder was discovered. The train officials wanted to leave the murder car there for investigation, but the Monte Carlo officials said absolutely not! They already had too many murders and suicides of their own by desperate losers at the gambling tables. So the murder car was taken back into France, since Monaco was a separate principality, and on to Mentone. This was our destination and the end of the line, since it was near the Italian border.

It turned out that this murder was a virtual reenactment of Agatha Christy's book, *Murder on the Blue Train*—a classic case of life imitating art. The victim was the proprietress of a tea room in Nice; the poor lady had been robbed and strangled. The English press, hungry for any intrigue involving Edward and Wally, discovered that this tea room had been a favorite trysting place of the star-crossed lovers and played the story to the hilt. Months later, the *New York Times*, Sunday edition, reported the case was still an unsolved mystery. They should have put Hercule Poirot on the case!

In Mentone, we were just enough preseason to find the hotels still closed for refurbishing. However, Diana talked us into the Hotel de Orient, even though they had only a minimal staff and the hall rugs were still at the cleaners. Our meals were served in the sitting room of our three-room suite by the head waiter, with great flourish. We learned later he was also preparing our meals.

Diana located a highly recommended physician, Dr. Pierre Pouget, who graciously came to the hotel to see Phil. After an examination and some consultation (with Diana as interpreter), Dr. Pouget gave Phil a prescription to help him relax and suggested at least two weeks in bed. Phil rebelled. As a compromise, we hired a chauffeur with car and arranged to spend this time in the sun and air, seeing the sights at the same time.

Phil and Pem during trip to Europe. Above: at Hotel de Orient in Mentone, French Riviera
Left: just below the village of St. Agnes.

Bertrand, our chauffeur, arrived at ten each morning in his vintage convertible seven-passenger Hispana Suisa, purchased with his pay as a World War I fighter pilot. Diana would collect the well provisioned picnic basket from the kitchen, and we would be off. Bertrand made his living in this way and knew all the interesting places to go. At Phil's request, we first drove up the coast to Monte Carlo. He had cabled George to sell some of his stock and send the proceeds to him at Monte Carlo, the nearest American Express Office.

Monte Carlo was a colorful place. The central square was paved in colorful mosaic tile, the uniforms of the gendarmes were lavishly adorned with gold braid, and along one side of the square was the imposing structure of the gambling casino which paid for it all. We were told there were no local taxes. On the other side of the square were haute couture boutiques, and it all looked out over the blue Mediterranean.

There were three roads leading from Mentone to Monte Carlo, the Grand, Middle, and Petit Highways. These roads, although paved, were narrow, two-way highways, as were most roads at that time. George had not failed us; the money Phil had requested was waiting for us at the American Express office. We returned via the Petit (or upper) Highway. Bertrand pulled off where he could park near a trail leading farther up the mountain to a small picnic area, where we ate our lunch while feasting on the view. From here, we could see Crete, far across the Mediterranean.

After Edward's abdication, Mrs. Simpson had fled London and the attendant publicity and was being sheltered by friends on the Riviera. One day, when we were stopped on the way from Monte Carlo to enjoy the view, Bertrand called our attention to her car as it passed. Her driver was a good friend of his.

Ville de France, situated between Mentone and Monte Carlo, is a lovely place. Picturesque villas nestled in lush green shrubs and flowering vines along the hillsides. The yacht harbor below was sprinkled with palatial seagoing yachts. In contrast we were captivated by quaint little villages high up in the tops of the mountains. This was the end of the French Alps. It was sad to see the laboriously built terraces up the sides of the mountain slopes, where for an untold time grapes had been grown to make the family wine, now long abandoned. In the village square we would find the answer. There was the ever-present monument, with the names of all the brave young men who had died to protect their homeland. Now, there were only old men, women, and a few children.

One village was different, although it had the centuries-old weathered look of all the others. Obviously constructed of materials at hand (dirt and rocks), it was, like the others, one continuous structure, each room added as the need arose. The more affluent members of the community had a milk goat, housed in its own tiny cubicle next to the family quarters.

The only colors to be seen were the stained-glass windows of the small chapel in the square and the ever-present flowers. The only break in this contiguous structure which was the village was the narrow cobblestone thoroughfare, just wide enough to accommodate a loaded donkey. What made this village stand out was one large wall, taller than everything else, on which, plainly visible as one approached the village, was a large illustrated sign shouting the virtues of the Singer Sewing Machine!

From our balcony on the second floor, we could see the small French and Italian guard huts of the border. We could hardly overlook the opportunity of at least a peek into Italy. So one day, when Diana's gentleman friend came from Nice, we went to San Remo, a small, pleasant city several hours drive into Italy.

After a delightful luncheon, we returned via the "Village of the Flowers." In the village square was an open thatched-roof market. Vendors crowded the market, carrying large, drab, covered baskets. Promptly at two o'clock, the church bells began to ring; then the covers were removed from the baskets. The color was spectacular. One could see almost any variety of bloom. Buyers came here from all over Europe to buy flowers for their shops and vendors. Phil bought me some lovely red roses to decorate our suite.

Phil was looking better and eating well, but the strain of the past ten years could not be erased in a week or two. Dr. Pouget, who visited him once a week, advised him to take a minimum of three weeks, which meant we would not be home for Christmas. How could we face a Christmas without our dear little sons? We didn't worry so much about little Skeezix; he was only fourteen months old. We had written cards and letters to Mother and seven-year-old Philo, but they would really miss us as much as we would miss them. However, since it had to be faced, Phil cabled his secretary, giving her a list of presents to buy for Mother and the boys; then we decided we would just have to ignore the fact it was Christmas.

As we were trying to become accustomed to this idea, Phil had a wire from Captain West at Baird, with devastating news. The Crystal Palace had burned down, taking with it all Baird's equipment, along with all its hopes for a place on the English television scene, at least for the time being.

After New Year's we returned to England just long enough to visit the mass of melted glass and twisted steel that was the ruins of the Crystal Palace. Sifting through the rubble, Phil stumbled on a macabre souvenir of the tragedy—the charred, melted remains of one of his Image Dissectors. This discovery was a grim reminder of Baird's situation, but at this point, there was little Phil could do to help the company.

All this while, Hitler was stepping up his preparations for war. All Europe was on edge, but the consensus was that England would be the ultimate target. In France, everywhere we turned, there were excitedly gesticulating Frenchmen discussing where Hitler might be planning to strike first, fearful it might be on French soil. In England, people were just as worried, but due to their traditional reserve, it was hard to know what they were thinking.

Despite our reservations and warnings from Captain West about the political situation in Germany, after our brief return to London we flew to Berlin. Phil hoped that by visiting Fernseh A.G. he could free some of the considerable royalty funds due the Farnsworth Company from Fernseh. Fernseh was still using Farnsworth equipment both in its studio and its mobile television van. It was still receiving very good press all over Europe as well as in the United States, and Phil was anxious to check it out.

We landed in Amsterdam for lunch and customs. Our cash and travelers checks were confiscated, and we were issued only sufficient marks to pay for our expenses. We were met at the Berlin Airport by a car with two uniformed men who introduced themselves as our courtesy drivers, who would be at our service as long as we were there. We were delivered to the Eden Hotel, which catered mostly to English and American visitors. Captain West arrived the next day, followed shortly thereafter by another Baird director who said he was persona non grata in Germany and so had "slipped in quietly." Baird also had connections with Fernseh.

Phil was very uneasy about our drivers (who, we learned later, were reporting to the German Intelligence). Dr. Goerz, president of Fernseh, arranged for one of his men to drive us, thus sidestepping the Reichpost men. Dr. Rolf Mueller, Fernseh's director of research, who had spent several weeks in Phil's laboratory in Philadelphia, took us for a drive out to Pottsdam to see the elaborate castle built there by Frederick the Great. The castle was on a hill, and the terraced grounds were glass enclosed and filled with exotic fruits and flowers imported from all over the world.

Paul and Lilli Goerz entertained us royally. On Saturday, they took us to lunch, then to their home, where their two teenage daughters were having a tea dance. We observed them from the hall. Crystal, their thirteen-year-old, who was attending her first dance, was sitting nearby with a young man. Lilli was shocked when she turned to the young man and asked, "What do you think of Mrs. Simpson?"

One of the visitors to Phil's lab had been a German government official, who had exacted a promise from Phil to return his visit when he came to Berlin. Upon hearing the name of this man, Dr. Goerz seemed quite agitated. He said he would take Phil to the building and give him directions but would not accompany him inside. When Phil met him outside later, Dr. Goerz told him that this man was very close to Hitler; in fact, his office was just a door or two away from that of Hitler. Phil, whose instincts were usually keen, began to question the wisdom of this visit, and as the days passed, we became increasingly uneasy. Hitler had probably been notified by customs in Amsterdam that we were coming and was no doubt getting daily reports on us.

Philo, left and Dr. Paul Georz, 1937

We later learned why Dr. Goerz wanted to stay out of Hitler's sight. He had been a member of the Elite German Cavalry, and since Hitler saw them as a threat, he had ordered them all shot. It was only because Dr. Goerz was useful to him that he had been spared.

We witnessed an extensive parade of large war tanks, long-range cannons, and ranks of goose-stepping soldiers. A few days later, there was an even larger military parade. This one was led by large official cars bearing Herr Hitler himself, with General Goering and several other dignitaries. The smell of war was in the air so thick one could cut it.

As we toured the Fernseh plant, there were many closed doors bearing the sign "VERBOTEN." One such door was open, and as Dr. Geortz started to take us in, we were stopped by a military man putting his rifle across the door. Dr. Goertz told him in German, "It's all right; they are making his tube in there."

At dinner that evening in a famous old German restaurant with Lilli and Paul Goertz, we were told that all manufacturing plants in Germany had their "VERBOTEN" areas. Security was so tight that one shop made only one part of a larger military item, so they had no idea what it was they were making. Then he told a story about two friends who met on the street after a long separation. When one friend said his wife was expecting a baby, the other man congratulated him and, since he worked in a baby carriage factory he could smuggle the parts out one at a time and his friend could put them together and make a carriage. Some time later they met again, and when asked if he had put the baby carriage together, the new father said he had put it together several times, but it always turned into a machine gun.

Dr. Goerz was also connected with the Zeiss Ikon Optical Company. Herr Wild, president of the company, was insistent that Phil visit their plant in Stuttgart. Herr Wild was in his seventies . . . and being a Jew, he was having trouble with the Third Reich. His cars had been confiscated, and he was obliged to ride a bicycle to and from his plant. He smilingly said he didn't mind this; it kept him in shape for the winter skiing he loved.

When Herr Wild had Phil alone, he told him confidentially that he was concerned for his son Rudolph, who was attending law school. He thought if Phil could offer him employment in the United States, he would be out of the turmoil which was sure to come. After meeting and talking with Rudolph, Phil agreed to take the matter under advisement. Later, he was able to get Rudolph out of Germany, and he became a valuable asset to Phil's lab.

The trip to Stuttgart was to keep Phil away overnight, so I stayed on at the Eden Hotel. The lower level dining room was a popular place, and we ate there because we enjoyed the music of the resident pianist. At one side of this room was a bar. Early in the evening, a number of smartly dressed young ladies would line up on the bar stools. One by one they would relocate to join some lone male diner, of whom there were many. Our English friends told us they were Hitler's girls, whose job it was to glean information from visiting English and American businessmen. This was obviously no place for me to come alone.

When Phil voiced his concern about leaving me there alone, I told him not to worry; I would eat in the main dining room. This I did, and I had the entire dining room to myself. The orchestra played for me, and royalty could not have commanded more attention than was lavished upon me. I even learned some German from the elevator boy: "Fimph de stock!" At least that is how it sounded, meaning "fifth floor."

Phil's efforts to get permission to take out of the country the money due our company from Fernseh were to no avail. Hitler had completely stopped the flow of Reichmarks out of Germany. However, Phil was allowed to take equipment, so he did the best he could for the company. Then we were more than ready to leave for home.

Phil arranged our passage, but mysteriously, our exit visas were cancelled. We obtained new exit visas, but when these were also cancelled, we began to feel very uneasy about our situation there. We felt quite sure our every move was observed and reported to Hitler. When our exit visas were cancelled for the third time, Phil threatened to go to the American Consulate.

Dr. Goerz then took over. He made the arrangements himself, then told us he would call for us at eleven that night to take us to the boat train. This train ran between Berlin and the seaport of Hamburg. We were smuggled on board by eight of our English and German friends. We all crowded into our drawing room, and someone opened a bottle of champagne to toast our safe departure. Dr. Goerz brought me a box of German chocolates. Having no paper available, I had each of them sign the wrapping paper on the candy. This memento of those hectic days is still in my file. Captain West told Phil his reason for coming to Berlin was that he had been concerned about our safety. They all stayed with us until time for the train to pull out.

A feeling of great relief flooded over us as the *S.S. Europa* weighed anchor and we headed for home. Phil said that even though they had not returned his money as promised, he had been allowed to keep his passport and sailing papers. He thought he had paid a small price for our freedom.

This January crossing was a far cry from our peaceful voyage on the *S.S. Hansa*. We ran into very heavy seas and then a violent storm. The waves were breaking over the top deck. There appeared to be few passengers aboard. After a crossing so rough it took an extra day, we steamed into the New York Harbor. I could have kissed the Statue of Liberty, she was such a welcome sight. By this time, the decks were filled with people. It turned out the ship had been filled to capacity.

Reports later came out that not long after our return, Hitler began forcibly detaining visiting scientists. Some who refused to do his bidding or were of the Jewish faith were never seen again.

CHAPTER 21

The Last Straw

It was heaven to be home with our boys again. Mother Farnsworth had taken good care of them. She didn't mention it, but Philo told me years later that he was more of a problem than he should have been—like making slice after slice of toast that he had no intention of eating, just to see it pop up. Our maid, Gertrude Gaskins, came daily to do housework and laundry, and Phil's secretary, Mabel Bernstein, took them shopping and ran errands for Mother Farnsworth. Skeezix had a scar on his nose from falling down the stairs, but otherwise the boys were in fine shape. Even Mother Farnsworth, with the constant care of our boys, seemed to have come through with flying colors.

The lab was another story. Phil had left Arch Brolly in charge of his Philadelphia lab crew. Arch had very ably managed the San Francisco lab after we left to build Philco's television setup. No sooner had we left than Jess McCargar sent in his own henchman, a stock-broker friend named Russell Pond, to manage the lab in Phil's absence. George Sleeper*, Jess's new son-in-law, was still on the scene, officiously trying to tell the engineers what to do. Between the two of them, they had completely undermined the credibility of Arch and his men with Jess. Phil fired them both on the spot. Phil came home from his first day back at the lab sick in body and soul.

Cliff, who had always been Phil's right-hand-man, reported that several patents had been allowed to lapse. After a patent is filed, there are usually revisions required by the Patent Office; such as change of wording, claims not allowed as described, and sometimes infringements in one or more claims. The inventor's counsel is given a certain time to answer the questions or make changes. If this is not done in the time allotted, the patent application is no longer valid and is allowed to lapse. Another important patent had been about to lapse, so Cliff told Jess that if he didn't see that it was kept alive, Cliff would do it himself. Jess reluctantly told Don to go ahead with it.

The travel and fees involved in revising a patent application were very costly, and Jess had refused to authorize the funds for Don Lippincott to file the necessary papers within the time allotted. One of these was Phil's patent application on a Velocity Modulation Radio Frequency Amplifier.

None of Phil's men understood the concept; they even had doubts that it would work. This uncertainty, along with the general confusion within the company due to Jess's erratic behavior, may explain why they failed to cable Phil in France. Both Jess and George thought it rather inconsiderate of Phil to go running off to France, even though Phil had told them his reasons for doing so. Phil's Velocity Modulation patent did issue in Australia on October 22nd, 1937, as patent number 102,330.

A patent was issued to Russell Varian on the Klystron, a form of Velocity Modulation Radio Frequency Amplifier similar to Farnsworth's concept. Evidently Russ had been thinking along the same lines. Who was his patent attorney? Herbert Metcalf, of Don Lippincott's firm. Phil had disclosed this invention to Don early in 1936. Phil refused to enter into a contest with Russ, however. He said, "Let Russ have it." This patent was the basis upon which Russ formed his very successful company, Varian Associates. We were happy to see his success. He later endowed a building bearing his name at the Stanford University.

The day after our return from Europe, having recovered somewhat from the shock, Phil called Jess in San Francisco and told him he could not condone his actions and that he had fired Pond and Sleeper. Four days later Jess arrived in Philadelphia. He stormed into Phil's office with, "You go out there and fire all of those men!"

"No, Jess, I will not do that. I've spent too much time training them. They are too important to our continued success. There is not one of them who doesn't contribute his share to our operation."

"Either you go out there and fire them all . . . or I will!"

"I think you'd better calm down and consider the consequence of what this would mean for the company, Jess. I'm certainly not going to fire my men."

"Well, then, I will!"

With that, Jess strode out to the lab and shouted, "You're all fired!

---

*George Sleeper later went to work for the Columbia Broadcasting Company. In those days, any engineer who had worked for Phil Farnsworth could easily get a position at higher pay. Most recognized that the unique advantage they had in working for Phil offset the extra pay.

Pick up your stuff and leave!"

There was a stunned silence. The men found it hard to believe what they had heard.

"Well! Go on . . . Get out!" Jess was livid.

Pale and shaken, Phil came home and told me what happened. I was furious with Jess. This was the act of a demented man. Phil reported the situation to George in New York then called each of the men. He told them to hang on; he was going to do some reorganizing and hire them back. However, the men who had come with us from San Francisco and some of the newer men replied that as much as they had enjoyed working with Phil, they would never come back as long as Jess McCargar was on the scene. Who did Jess think he was to talk to them in that fashion? This included Tobe and Rom Rutherford, Archie Brolly, and Bill Eddy. Cliff would liked to have said the same, but his loyalty to Phil went too deep. He told Phil he would stay and do what he could to help pick up the pieces.

George Everson came down from New York, and with his usual talk about a "spirit of graciousness" smoothed things over to the point that Phil could put those of his men who would return back to work. It took great self-control, but Phil had too much at stake to let it go now. He had put too much of his very essence into the project. It was a part of him. Since Jess was still president of the company, Phil would put up with him, but only until he could find a way to relieve him of his duties. Phil was still vice president in charge of research and the largest stockholder.

After Jess blew his top and decimated Phil's carefully built lab crew, Phil's world was very much shaken. He sorely missed his old standby men, especially Tobe Rutherford, who was closer to him than anyone except Cliff. He was certain of one thing; life was too short to put up with Jess McCargar any longer.

George Everson did his level best to make peace between Phil and Jess.

"I think we have to make allowances for Jess, Phil. He tells me his wife is divorcing him."

"I'm not surprised," Phil answered ungraciously, "Jess is just plain mean. I don't see how anyone could live with him."

"Show some compassion, Phil; this is the second time this has happened to Jess."

"No, George, my compassion as far as Jess is concerned was all used up some time ago."

"Well, I have some good news for you," George said, changing the subject, "I've made another stock sale. This should carry the lab for at least another two months. I think before this money is gone, I should go back to California. I've been thinking of taking Moli and his demonstration to Hollywood." George was referring to Bart Molinari, who had been left in charge of the San Francisco lab when Arch Brolly came east to work with Phil. Moli, with tubes supplied by Cliff and some he made himself, had maintained a remarkably good picture demonstration.

"There's a lot of interest in television there," George continued, "and money could easily be raised. You just keep things going and don't worry about Jess. I'll try to calm him down."

"I'm going to have to hire several more men, George, if we intend to keep the broadcast studio going, and I strongly suggest we do."

"Go ahead Phil, but do the best you can to keep expenses down; and if you plan to make any moves, check with me first."

"I'll do that, George."

Our time in France restored Phil's health to some extent, but the events of the past few days reversed his progress. He managed to get the new men settled in on their jobs and both the lab and studio back in business, but the old magic was gone. Creating had been his life. The joy of breaking new ground, riding on the edge of discovery—these were the things that kept him going even in the most difficult of times. More importantly, the pioneering spirit he had forged in his men and the unique camaraderie they shared were the source of his inspiration. Without that spirit, a day at the lab was just another day of work.

Phil had resisted my suggestion that he take some time off and get away from it all for a while. Then one day he came home from the lab and asked how I would like to go to Bermuda. We had often talked about someday visiting this fabulous isle but never felt we had the time or the money for such extravagance.

"Won't that be very expensive?" I knew he had been under some criticism from Jess and George for the expenses of our side trip to the French Riviera. They had been asked to sell some of Phil's stock to cover that.

"Yes," Phil agreed, "it probably will since I intend to take the boys with us, but I'll sell a hundred shares of stock. I think we should take Gertrude to care for the boys when we need a little freedom."

"That sounds wonderful, dear." Anything, I thought, that would take him away for a rest. Then I remembered my eighteen-year-old sister Lois who had just come east for a visit and was staying with Cliff and Lola. I had been looking forward to a nice long visit with her. I voiced my thoughts to Phil.

"I'd hoped to spend some time with Lois."

"Let's take her with us!" Phil was fond of Lois, as most people were. She was so pert, pretty, and full of fun.

"Could we? It might make up a little for my deserting the family when she was only eight years old. How long do you plan to be gone?"

"Just as long as it takes me to make some decisions. This may cause some big changes in our lives. I think you should plan on a week. Can you be ready by Saturday?"

"That just gives us two days! Let me call Lois." By now I was more or less accustomed to these spur-of-the-moment plans. Long-range plans had a way of never working out for us.

After Lois recovered from the shock, she said she would be ready with bells on. Gertrude, overjoyed at the prospect, was a veritable cyclone of energy, packing for the boys and herself, doing last-minute laundry, and getting the house in shape to leave. Late afternoon Saturday saw us all safely ensconced in our staterooms on the *SS Queen* of Bermuda. There was a large arrangement of long-stemmed roses and a basket of fruit, compliments of our good friend Skee Turner, who came to see us off.

During the night we ran into rough seas, and I awakened with a severe case of mal de mer. The beautiful red roses had come to life. Their movement followed the up and down movement of the ship, but just enough out of phase to make the combination very upsetting to me. I shut my eyes, but I could hear their movement. Finally, I asked Phil to call the steward and have him take the flowers to Lois, and while he was at it, take the fruit to the boys. The smell was upsetting me.

Approaching Bermuda, we could see the white-roofed houses nestled

Globe trotter Philo on the SS Queen of Bermuda

among the lush greenery. As we neared the Hamilton docks, the quaint landing platform, the horse-drawn surreys, and many bicycles made me feel as though we had been transported back in time to provencial England. Beyond the docks we could see the downtown central square, where an English bobby stood on a small platform directing traffic, although the only motorized vehicles on the island were those used for road repair. It was not unusual to see couples in their evening clothes on bicycles-built-for-two, on their way to a night on the town.

We found the Elbow Beach Hotel, where we had reservations, to be a very charming place. It was built on an elevation and commanded a spectacular view of the ocean. Terraced flower gardens flanked the walk down to the beach, a generous length of fine white coral sand. To one side of the hotel was a large beach house with ping-pong and other games to entertain the guests on rainy days.

We were thoroughly enchanted with Bermuda. The only other time we had seen the ocean so blue was when we had seen the Mediterranean from the Grande Chaussee between Monte Carlo and Mentone. The three newlywed couples who arrived with us were jolly company, and we thoroughly enjoyed dancing every evening to an excellent orchestra (refugees from Turkey). Lois at first felt strange being the only one in our group without a partner; however, by the second day several young men had crashed our group and were competing for her attention. She liked dancing with them, but her heart was with her sweetheart, intern Rees Anderson, back in Utah.

One day when we tired of the beach, we rented bicycles and were on our way to Hamilton, on the other side of the island. Startled by a fast-moving carriage suddenly appearing around a corner just ahead, I slipped in the loose gravel at the edge of the unpaved road, and landed, bicycle and all, on a path some distance below the road. Even more startled than I was the elderly English lady at whose feet I found myself. My shorts had been little protection, and I left considerable skin on the rocks behind me when I slid. I was most concerned about the English lady, however. Fighting for breath, she gasped, "I didn't know whether . . . I should try to catch you . . . or not!" I was relieved that she didn't have a heart attack right there.

I had not fully regained my confidence when the group decided to take a trail ride. I agreed to go, provided they had a gentle horse for me. Too late I recognized my mistake. This horse was old, tired, and stubborn. He refused to go faster than a walk. The other horses were raring to go, so I told the other riders to go on ahead. Phil stayed behind to assist me. When I hit my horse on the rump with the green switch Phil brought me, the cantankerous animal stopped and laid back his ears. In my experience with horses that meant, "I don't have to put up with you; I can dump you."

Phil's horse had been dancing around, eager to hit the trail. He now whirled and kicked my horse in the rump, which got my horse going but only at his former pace. The trail ended at a deserted beach, and Phil joined the others who were running their horses up and down the beach. I had had it with my horse and was about to dismount when he pawed the sand and rolled. I was able to free my feet from the stirrups just in time to escape being crushed beneath him. This ended our riding in Bermuda.

Our scheduled week was about to come to a close, but Phil was not yet ready to leave. He decided to send the rest of our party home while he and I stayed on for another week. He needed more time to evaluate his situation.

The evening before our family and friends were to sail, Phil gave a wienie roast on the beach. The boys had gathered a large pile of drift-wood. After we had cooked and eaten all we could hold, we sat around the fire and sang. This was something new on the island, and for days people were talking about it.

After what had happened to me the last week, I began to get the feeling Bermuda had me jinxed, but this was not the end of it. We had been warned to avoid the severe undertow at the end of the hotel beach; beyond the shallow waters along the beach lay a razor-sharp coral reef. One day Phil and I were floating. With my ears under water I had not heard him say he was going in, and I drifted out too far. Before I knew it, I was caught in a swift current. Not a very strong swimmer, I exhausted my strength before fully realizing my predicament. I shouted for help and began to frantically fight the waves. As the strength left my arms and legs, I found myself under water, just drifting along. A peaceful feeling encompassed me, and in a semiconscious state, I felt one with the water. All fear left me. As though in a dream, I felt this was really a rather peaceful way to die.

I regained consciousness on the beach, coughing and sputtering, encircled by people. There was no lifeguard on the beach, so it was left to Phil to perform a heroic feat. Seeing me floating limply in the water, he swam out to my rescue. He had little chance of swimming out of the current with me in tow, so he took a deep breath, grabbed hold of me, and then walked on the bottom to give him more strength against the current, holding me high over his head until he was out of deep water. When I asked him later how he ever held his breath that long, he said we never know what our capabilities really are until faced with an emergency. Phil was careful not to let me out of his sight for the rest of the trip.

The next week was devoted to some serious thought and discussions about the course our future should take. A week of diversion gave Phil the opportunity he needed to back off and study his situation. He could see no way to override the strong lobbying in Washington against commercial television. RCA was not yet ready for it, so the longer they could stall, the stronger would be their position. It was obvious to us, and I am sure it was equally obvious to RCA, that they would eventually have to obtain a license to use the Farnsworth patents. Phil was also aware of the necessity of having a license from RCA for certain radio-type parts. Meantime, RCA was doing very well selling radios and other communication equipment and improving its own television system.

As for Farnsworth, there seemed little chance that more license agreements could be negotiated as long as the newly formed Federal Communication Commission refused to designate spectrum space for commercial television. Perhaps our only course was to enter radio manufacturing ourselves. This would not only provide a shipping room door and a new source of revenue but would put us in an advantageous position to convert to television sets when the time came. In any case, Phil was sure of one thing: he could never work with Jess McCargar again.

The day after we returned home, Phil called George in New York, asking him to arrange to bring his friend Hugh Knowlton, a partner in the Wall Street firm of Kuhn, Loeb & Co., to our home for a planning meeting. They had been given an option on a block of Farnsworth stock for services rendered. Two days later, they, along with Mrs. Knowlton, arrived at our home. Erica had been curious to see this television thing about which she had heard so much.

Phil laid it on the line to George and Hugh. Somewhat to his surprise, they agreed wholeheartedly. Phil wanted a complete reorganization of the company, with the new company to be known as Farnsworth Television and Radio Corporation. George was worried about the expense of setting up to manufacture, but Hugh spoke up with the suggestion that this might be an opportune time for Kuhn, Loeb & Co. to exercise its Farnsworth Television stock option. He also suggested floating a stock issue as Kuhn, Loeb & Co. was expert in that sort of thing. As an investment house, they also had a finger on the nation's pulse and could help Farnsworth find an existing plant for manufacturing.

They decided to start looking around for a man with a good track record in the radio manufacturing business to take the helm of the new company. George said Jess could be offered the position of chairman of the board of directors but it was doubtful if he would accept. As the meeting was coming to a close, Hugh gave Phil a bit of advice. He said this transition would take time, perhaps six months or even a year. It was important that Phil keep a good demonstration capability at all times. At the same time, expenses would have to be kept at a minimum, but because commercial television was not yet in sight, more improvements were not all that necessary.

After they left, Phil was preoccupied. Going to the kitchen to check on dinner, I heard him playing *Nola* at the piano. This was good emotional release for him, and later we talked about it.

"Don't be too upset with Hugh's parting remarks about not making improvements," I told him.

"None of them seem to realize how hard I've worked to keep ahead of the competition. I just cannot allow myself to fall behind technically. I'd never catch up with RCA, with all its resources."

"Honey, you'll never stop making improvements as long as there is a need for them. Just try to keep expenses down. That's all they're really saying." Talking about it seemed to relieve him somewhat, but we both knew this would be a difficult period.

Phil had depended upon me to answer his mother's frequent letters, and keep in touch with other members of the family. On April 25th, 1937, he penned one of his own infrequent letters to his mother:

Dear Mother,

Since you left, business matters have gone from bad to worse . . . this finally resulted in a meeting of the Board of Directors here at home on Saturday. I will give you the highlights. The company will change its policy to one of active operation. We will manufacture both receivers and transmitters. We will erect and operate television broadcasting stations. We will modify our licensing policy to provide the greatest use for all the radio industry. We will negotiate all the cross-licenses necessary to permit us to enter the entire radio and television field.

Jess is resigning from the company in favor of a highly paid technical executive . . . I have been suggested as the new chairman of the board of directors. I don't care particularly whether I get this title or not, because I have always in the past performed this function anyway and see no difficulty in maintaining this position in the future. This policy is one I have been fighting for this past few years and I feel the greatest relief in its adoption— as though a ton of weight had been lifted from my shoulders. By the way, don't permit anyone to sell any more stock while it is at such a low figure, because it will only remain there for a matter of a month or so.

I have received one other bit of news, which has meant more to me than any other thing that has happened in years. The BYU has voted me a citation as A Distinguished Alumnus, who has been outstanding in his contribution to the reputation and prestige of the University, and an inspiration to the students. I found it almost impossible to compose a letter accepting

the award, and my hand shook till I could hardly sign it. It was, I am afraid,
a rather extravagant letter, but I did try to convey my deep feeling in the
matter.

Please give our love to everyone and take a great big hunk for yourself.

Phil, Pem, Philo and Skeez.

In the spring of 1938, work was slowing down at the lab, and the finance people were still working on organizing the new company; so taking Cliff and Lola with us, we went off on another trip, this time to Maine. In Baxter state park, near the base of Mt. Katahdin, we engaged a guide who led us on backpack trips to remote streams and ponds where hungry trout leaped for our dry flies.

Phil and Cliff liked to play as hard as they worked. Phil's determination to get himself in shape was equaled by my and Cliff's eagerness to help him do it, and Lola seemed to enjoy being a part of it. We even spent a morning wading in the Upper Sardnehunk River in our sneakers. When my feet hit that icy water, I could not believe we were actually going to do this, but after a while, it didn't seem cold any more; my feet were numb. In any case, the thought of getting lost in the woods if I tried walking back to camp alone was even less inviting. Those boys were a hard act to follow!

The highlight of the entire trip came when Cliff and Phil decided to pack in for an overnight on Slaughter Pond to catch some early morning fishing. The next morning, we girls had been up just long enough to build a fire on the camp grill and heat water for coffee, when the boys dragged into camp, wet and shivering with the cold.

As we thawed them out, we got the story. Being good woodsmen, they had made their beds on pine needles under a tree, scooping out holes to accommodate their hips. In the middle of the night a severe storm from the north swept through the area. The rain fell in torrents, running under their blankets and making puddles of their "hip holes." Twice the high wind blew their covers off and down the hill. Camp fires were strictly forbidden in that area; anyway, there was not a dry stick anywhere.

Utterly miserable, they huddled in the lee of a tree, and with the first light hit the trail for camp. About half way back, they found a large wild raspberry patch. They were so shaky they stopped to eat a few berries for strength to go on. In their misery, they totally ignored the hungry bear feeding on the other side of the patch. The bear saw them, but seemed not to mind sharing nature's bounty with them.

While we were eating breakfast, the elderly gentleman who managed the campground came by with the news that two men who had camped on the other side of the Pond had actually died from exposure that night. Phil and Cliff felt very lucky to be alive. With that, and considering the fact that our time was up, Phil shaved off his seven-day beard, and we headed for home.

On our way home, I took some kidding when, coming south from Millinocket, we passed Lake Pemadumcook. Phil wanted to stop by the town of Brownfield to check out a property George Everson had told us we should use for vacations. He and a friend had acquired the property from the owner, George Haley, who was then teaching at the University of San Francisco, but they had never seen the place. Following George's directions, we arrived in Brownfield and stopped to ask a farmer where we would find the old Haley farm.

"Ta Haley fom?" the man repeated Phil's question, "Weall jus ga ta rud dan a piece ta the next lef tun. Go in theah a piece on hits ta fust place on ta lef. Kinda run down tis, be'en umpty nigh onta fifteen yeaws naow. Doahs an windas been stole th'ave. Shame's what tis."

Phil thanked him and had no trouble following his directions, after we all agreed on what they were. The lane leading to the house was lined with venerable old sugar maples. In the house we found the calling cards of various small animals who had exercised squatter's rights. The narrow parlor led into a dining room that was straight out of the history books. It had a large walk-in fireplace, with its iron bar for holding the iron soup kettle still in place. Of course, the iron kettle was long gone. At one side of the fireplace was a built-in brick oven and a place beneath to hold bricks or rocks heated in the fireplace to bake New England beans and brown bread.

Beyond this was a kitchen with an aged wood-burning cook stove. A doorway on the other side of the fireplace led to what was probably the master bedroom, with its own small fireplace. Narrow stairs led from the parlor to the floor above and two more sleeping rooms. On the other side of what we assumed to be the parlor was a door leading to a shed. This had obviously been used to shelter cows and probably a horse during the winter to avoid wading through the deep snow to the large barn outside. At one side of the manger, a walkway made of boards led to an indoor privy, which must have been built with a family in mind, since it had three holes—one for Papa, one for Mama, and one for a small child . . . just like the three bears.

Standing on this walkway, Phil's attention was riveted on the beams overhead. The glossy rich chestnut marks of an expertly wielded hand-adz were visible. As we learned later, they and the house were close to two hundred years old. The land had been a grant to the original Haley ancestor from the queen of England. The first deed to the place had been handwritten by Daniel Webster, who had worked at the deed recorder's office to pay his way through Fryeburg Academy. I could tell Phil was becoming captivated when he said he would like to buy the place and build a living room around those beams.

Exploring further, we found a large barn and beyond that a ravine. Phil led us down the slope where, as he had suspected, we found a crystal-clear stream. Phil had been like a bird dog scenting game. Finally, he could resist the temptation no longer.

"I'm going to buy this place and build a dam right down there and make my own trout pond."

"This is a long way from Philadelphia, Phil." I pointed out.

"That's in its favor," Phil said. "It's far enough away that we will be less disturbed when we want to get away."

"Guess you're right about that." I was beginning to catch Phil's feeling for the place, "It's so beautiful and peaceful here, with woods as far as you can see in every direction."

True to his word, Phil wasted no time purchasing the farm, including sixty acres of mostly wooded land, with two mountains in the immediate background. He was anxious to get started on the dam, because his greatest need was physical exercise. He suggested we invite my father, who was good at building almost anything, to come and help us make the house livable. Dad's second marriage had not been a very happy one, especially since Lois had married and moved away. He welcomed the chance to come.

By the end of August, Phil had accomplished all he could at the lab and was again in need of a build-up, so we headed for Maine with Dad and our camping gear. The schedule Phil set up was meant either to kill or to cure. He decided to ignore the house and start on the dam first, hoping to get it to the point where it could be left to finish in the spring.

Every day we arose at daybreak and ate breakfast prepared by Dad, who loved to cook on camp fires. We used the small bedroom fireplace, since the other flue looked unsafe, and had rolled our sleeping bags out on the floor in front of it. We started work at seven, when our helpers arrived. After taking an hour at eleven for lunch and a rest, we worked until 4:30 p.m., by which time Phil and I were exhausted. After an early dinner, we sat around the fire and listened to Dad's endless stories of his lifetime of exciting and often amusing experiences. At dusk, we were more than ready for bed, so we seldom had reason to light the Coleman lantern.

Phil hired more men to help him put in a concrete core for the dam, expecting to reinforce it with earth and rocks on either side. The place was surrounded by ancient rock walls, built from glacial rocks collected long ago from fields to be put under cultivation. These were hauled to the site on a rock slide pulled by a team of horses. While this was going on, Dad installed windows and doors in the downstairs part of the house. We had Gertrude bring the boys up for Thanksgiving, by which time the core of the dam was poured and ready for the dirt, sand, and gravel reinforcement. Phil was concerned, because winter was close on our heels, and he was needed back at the lab. Questioning a neighbor about whether it would be safe to leave the dam like that over winter, he was told, "Showah, aint nawthin'll take er ott. She'll freeze solid and stay thet way til spring."

Philo had the time of his young life, exploring the place, but Phil had to lay down strict rules about wandering off into the woods alone. Skeezix, now three, had to be watched constantly to curb his urge to wander.

Our plan was to drive back to Philadelphia the day after Thanksgiving. Before we had finished our Thanksgiving dinner, it had already begun to snow. However, since it was the first snow of the season, we thought it would not amount to very much. We didn't know Maine! By morning there was a foot of snow on the ground, and none of us were dressed for it. While we were getting the place ready to close up, Dad trudged through the snow to Everett Perry's house, our nearest neighbor. Everett agreed to bring his team and pull us out to the highway nearly a mile away.

Phil asked Everett to do a few cleaning jobs around the place and offered him the going local wage of three dollars per day. Everett said he would do the work, but only wanted two fifty a day for it. When Phil asked why he didn't want three dollars, he said, "Cuz aw dunt want to wok thet hawd."

CHAPTER 22

Company Reorganized

The search for an executive capable of taking charge of the new Farnsworth Radio and Television Company ended with the hiring of Edwin A. Nicholas, previously the head of the licensing division of RCA. "Nick," as he liked to be called, agreed to come on just as soon as the capital necessary to start the company was in place.

The financial experts at Kuhn, Loeb & Co. suggested floating a stock issue to finance the purchase of manufacturing facilities and start-up operations. While this step would assure the long-range future of the company, it was still left to George to raise enough money to cover expenses until the underwriting was complete. George figured the best place to find new money was Hollywood, so he arranged to have Bart Molinari bring the San Francisco demonstration unit and meet him in Los Angeles. The movie industry still feared it might be displaced by the young upstart, television, so, just in case, it wanted in on television.

Moli set up in a studio next door to the old Palomar dancing studio, which proved to be a fertile source of lovely young ladies who gladly seized the opportunity to be televised. This wide selection of talent gave George and Moli a chance to study which types of hair and skin were the best subjects for television. Carter Wright, a producer with Franchon & Marco, the leading producers of vaudeville acts which toured the country and performed between movie features, kindly provided much material for the television programming. Of all the people who were televised, Billie Dove and John Boles, both leading movie personalities, possessed the features and skin most suitable for television.

Bart Molinari with Farnsworth television camera.

A representative of Scientific Films, Inc., who did short scientific news subjects for Paramount Eyes & Ears of the World, saw the demonstration, and wanted to make a film of Phil and his equipment. Arrangements were made, and Scientific Films came to Philadelphia. They filmed Phil working on equipment in the lab, and at the Wyndmoor studio they filmed him giving a talk about our operation there.

We wanted to demonstrate the simplicity of the television receiver, so after they were through with Phil's talk, they went into the small reception room where we had a receiver in a typical living room setting. Seven-year-old Philo and I sat in a large chair. Philo asked, "Mother, can we see a television show?" and I replied, "Yes, Philo, will you please turn it on?" He then went over to the set, and when he turned a knob, the picture came on bright and clear, proving that the set was so easy to use that even a child could operate it.

A few weeks later, all the way across the country in Provo, Utah, my young sister Rhae was seeing a movie with a friend, when this Paramount newsreel segment came on after the first feature. Rhae could hardly believe her eyes when she saw Phil, but when I came on, she was absolutely ecstatic! Here before her on the silver screen was her sister whom she had not seen for over five years. Excited, she jumped up and shouted, "That's my sister!"

This newsreel was filmed in technicolor and given worldwide release. The exposure was an enormous help to George, who raised over one hundred and fifty thousand dollars in stock sales in the Los Angeles area. He felt this would carry the company through the underwriting period.

However, the Farnsworth group in New York, headed by corporate attorney John Wharton, was running into difficulties with the newly set up procedures of the Securities and Exchange Commission. There were frequent and expensive trips to Washington by accountants, lawyers and executives. The pile of documents and printed matter grew to nearly four inches in height. Expenses doubled, then tripled beyond the original estimates. During this process, Kuhn, Loeb & Co. was working with the underwriters on the other side of the table from the Farnsworth group, who had to bear the brunt of all this expense. Such are the rules of the game.

At this time the situation in Europe was getting critical. British Prime Minister Chamberlain's attempts to avert an all-out war by appeasing Hitler were reflected in an unstable Wall Street market. Since the success of the Farnsworth stock issue depended upon a certain stability of the stock market, everyone was on pins and needles worrying about it. The time allowed for this underwriting was running out like sand in an hourglass.

Phil and the rest of us were sweating it out in Philadelphia. These days he seldom worked at the lab in the evenings. He had reserved the after-dinner time to spend with the boys and me. He not only spent more time playing with them, we even started spending more evenings playing the violin and piano, which brought back old times and helped relieve the tension.

We were very much aware that the situation in New York was touch-and-go. There was one delay after the other. On March 31st, the very last day, there were still over one hundred legal documents to be ratified. The attorneys were jittery for fear some last minute forgotten detail might yet dump the apple cart. Bankers, government officials, lawyers, business executives, and their advisors and assistants were at the meeting. Finally everything was thought to be in order . . . but not so. One paper was missing; they could not close without it—and Allen G. Messick, the man responsible for the document had calmly gone to lunch.

To shorten a long story, Mr. Messick and the paper were located, and the papers were all properly signed. George and Jess breathed a sigh of relief when a check for three million dollars was presented to George as secretary of the Farnsworth Company. George called Phil with the good news. There was great rejoicing at the lab . . . and at home! The situation of the signing was so ludicrous to Don Lippincott that, upon going back to his hotel, he sat down and penned a satiric verse about the incident, which was later published in Savoir-Faire.

A Television Picture
By Donald K. Lippincott

The clans are here from far and near,
And on the desks reposing
Are bales and blocks of common stocks;
There's going to be a closing.
Exchanging rafts of checks and drafts
And instruments of title
And all our fears and tears of years
Will meet with their requital.

So here are ranks of men from banks,
And many secretaries
And legal lights and parasites
And fiscal functionaries.
But what's this pall that grips them all
And stifles all this bunch:
They're waiting for an I. O. U.
And by the Gods they need it too
And Messick has the I. O. U.
And Messick's gone to lunch.

O praises be to Allen G;
Chambers of Commerce praise him!
No banker grim can trouble him
Nor tax collector faze him.
When tempers fail and strong men pale
He just plays out his hunch;
He knows the thing he has to do
And by the Gods he does it too!
He just writes out an I. O. U.
and calmly goes to lunch!

The very next day Hitler invaded Czechoslovakia and the stock market plunged, but our stock issue was secure. Now that they had the money, the next objective was to locate a manufacturing facility and get tooled up to make radios while awaiting the time to turn out television sets. The Capehart Company, which manufactured phonographs and juke boxes in Fort Wayne, Indiana and another plant at Marion, Indiana, fifty miles south, were purchased. Now the company needed an in-house legal department. Don Lippincott was invited to fill this position, but he and Ruth preferred to stay in California. Edwin M. Martin was hired from the patent department of the Hazeltine Company.

Meanwhile, in July 1938, Albert Rose and Harley Iams, two engineers at RCA, applied for a patent for a revolutionary new type of camera tube, whose principal feature was a low-velocity scanning beam. This work seemed to point the way for the future, because the resulting tube seemed to combine the relative advantages of both the Iconoscope and the Image Dissector into one all-purpose tube—without apparently infringing on any of Farnsworth's patents. Work on this tube proceeded apace, and the trademark division of RCA came up with a name for it: the Image Orthicon.

Not long after the application for the Orthicon was submitted, the legal division at RCA received shocking news: there would be no patent for the Orthicon. The patent office, after yet another interference case, ruled that all the novelty in the Orthicon tube was in fact covered by Farnsworth patent number 2,087,683, filed in April 1933 and issued in July 1937, and four other Farnsworth patents. Thus the Image Orthicon—which would serve as the workhorse of the industry in the 1940s and '50s—was ruled to be a Farnsworth invention.

By the time this decision was handed down, the Patent Office had grown quite weary of RCA's monopolistic tactics. After all claims relating to the Orthicon were awarded to Farnsworth, one of the patent examiners told Don Lippincott he was sorry they were unable to give us the name as well, but RCA had registered "Image Orthicon" as a trademark. To this day, RCA claims this tube, but all it really invented was the name.

While this last patent interference case with RCA was being resolved, Nick Nicholas lost no time in getting Farnsworth Television and Radio organized. By the first of April 1939, he had two well equipped plants and the necessary funds to launch a radio manufacturing business as Farnsworth Television & Radio Corporation. Within the next four to five months, he had a complete line of radios ready to sell, with distribution arranged for a large portion of the United States. According to reports, at the first distributor's conference, over one million dollars worth of radios was sold. Phil's research department was moved to Fort Wayne, and Phil and I planned to arrive in the fall.

Nineteen thirty-nine was an important year, not just for Farnsworth, but for the television industry as a whole, for it was the year that RCA realized it could no longer stem the rising tide. Not only was industry reaching a level of technical maturity that could no longer be denied, but David Sarnoff must have felt the questioning glare of his own board of directors. By 1939, RCA had invested many millions of dollars on its television research—Fortune magazine estimated the sum at more than thirteen million dollars. The entire Farnsworth effort, by comparison, had spent something on the order of one million dollars.

What did Sarnoff have to show for this investment? He had certainly managed to avoid licensing the Farnsworth patents, but at what cost? The best his researchers had been able to come up with was the Iconoscope, a device dubious in both its origins and its capabilities. Even those who extolled the virtues of the Iconoscope's signal strength admitted to its many shortcomings. Its angular configuration made shading and signal filtering a nightmare, while the signal produced by the Image Dissector was clean and sharp.

In any event, Sarnoff could no longer afford to postpone the advent of commercial television, and a date was chosen for its formal introduction—April 30th, 1939, at the opening of the New York World's fair. The date was premature in many respects—the FCC had yet to adopt uniform signal standards or grant licenses for actual commercial operations—but Sarnoff was determined to demonstrate that RCA was "first in television," so he opened the RCA exhibit at the New York world's fair with his famous pronouncement: "Now we add sight to sound." There was no mention of any of the individuals whose seminal work had made the event possible.

Gets Place on 'Top Ten'

This event was, in many respects, precisely the moment Phil had dreamed of since that day in the potato field nineteen years earlier when he first conceived his system of electronic television. But even as it happened, Phil's attention was beginning to turn elsewhere. The many months of stress and anxiety over the reorganization had worn Phil down to a frazzle, so we decided to spend most of the summer in Maine, where he was hoping to build his strength for the big move to Fort Wayne.

Philo Farnsworth, former Utahn and young developer of television's basic principles, was listed as one of America's ten "Young Men of 1939" by Durward Howes, biographer.

Shortly after we arrived in Maine in May 1939, something happened that gave Phil a much needed boost in morale. He was chosen as one of "America's Top Ten Young Men" by biographer Durward Howes. He received a copy of the write-up in the Salt Lake Tribune carrying his photo. The article listed the 10 men so honored:

Philo T. Farnsworth, 33, formerly of Utah and now of Philadelphia, for developing television's basic principles.

Lou Gehrig, 36, New York City, for accepting with true sportsmanship the close of his career as "baseball's iron horse."

Earnest O. Lawrence, 38, Berkeley, California, winner of the 1939 Nobel prize in physics for building the atom smasher.

Fulton Lewis, Jr., 36, Washington, D. C., radio news commentator.

William S. Paley, 38, New York City, president of the Columbia

Broadcasting System.

Perry Pipkin, 35, Memphis, Tenn., president of the United States Junior Chamber of Commerce.

Philip Reed, 40, New York City, chairman of the General Electric Corporation board of directors.

Harold Stassen, 32, St. Paul, Minn., America's youngest governor.

Spencer Tracy, 39, Hollywood, twice winner of the Motion Picture Academy of Arts and Sciences award for the best performance for an actor.

Dr. Herman B. Wells, 37, Bloomington, Ind., president of Indiana University.

Naturally, Phil was very pleased to be singled out in this manner and included in such company, because he had a high regard for all of these people. It gave him the spiritual lift and encouragement he badly needed at this time, and was particularly helpful in its effect on the new management people with whom he was to work.

When we arrived in Maine, we made a discovery that Phil found most disheartening. The core for the dam which he had built the previous fall had been washed out by the heavy winter, despite assurances from the local folks that it would freeze in place. Phil resolved to restore the dam, but first there was a lot of work to do to the house.

During the winter, my father and our good friend Tom Cosgrove had installed a bathroom, windows, and doors, and in general had made the house in Brownfield somewhat liveable.

Phil wanted to populate our place with pheasant, and was presented with ten dozen eggs from the Maine Fish and Game Department. A secondhand incubator was purchased and the job of turning the eggs twice daily and regulating the temperature was left up to me.

Now the dining room and sitting room flues had to be rebuilt. The old fireplaces were torn out and, the walk-in fireplace in the dining room was scaled down to a stoop-in size. The old configuration was copied, down to the brick baking oven and the space for hot bricks below for baking beans and brown bread. The old wrought iron doors were retained.

The stairs to the second floor were rickety and very worn, so Phil had them torn out. In the process, a secret double wall was found, revealing a space of about a foot and a half wide by eight feet long.

In this space we found an ancient flintlock rifle, a Civil War hat, powder horn, and rusted spear, all with Confederate emblems. Because the Civil War was fought at times with brother against brother, there were many deserters. We surmised that a Confederate deserter had hidden here and the evidence sealed up, away from prying eyes forever.

While a bricklayer was rebuilding the big fireplace, Phil went to work on the sitting room fireplace. Phil was down on his knees, laying the fireplace foundation, when he was startled by a voice behind him.

"How be ya?" He turned to see an elderly man with a gray, straggly beard. He wore an ancient wide-brimmed black hat, a coarse blue shirt, and bib overalls, all giving the impression of having been lived in for an indefinite period of time. He came in through the open door so quietly he seemed to have just materialized there. He was studying Phil through small eyes, shriveled with age.

"Well, hello!" Phil greeted him as soon as he could find his voice. "Where did you come from?"

"I be Dan, live dun tha rud a piece."

"Glad to know you Dan; I'm Phil Farnsworth. We're going to be your neighbors." Phil placed another brick.

After a long silence. . . . "S'place ben umpty fa yeahs."

"Yes, I know," said Phil, as he broke a brick smartly with the edge of his trowel. "We're rebuilding it."

"Yeawh."

Phil laid his brick and turned around. Old Dan had left as quietly as he had appeared. In the following days, we became accustomed to Old Dan's silent comings and goings. He traveled in a little old buggy, pulled by an old brown horse, and always trotting behind was his faithful old dog, Prince.

The Haley farm in Brownfield, Maine. The pheasant house and run replaced the large weathered barn destroyed by the 1937 hurricane.

Since nothing much in the way of research was going on at the lab in Philadelphia, Cliff, Harold Bernhardt, George Huffnagle, and Joe Schantz came up to Maine to see what they could do to help us. Phil turned the building of the sitting room fireplace over to the bricklayer so he could devote his complete attention to working on the dam. He was determined to rebuild it—this time to withstand anything.

Phil intended to dig all the way down to bedrock for the footer of the new dam. However, soundings made to a depth of thirty feet found only very hard packed glacial silt. This did not phase Phil. He was accustomed to finding his way around obstacles. He redesigned the dam as a floating structure, with twenty-foot wingwalls embedded in the banks of the ravine, and a footer thirteen feet wide at the bottom and twelve feet below ground level. This tapered up to two feet at the top, then rose another ten feet. This formidable structure, laced with reinforcing rods, formed the core of the dam, with tons and tons of rocks on either side to make certain it stayed put.

The heavily reinforced forms were fabricated and a large cement mixer rented. A call went out for men to push the wheelbarrows full of cement from the mixer along a ramp which extended the length of the dam, there to be dumped into the forms. By this time Phil had hired a civil engineer to check his plans and oversee this part of the project. Because he wanted a continuous pour to avoid any weakness in the structure, he needed three shifts, requiring thirty men. He hired a young doctor to be on hand through the pour in case of accident.

Phil's strength gave out early, and Cliff took his place as general on-site manager of the project. Twenty-four hours later, Cliff came to make one of his periodic reports to Phil. Cliff kept insisting he was doing fine, but this time he sat on a couch and went to sleep in the middle of his report. The pour lasted approximately thirty hours. One man was overcome by heat stroke, but for the most part these were sturdy young men who were accustomed to hard work.

The baby pheasants had hatched and were moved to a hexagonal shaped brooder, with a wire run extended from each of the six faces of the brooder. One day Phil had an important telephone call from New York, but he was nowhere to be found. As a last resort, I went to the brooder house. There was Phil on his belly in one of the twenty-four-inch-high wire runs watching his baby pheasants. They were dying and he had to know why. He discovered that his problem was a leak in the kerosene line in the brooder house.

When it came time to leave Maine, Phil decided to house the pheasants in our unfloored living room for the winter and hired a man by the name of Fred Doane to take care of the place.

We had planned to be in Fort Wayne in time for Philo to enter the fifth grade. However, since Joe Spallone was late finishing our living room windows, we sent the boys off with Cliff's family, so Philo would be there in time for the beginning of school. Phil was scheduled to give a talk at Syracuse University in November, so he decided to wait and take care of that on the way to Indiana. My father was coming that far with us on his way home to Utah.

Phil's Syracuse talk was enthusiastically received, and after a delightful luncheon, Phil was prevailed upon to visit several math and science classes and talk with the students. While he was thus occupied, I drove Dad down to Palmyra, where we visited the sacred grove, site of Joseph Smith's first vision, and the Hill Cumorah, where the angel Moroni hid the golden plates containing the history of the Jewish families who were led away from

Jerusalem before its destruction in 600 B.C. As foretold by prophets of old, the record was once again brought forth, through the Latter-day Saint prophet Joseph Smith, for the edification of these generations, as the Book of Mormon. This was a wonderful experience for both of us, strengthening our faith in the gospel of Jesus Christ. Many times over the years, my father mentioned how much this meant to him.

By the time we arrived in Fort Wayne, Cliff had found us a nice house south of town, and Philo and Jean, Cliff's daughter, had already made school friends. We had missed Russell's fourth birthday on October 5th, so we had a belated party for him and bought him his heart's desire, some long corduroy pants and a hat like his daddy's.

Phil was very pleased with the new plant. When he took me to see the radio assembly lines, I was fascinated to see the empty chassis at the beginning of the line and how it progressed down the long line of seated workers, ending up a finished radio, ready for testing.

Phil found creative work in these surroundings to be quite difficult, however. His reputation preceded him. Every morning

Skee, wearing his birthday present - long corduroy pants and a hat like his daddy's

when he came to work, there would be several engineers waiting to grab a minute—or ten, or fifteen—with him on his way to his office. Often this was just an excuse to meet him and shake his hand and had nothing to do with television. While Phil always stopped and heard them out, he came to feel something like a show fish in an aquarium—a role in which he was very uncomfortable.

It was clear to me now that a major period in our lives was drawing to a close. It seemed Phil had given all he could to television; the technology itself was refined to such a point that it was quite ready for commercial consumption. All that remained was for the industry to adopt uniform signal standards and commercial broadcasting would begin. On the home front, with the company reorganized and moved to Fort Wayne, Phil's struggles for adequate financing seemed a thing of the past. Radio sales were strong, and the company was well situated to begin manufacturing television sets just as soon as the FCC gave its approval. There was only one matter of unfinished business: a license with RCA.

In the months following David Sarnoff's dramatic publicity stunt at the New York World's Fair, we began to notice a not so subtle shift in RCA's public attitude toward Philo Farnsworth. Mr. Sarnoff even took the unheard of step of acknowledging Phil in his speeches. A little investigating by our Wall Street people revealed that the change in tone was genuine:

RCA was ready to negotiate with Farnsworth.

Late in 1939, RCA conceded the futility of trying to circumvent Farnsworth's patent structure, and negotiations for a license between the two firms commenced. RCA, once determined that it would never pay patent royalties, was at last ready to admit that there was no alternative. Their attempts to grind Farnsworth down with endless litigation had failed.

With FT&R President "Nick" Nicholas, the former head of RCA's licensing division, leading the negotiations, ably assisted by Edwin M. Martin, now head of patents for Farnsworth, suitable terms were eventually arranged with RCA's vice president in charge of patents, Mr. Otto Schairer.

And so the struggle for television came to a close in October of 1939, in an office high above Rockefeller Plaza. Before signing the license, Mr. Schairer reminded the Farnsworth group what an historic agreement he was about to sign—the very first patent license that ever obligated the Radio Corporation of America to pay patent royalties to another company. The bitterness of the defeat was evident: Mr. Schairer had tears in his eyes as he signed the document.

CHAPTER 23

Dashing of Hopes

From the vantage point of 1940, it was amazing to consider how far we had come. Starting in 1926 with an empty loft, a year, and twenty-five thousand dollars, Phil had created an entire industry.

For Phil, the value of the past decade and a half was impossible to express in mere dollars and cents. The value of the experience could not be counted in royalties or recognition. The wealth that motivated Philo T. Farnsworth was not the wealth of capital gains but the wealth of ideas and knowledge.

The idea that germinated in his brain for electronic television must have been a gift from God, a partnership between divine inspiration and temporal genius. From that single seed of inspiration he peeled away many of the mysteries of the physical universe and commanded the forces of nature to do his bidding.

At the outset of this adventure, Phil always worried that he lacked enough formal education. But his experience was his education, more than any number of years at BYU could have provided. His laboratory was his class room, and he was both student and professor. He learned as much as he taught and taught as much as he learned. Phil's lack of formal training was perhaps his greatest asset, rather than the liability he feared it would be, because it enabled him to structure his observation according to the unique framework of his God- given genius. He had been spared the burden of conventional wisdom and had been deprived only of the knowledge of what was impossible. So enabled, he simply proceeded to do whatever needed to be done. As Phil was fond of saying, the difficult we do right away; the impossible takes slightly longer.

Inventing television was an achievement worthy of recognition among his mortal peers—and a training ground for the journey to come, where he would find himself traveling alone in territory where only immortals had gone before. But first, there was still work to be done.

We spent the winter of 1939-40 getting used to our new location in Fort Wayne. Phil was determined, for the good of the company, to continue perfecting television. But almost immediately he found it difficult to adapt to the new environment, where the priorities revolved around manufacture instead of invention, where the principal objective was making money instead of progress.

Despite the difficulties, Phil was pleased with the direction the company was taking. He had always felt the big returns from television lay in broadcasting, not in manufacturing, so he was happy when Nick agreed with the wisdom of acquiring the local radio station, WGL. Thus, not only would Farnsworth have the facilities to manufacture television receivers, but it would be a simple matter to convert to television broadcasting when commercial licenses became available.

During this period Phil applied for sixteen more television patents. Some of this work had been disclosed previously, but the patent applications had been held up for lack of funds to cover filing fees. However, his feeling that commercial television was going to be held up by international politics and Hitler's war was undermining his former drive. The thrill of achievement that had driven him up to this point was dwindling.

There was also the sticky matter of signal standards, which were still needed so that any receiver would be able to receive any broadcast. While the FCC was charged by law with the legal responsibility for setting such standards, the commission was unwilling to take the task entirely upon its own shoulders, and so turned to the Radio Manufacturers Association (RMA) to form a committee.

The RMA was an organization formed to represent the mutual interests of such companies as Philco, General Electric, RCA, Hazeltine, and Farnsworth. Each of these companies was invited to name a member to the panel, and Phil agreed to represent Farnsworth. Of course, RCA was not only one of the largest members of the RMA, it also held considerable influence over all the others by virtue of its patent monopoly, so Phil feared that the committee would recommend whatever standards RCA dictated. After the first few meetings, Phil made clear his position of complete cooperation and then appointed his chief assistant to take his place.

Phil, becoming very depressed, came home from the last meeting he attended sick at heart.

"Pem," he said, "you know how hard my men and I have worked to keep ahead of the pack. What has it bought us? True, anyone entering the television race will have to take a license under our patents, but my first patents have only seven more years before they become public property. We both know that, barring a miracle, we're facing a second World War, and this may go on for many years."

"Do you really think Hitler is big enough to take on the whole world?"

"No, but I wouldn't be a bit surprised to see Mussolini join up with him. Together, they might have a chance to do just that. In any case, since my patents are open to my competitors for study, they are really going to town. Of course I knew this would happen; that's why I've been pushing so hard for commercial television."

"Yes, Phil, but you've been constantly improving your system and filing new patents."

"Even so, our most controlling patents will expire by 1954. Sanford Essig, who came to us from RCA, brought me a brochure RCA put together, showing each of our patents and their dates of expiration. All they have to do is hold commercial television off until my patents expire, and we will not collect a single royalty check."

As Phil had predicted, by the time television standards were agreed upon and submitted to the FCC, Washington had decided there was too much danger of war to launch a new industry such as television. The White House had other plans for the manpower and expertise of the industry, to say nothing of the dollars saved, which could buy war bonds instead of TV receivers.

Phil's health began failing rapidly after that. One day he came home looking really ill.

"Pem, I just can't go on like this. I guess I've trained my brain too well; now I have a hard time turning it off. I think I'm going crazy."

"Phil, honey, you can't be serious! So that's what has been driving you to have several highballs every night! I knew something was eating you."

"I'm deadly serious, Pem; it's come to the point of choosing whether I want to be a drunk or go crazy."

"Now wait a minute, Phil. Let's get medical help. There must be someone here who can help you."

"Oh, they're no help. It's unlikely that Fort Wayne will have better doctors than those we found in Philadelphia, and you must remember their advice. 'Why not take up smoking? A finger-habit may soothe your nerves.' Well, I did. Now I'm even worse off than before."

"That was bad advice, honey, but we can't give up. Let's try again. I'll talk to some of the old-timers at the plant and get a recommendation."

Phil had good reason to be disenchanted with the medical profession. He had gone to several highly recommended doctors in Philadelphia, ending up with the psychiatrist who had advised him to smoke. Had they known then what they do now about treating depression, they could have saved us both years of pain and anguish.

As it was, Phil spent less and less time at the plant, until he finally called Mr. Nicholas and told him he was taking a few weeks off. Then he drank—not only in the evening, but all day long. This went on for some time. Then in an effort to show him what he was doing to himself and our family, I threatened to leave and take the boys unless he would agree to try again for medical help. Faced with this ultimatum, Phil agreed to see a doctor, but only if the doctor would come to see him.

A doctor was recommended and agreed to come to the house. He gave Phil a prescription for an elixir which he said would give him the relief he needed. This worked very well for a few days; then Phil doubled the dose and just stayed in bed, refusing to eat. Frantic, I called the doctor. He said the medication he had prescribed was harmless and non habit-forming, and he thought Phil really needed several weeks of complete rest. I agreed with that, so this went on for three weeks.

When I tried to pull Phil out of this state, he wouldn't respond. He was uncommunicative, talking to me only when necessary, mostly to refuse food, and would walk only so far as the bathroom adjoining our bedroom and back to bed. Otherwise, he just slept. I called his doctor again, who told me to cut down on the medication. This was more easily said than done. Phil was now dependent on the stuff, and the situation was more than I could handle alone.

I was trying to keep the family and the house going and at the same time act as Phil's nurse twenty-four hours a day. Philo, though only eleven, was very helpful. He set his alarm, prepared his own breakfast and school lunch, and never missed the school bus which passed by our gate. This gave me enough rest to keep me going. Skee was not yet in school, but was very good at entertaining himself. One morning I found him sitting up straight and stiff in his bed. Alarmed, I asked what was the matter. Not moving his head, he looked down at his arm. Following his gaze, I saw a movement under his pajama sleeve. Then I knew.

"Honey, have you been playing with Philo's white mice again?" At his slight nod, I cupped one hand over the moving sleeve and reached under and rescued the mouse and put it back in the cage.

"Where is the other mouse, dear?" He still had not moved.

"It's in my bed, Mommy, and I don't dare move; I might smash it."

A careful inspection of the covers revealed no mouse. On an impulse, I reached cautiously under the pillow. Sure enough, Mr. Mouse had found a peaceful place for a snooze.

With both mice back in the cage, my chastened son breathed a sigh of relief, and said, "But Mommy, they are so cute and soft." I told him he could have a pet of his very own that he could play with, but he shouldn't let Philo's mice out again. They were so small they might get lost.

Like the mouse under the pillow, Phil had found a haven from his tortured mind in his medication. We were all very concerned. Mr. Nicholas called frequently from the plant to see how Phil was doing. When Hugh Knowlton heard about it, he came out from New York, and he, Mr. Nicholas, and Ed Martin came to see Phil.

Obviously, Phil was badly in need of medical attention. Hugh Knowlton suggested a famous physician friend of his in Boston who would make sure we had the best possible medical help. When the doctor agreed to see Phil, Cliff and Lola offered to take care of our boys while we went to Boston.

Now all I had to do was get Phil out of bed and all the way to Boston. Knowing I could depend on him, I called on big, gentle Tom Cosgrove to help me get Phil on a train and to Boston. Phil had given Tom work at the plant after Tom's wife had been killed in an automobile crash in Maine and their daughter Ann seriously injured. After the accident, we had brought Ann to our home, where she was nursed back to health. Phil had also taught thirteen-year-old Tom, Jr., to use our new John Deere tractor and given him the job of plowing up a field for planting. Tom senior, always helpful, was more than happy to do anything he could to assist us.

Phil had lost twenty of his sparse one hundred and twenty-five pounds, and Tom carried him tenderly, like a baby. In Boston, we were welcomed at the Peter Bent Brigham Hospital. The elixir Phil had been taking was chloral hydrate—a highly addictive potion. He remembered nothing that had happened after the first week of using it. After a week in the hospital, Phil began to respond to the treatment he was getting, but as he gained strength, he decided he would make better progress at our place in Maine. After three more weeks, he could stand it no longer. He arranged with his physician to take his male nurse with us up to our place in Brownfield. This nurse suggested taking his wife along to do the cooking for their room and board. When we told them the conditions at our place in Maine were, to say the least, rustic, they said that sounded like fun, and so it was.

They stayed with us for several weeks, after which time Phil's doctor released him, but arrangements were made for me to bring Phil for monthly checkups to the doctor's vacation home on Lake Winnipesaukee, in New Hampshire, about fifty miles southwest of our place. We kept up this schedule all summer. However, Phil's dream of seeing television through to its commercial conclusion, the quest that had occupied him for almost twenty years, had burst like a bubble, leaving him in a deep depression. He seldom talked about it, but I knew it was eating at him.

Upon our arrival in Maine, we discovered that the large old barn had blown down in a recent hurricane, and the lovely old weathered boards and timbers had been mostly hauled away by enterprising townsfolk, since weathered boards were becoming fashionable.

The pheasants, now half grown, had found the fresh wood of the new windows to their liking and had pecked away extensively at the frames. We drew up plans for a pheasant house and run, which local carpenters and Tom Cosgrove soon had ready for occupancy.

We all loved this place. We called it Fernworth Farm, because of the shoulder-high ferns growing there and also because of a legend. One family historian found some indication that the family had descended from one of two brothers who came to England from Fernworth Castle in Scotland, anglicizing the name to Farnworth, since the two countries were even then at loggerheads with each other. The "s" was added by one branch of the family after Joseph and Matthias came to America in the early 1600s. Phil's ancestor Matthias and his family appear in the earliest Groton, Massachusetts, records as founders of the town.

Be that as it may, at Fernworth Farm we found peace and tranquility. Phil bought a guide's model canoe, and we spent many hours paddling around on our pond or tramping in the woods looking for berries or wild flowers. The blueberries growing everywhere were a particular treat.

Philo loved to read, and he became enchanted with comic books. For a while he was spending his whole allowance on them. Phil offered to buy any books Philo wanted, if he would read them instead of the comics. Philo took him up on it. He first ordered a set of encyclopedias, which he read like story books. Then he became interested in the snakes, frogs, and turtles he found on the place, so he ordered an advanced treatise on herpetology, the study of cold-blooded animals.

We had given Philo a registered cocker spaniel which he named Count Noah of Fernworth. About a year later he purchased a female which he registered as Soma Countess of Fernworth. The next thing we knew, he was a card-carrying member of the American Kennel Club and in the dog raising business. No one suspected that the carefully composed letters painfully pecked out on my typewriter had been written by a thirteen-year-old boy.

Pem and Phil with Count Noah of Fernworth. Photo by Philo III.

We owned several good cameras and a well equipped darkroom which Phil and I used. Philo ordered a book on photography and soon was outdoing both of us.

In answer to his query, *National Geographic Magazine* invited him to submit an illustrated article on "cold blooded animals of the eastern seaboard." Unfortunately, *Nature Magazine* came out with a similar article before Philo's was ready, so he wrote *National Geographic* that he didn't think it was the right time to submit his work.

It was necessary to supervise closely five-year-old Skee's activities, because he loved the woods, and there was too much danger of him getting lost. Our neighborhood was mostly populated with deer, bobcat, bear, and fox. I learned after he was grown that he had seized every opportunity to slip away for short excursions into the woods with Philo's dog Count. Count was good protection. When we took him with us, he scouted the area ahead so thoroughly we never saw a wild creature. Phil saw to it that we all made a habit of carrying a compass, a knife, a water canteen, and a trail snack when setting off on a jaunt.

Both boys were interested in music. Harry James on the trumpet was Philo's idol. Before long he was taking the bus once a week to Portland—fifty miles away—for trumpet lessons. Skee was already composing simple melodies on the piano. He wanted to play the violin like his daddy, so Phil bought him a child-sized violin, but then became too busy to teach him, so Skee lost interest in that.

As Phil had predicted, he soon received the official word from Washington that licenses for commercial television broadcasting would be indefinitely postponed. He then began to make plans for shifting the center of his activity from Fort Wayne to Maine. Feeling he had to put television behind him, he entered into a frenzy of activity. He decided he would build his own lab and go on with what he did best, inventing. He had a number of ideas that had of necessity been put on a back burner, but first we needed a new wing on the house. So we sat down and designed it.

Phil's brother Carl, who was recovering from a bout with tuberculosis, had just been released from the sanatorium and, hearing of Phil's condition, came up to help. The previous year, Phil had marked off the dimensions (15 X 28 feet) for a swimming pool, to be placed under the new wing on a lower level. He now had two of our "boys," Charles Harmon and Donald York, excavate it with his John Deere tractor and a hand-operated farm scraper. While we designed the new wing, Carl took over the job of overseeing the finishing of the pool.

We extended the shed, which was now to be our living room, and added a new wing. In the new wing at the front of the house was a large master bedroom. I insisted on plenty of closet space, so we had our separate closets, plus one for out-of-season clothes, all cedar-lined. We had a fireplace, with a wood box in the window seat that could be filled from outside the house. Next to the bedroom was a large bathroom, with separate tub and shower. On the second floor, this room and bath were duplicated for guests, even down to the fireplace, but it had to wait its turn in our plans for its finishing touches. Outside our bedroom door was the door leading down to the pool.

The remainder of the wing was Phil's study. This was raised three feet to allow for diving room at the deep end of the pool below. At the end of this room was a 6 X 10 foot plate glass picture window, giving a beautiful view of our pond, miles of woods, and in the distance, the picturesque Chicorua Mountains of New Hampshire. There were two windows on each side of the room. At the end opposite the picture window was a large fireplace, faced from floor to ceiling with three shades of polished granite from a nearby quarry, a masterpiece by an artist in this craft. This wing and the living room were paneled in knotty pine, to fit in with the aged beams of the living room.

By the time this was completed, Phil had his lab plans ready, and the building crew started with that. This was a three-story building twenty by thirty-five feet, ten feet south of the new wing. Phil installed a large

Timken oil-fueled furnace with three circulators, one for the house, one for the pool, and one for the lab. On the side of the lab toward the house was a small enclosure for the large cylinders of oxygen, helium, and hydrogen which were piped up to the glassblowing room on the second floor, for making vacuum tubes.

One day, old Dan came to visit Phil. Old dog Prince, his best friend, had died, and he was very sad. He wanted Phil to make a headstone with about a fifteen-word epitaph engraved on it for the dog's grave. Phil came to me. I told them I would make the form in wood so it could be cast in cement, but the epitaph had to be shorter. We ended up with: "TO MY BEST FRIEND, PRINCE" and the date. When it was finished, Phil cast it in very fine-grained cement. Dan was very pleased with it.

After that, Old Dan was indeed a sorry figure. One day he stopped by in his black buggy and asked Phil if he would take him to South Paris, the County Seat, about thirty miles away. He said he had been there once as a youth, and wanted to see it again before he died. Carl heard this, and knowing Phil was quite busy, offered to take Dan. They visited several towns in the area while they were at it. It had been many years since Dan had been farther than the town of Brownfield, only five miles away. This was not unusual in the older generation of Brownfield, who still existed in the horse-and-buggy days.

Not long after this, Dan asked Phil if he would buy his eighty-acre farm, which adjoined our land. Fred Doane, who had been our caretaker last winter, and his wife had offered to give Dan a home for the rest of his life, if he sold his farm so he could pay for his keep. Phil and Dan agreed on a price, and Phil sold some Farnsworth Television stock to buy the farm. My father gladly accepted the opportunity to come and run the farm and stock it with animals. Carl bought an abandoned house on twelve acres about a half mile on down the road and rehabilitated it so he could bring Vady and their two children from California.

Carl was unsuccessful in his attempts to drill for water, and Vady found Maine to be just a little too rustic, so Carl took his family back to California. That winter, their baby, little Carl Wendy, became gravely ill with meningitis, which left him totally deaf. This was a hard blow to all of us, but devastating to Carl and Vady. Phil and I felt they were very fortunate that at least their darling baby was allowed to live.

By now Phil's predictions of war had begun to come true. Germany invaded Poland one week after signing a mutual nonaggression pact with Soviet Russia, and Great Britain and France declared war on Germany as part of their alliance with Poland. There were also major political changes in Spain and other European nations.

Hostilities began one week after the August 23rd signing of a mutual nonaggression pact between Nazi Germany and Soviet Russia. German troops and aircraft attacked Poland on September 1st.

September 3rd, a German U-boat sank the British ship *Athenia* off the Irish coast. Soviet troops invaded Poland from the east on September 17th. Warsaw surrendered to the Germans on September 28th, and that day Poland was divided between Hitler and Mussollini. Then the women and children were evacuated from London, which was being unmercifully bombed by Hitler. All this happened within the one infamous month of September 1939.

The United States economy, having suffered a decline in 1938, was now booming, due to orders for arms and war equipment from England and France. When the United States entered the war after the Japanese bombed Pearl Harbor, President Franklin Delano Roosevelt created many agencies for domestic controls. Everything was rationed, from food and shoes to anything made of steel or rubber. All armed service reserves were called to active duty.

Don Lippincott, who was in the signal corps reserve, was called to active duty, given a commission, and put in charge of the patent department for the armed forces. His superiors scoffed when he suggested getting the television industry to pool their patents for the duration of the war for use of the armed forces. To get this dog-eat-dog industry to agree to such a proposition looked to them impossible. However, Don obtained their approval to at least let him try.

Don and his wife Ruth spent several days with us in Maine. Phil agreed to take the idea to the Farnsworth Board of Directors. With their approval, Don then confronted David Sarnoff with the idea. When Mr. Sarnoff heard that the Farnsworth Company had agreed, he went along. After that it was no problem to get the other companies to agree. For this major achievement, Don was advanced to the status of colonel, and David Sarnoff was advanced to the rank of general.

With the war dominating all the headlines and work in Fort Wayne at a temporary standstill, Phil saw no reason to plan on returning to Fort Wayne anytime soon. Besides, we were now quite comfortable on our New England homestead, and so decided to settle in for the duration.

CHAPTER 24

Boxes for Bullets

The world that Philo Farnsworth walked away from in 1940 was very different from the world he had walked into when we left Utah back in 1926.

For twenty years Phil had devoted himself to understanding and mastering the electron, which forms the outer layers of the basic building block of matter, the atom. At the same time, other scientists around the world had focused their attention on the inner layer of the atom, the nucleus, and were beginning to unlock the awesome power concealed in Einstein's simple formula $E=mc^2$. As the war in Europe spread, the American scientific community grew concerned that Hitler had engaged his own physicists to deliver the power of the atom in the form of a bomb, so work along similar lines in the United States took on new urgency.

With his new lab in Maine, Phil found he had the time to explore some of the deeper mysteries that had appeared during his television work, which he had not had time or resources to explore.

Chief among these was a phenomenon he had observed in 1936, while experimenting with one of his multipactor tubes. At the time, Phil had built a special version of this tube, to see what effect a spherical configuration would have on the tube's performance. What he saw greatly exceeded his expectations; in the middle of the tube he observed an eery, star-like blue glow, which he was at a loss to explain. He resolved at the time that one day he would determine its cause, but the pressing responsibilities of refining television prevented him from doing so. Still, this unexplained specter had always bothered him, and now he had the time to investigate it.

I arranged for our Fort Wayne house to be closed and our furniture shipped to Maine. With our new wing and a heated swimming pool, we were quite comfortable. The Farnsworth Company offered to pay for part of the cost of Phil's lab operations and furnish him with three men. Phil chose Cliff Gardner, Harold Bernhardt, and George Huffnagle. Cliff sold some of his Farnsworth stock and purchased a home down on the main road about a mile from us. Harold and George settled in Fryeburg. Phil got them busy with some special tubes.

Phil had Cliff build a special klystron-type tube which embodied his invention of electron bunching. He had to discover the secret of that mysterious blue glow in his spherical electron-multiplier tube experiment. When this tube produced the same blue glow, Phil was even more puzzled. He resolved to pursue this phenomenon further. However, he was diverted by requests for special tubes from the Pentagon in Washington.

Skee, now five, loved his uncle Cliff, and was delighted when allowed to watch the men work. The dangers in the lab were very real, and the first rule was that Skee had to stay on the stool. The oxygen torches used in making the tubes held a fascination for him, and he would sit quietly for long periods of time watching Uncle Cliff do his wonderful manipulations with glass. Cliff would lift him up to a high lab stool and as he worked ask him questions about the safety rules he had to keep in order to be in the lab. There was usually a certain amount of kidding and foolishness involved. One day as Skee was lifted up on the stool he said, "Now let's not talk; just work." Cliff liked to hear "Skeezy's" wise comebacks. This had long since been a way for Cliff to tease him, and Skeezix had called him on it.

Russell (Skeezix) was becoming known for his sage remarks. He was three when my father first came to stay with us, and he loved to climb on Grandpa's knee and hear his wonderful stories and songs. These sessions would always start with, "Skeezix, whose boy are you?" The answer was always diplomatic, "Your boy, Grandpa." Then his daddy would come home and lift him in the air and ask, "Whose boy are you?" The answer was "Your boy, Daddy." This went on for a time. Then one day, my Dad asked, "Now Skeezix, for sure, whose boy are you?" Russell was silent for a moment, then said, "Ah phooey! Nothin's for sure!" He never had to make that choice again.

One day, Skeezix had a bad earache. None of our usual remedies gave him any relief. I called our neighborhood physician, Doctor Kenneth Dore, who examined Skee and told us the infection had spread to the mastoid; and immediate surgery was necessary. When Philo heard this, he turned pale and ran into the next room. I found him hitting his forehead against the wall, as though to relieve his anguish. When I hugged him and assured him that Skeezix would be all right, he said, "But that's what you thought about Kenny." Kenny died when Philo was only three, and since he had never mentioned Kenny, I thought he hadn't remembered him. He had kept this locked up inside, all this time.

Dr. Dore took Russell and me to Portland, where his diagnosis was confirmed. The next morning Russell had a mastoidectomy. It turned into a very touchy situation, because it was so near the brain casing. Russell was such a sweet, brave little boy, he won the hearts of everyone at the hospital. Even when he was told he was not to swim for six months and then only with ear plugs and nose clip, he bore up well, though he loved the water.

I had an experience with Russell one day that clearly depicted his developing character. He and I were on a bus coming home from delivering our car for servicing in Portland, when we ran into a violent electrical storm. Lightning was striking all around us. When it struck a tree which almost fell on the bus, the driver found an open place and parked the bus to wait out the storm. Several teenage girls on the bus were screaming hysterically. Suddenly, five-year-old Russell stood up in the aisle and started to sing "Praymates, come out and pray with me, we'll climb my apple tree . . ." and so to the end (he had trouble with "L"s). After the first phrase, there was a sudden hush in the bus . . . only Russell's firm but childish voice could be heard, plainly audible between claps of thunder, through the ferocious storm around us. When he finished, everyone applauded and asked for more. He sang several more songs, and by that time the storm had abated sufficiently that we could proceed. When we left the bus at our road, the driver said, "Young man, if I had a medal, I'd pin it on you." Russell walked proud and tall all the way home.

With the bombing of Pearl Harbor, December 2nd, 1942, Phil's worst fears were confirmed and he warned me, "Pem, this will be a long and difficult war. I think we should make ourselves as self-sufficient as possible. I'm going to buy more cows, some registered sheep, and pigs. We'll want chickens for eating and for eggs, and I'd like to try raising guinea hens. They're much better eating than chickens, almost as good as pheasant, but after raising pheasants I wouldn't eat one now. Next year we should plant a large vegetable garden. I'm sure Zeline (McAllister, our housekeeper and cook) will bottle any surplus, after we share with friends and family." That Christmas we bought savings bonds for all our gifts.

Dr. Thomas H. Johnson, chief physicist at the Aberdeen Proving Grounds in Maryland, and his wife Ann had acquired a summer home in the nearby town of Denmark. One day Tom called Phil to ask if he might bring Dr. David Webster, professor of physics at Stanford University, for a visit. Dr. Webster had flown his small plane all the way from California. He wanted to recruit Phil to help on an important government research project in Chicago. Phil wanted to know more about the project, but Dr. Webster was either unwilling or unable to say any more, so Phil declined the invitation. After Dr. Webster left, Phil confided his misgivings to me: he suspected the military was fast at work building an atomic bomb. Phil was very interested in unleashing the power of the atom, but he had no interest in building a bomb.

Meanwhile, back in the woods around our property, we found white and black birch, maple, and other hardwood trees. Phil decided to set up his own portable sawmill and make our own lumber to build furniture and built-in cabinets. The black birch he wanted for flooring in our dining room. We located and purchased a used mill and had it set up on our Frost Mountain lot. This was a recently acquired eighty-acre wood lot adjacent to our place.

Word came to us that the War Production Board (WPB) was looking for C-select lumber for boxes in which to ship ammunition overseas. The owner of the Fryeburg Box Shop was planning to buy the two-thousand-acre wood lot across the road from our land and slash cut it. Phil hit the ceiling.

"If he does that, I'll move out. That's one of our best views. I'll buy his box shop . . . and the lot, so it can be selectively cut." Phil bought the box shop, the 2,000 acres, and several more lots surrounding our place. Then he wrote to Carl asking if he would come to Maine and help run the operation for him. Carl suggested that Lincoln also come to Maine.

They talked it over with their wives and finally decided to come. We formed the Farnsworth Wood Products Company, with Phil as president, Carl and Lincoln as vice presidents, and me as secretary/treasurer. The operation was largely in their hands. Carl and Lincoln soon had things up and running, being already familiar with the lumber business through working with Agnes's husband, Claude Lindsay, one of the Bay Area's most successful real estate developers. Within a few months, they were shipping two railroad box cars full of cut boards for boxes (box shook) for the War Production Board every week.

Carl W. Farnsworth, vice president of the Farnsworth Wood Products Company.

For a while, having his brothers near was a big boost for Phil's spirits, but now the Farnsworth Television and Radio Corporation asked Phil and his men to return to Fort Wayne. Phil declined, so the company withdrew its support of his lab. They insisted upon keeping Phil on inactive staff—at a very small stipend. Cliff and Harold Bernhardt refused to go back without Phil and turned in their resignations. Phil could not afford to pay them a living wage, so Cliff went to work for Raytheon as head of their tube department, and Harold and his wife Carol went to Cambridge, Massachusetts, where Harold worked in research at MIT. George and Bernice Huffnagle went back to Fort Wayne, vowing to come back to Fryeburg as soon as they could. To lose Cliff after all their years of working together was hard for Phil, and he was not doing so well. His depression, always with him, was taking its toll, and he began to drink again. Nothing he did seemed to compensate for the dashing of his big television dream.

While we were in Fort Wayne, I had given Phil a Novachord for Christmas. This was one of the first electronic synthesizers, and the 240-tube keyboard instrument was a joy to play. The Novachord was in the living room, on the other side of the wall from Phil's bed. At night, I often played to him for hours to help him relax and go to sleep. He also liked to have me read to him. We read a lot of poetry in those days. Later, we got into science fiction. However, nothing I did seemed to help at all with his drinking. He seemed bent on self-destruction.

Doctor Dore and I tried repeatedly to persuade him to go to Maine General Hospital in Portland. But he was adamant. It was also almost impossible to get him to eat, although Zeline was one of the best cooks in all of New England.

This was a very hard time for the boys and me. Phil was bed-ridden and required most of my attention. I was very grateful for the help of my dad and Zeline. One day, Dr. Dore came on his usual rounds, and after one look at Phil, told me to help get a robe and slippers on him; we could not let this go on another day. We were taking him to the hospital right now. Phil objected, but was too weak to make much resistance when Dr. Dore carried him to his car.

At Maine General, the doctors asked why we had waited so long. Dr. Dore told them they didn't know this man; he did pretty much what he wanted to do. A specialist was brought in. Phil had been sedated at this point, and they thought he was sleeping. The specialist said he had a very bad case of peripheral neuritis in his feet, and he would never walk again.

As through a fog, Phil heard this, and it aroused his fighting spirit. He told me about it later and said, "That's what they think. I'll show them."

Eating was Phil's biggest problem. Dr. Dore knew just the nurse we needed, and luckily he was able to get Letitia Getchell off the case she was on, so she could help us. Nothing on the hospital menu interested Phil. To Letitia's question of what he thought he could eat, he said he would try to eat a not-too-thick tenderloin steak . . . if it were rare. With the doctor's permission, I brought an electric broiler and some tenderloin steaks to Phil's room in the hospital. I think just smelling the cooking steak probably did much for his appetite. In any case, he ate the steak and even some of the food from his hospital tray. Once again he was on an upward path.

The next day we cooked another steak. While it was cooking, we had a visit from the head housekeeper. She was horrified to see us cooking in the room, but Letitia told her to go see Dr. Hawkes. This was his patient, and we had been given special permission. The lady said she would do that, but in the meantime, we should keep the door closed and open the window; we were smelling up the entire floor. Cooking with the window open brought us no more complaints, and Phil began to gain strength. Even so, it was four weeks before he was able to go home—with a wheel chair and Letitia, who stayed two days to make sure everything was going well.

Now Phil planned his own therapy. With my help he could get the wheel chair to the pool stairs door. Then he would go down the spiral staircase on his buttocks, using his arms to let him down step by step, and slip into the pool. He couldn't have designed the pool better for his needs. The heating came from pipes recessed in the walls of the pool about eighteen inches from the surface of the water. This kept the top of the water quite warm. Phil just floated around in the almost hot water for an hour every morning and evening, but to put his weight on his feet caused him excruciating pain.

Seeing his determination to get rid of "that blasted wheel chair," Dr. Dore told him he could give him something, but anything strong enough to allow him to walk would be habit-forming. He thought pantipon would be the least troublesome drug to use. He gave Phil a dose of it, and after a few minutes, told him to try putting his weight on his feet. Phil was delighted. We had brought crutches from the hospital, and he found he could take a few steps, taking most of his weight on his arms. He never used the wheel chair again, and after a few weeks, he threw the crutches away. By now he was swimming as well as floating in the pool. I swam with him, and again it began to feel like old times.

When Phil threw his crutches away, we had a big swimming party to celebrate. We invited Carl, Vady, Lincoln, Iris, and many friends, including Dr. Ken Dore and his wife Dorothy. Zeline made sandwiches and her fabulous lemon meringue pie from my special home-grown lemon. Of all the blossoms produced by my dwarf lemon tree, only three set fruit. I had picked two and left the third to see how large it would grow. I thought it might weigh as much as a pound, and to put it on record, I had it weighed by my butcher in Fryeburg. It tipped the scales at thirteen ounces, which I thought must have been some kind of a record. Then I gave it to Zeline for the lemon pies.

After everyone was tired of swimming and full of food, we sat around and listened to Dorothy Dore play the piano. She was an accomplished pianist, and it was a delightful way to end a marvelous party. There was some dancing to records later, but Phil and I would never again dance in public. Phil said he didn't trust his balance, but later we danced to records at home. At the time he was still depending on pantipon in order to walk at all.

Phil hired Stephen Bukata, a very versatile engineer, to carry on some work in the lab. Phil was now financing his lab through sales of his Farnsworth Television & Radio Corporation stock, since Stephen's salary far exceeded his own.

During the war we had tight rationing on food, shoes, and almost anything essential. Phil had seen this coming and was able to furnish our woodcutters with beef and pork from our farm, as well as butter and eggs. The War Production Board gave Phil a AAAA rating because of the special tubes he was building for the Pentagon and the boxes for bullets.

One winter morning I was driving the boys to school in our Cadillac in a freezing rain, which made the frozen ruts on the road treacherous. We had just recovered from one scary spin, skidding a full circle, so I was just creeping along and worrying about what lay ahead. We were on a down grade, which ended in a sharp turn up and over the railroad tracks. As we came to the down grade, we were barely moving, but the car started gaining momentum. The brakes were useless. I could see we were in for trouble, and told the boys to hold on tight; there were no seat belts then. At the bottom of the grade I was unable to make the turn and rolled the car, the top landing on the guard rail and throwing the car on its other side.

This was one time I would have given anything for manually operated windows. We were shut up tight and being suffocated by battery acid. Philo was on the bottom, and I hadn't the strength to push the heavy door up and open. About that time, Roger Dunn, a lumber man from Brownfield, pulled the door up and said the most welcome words I ever heard: "Can I help you?"

Mr. Dunn helped us out of the car. Although we were very shaken, our only physical injury was a small bump on Russell's head where he had hit the "on" button of the car radio. We were driven on to Fryeburg to Carl and Vady's home. Carl said he was taking us home, but I was to drive. I could not believe it! I was shaking like a leaf.

"I know it's strong medicine, Pem, but it's good medicine for you right now." I drove home and continued to drive the boys to school all that winter, even though it took all the nerve I could muster. Several times when the roads were slick, I slipped into snow banks. If I were too late coming home from shopping, someone would come with a tractor to pull me out.

After I flipped the Cadillac, Phil called our dealer in Portland to order a new one.

"Are you serious, Mr. Farnsworth? Car manufacturers have not been permitted to build new cars. The steel is needed for war ships. I doubt if there is a single new Cadillac in all of New England. Anyway, there is a waiting list a mile long for any kind of a car."

"Well, my car has been wrecked, and I simply have to have a car up here. My 4-A rating should get one for me if there is one. Go beyond New England if you have to."

One Cadillac was found, in Boston. In due time, it was wrenched free of all the red tape and delivered at our door. Apropos of the times, it was gunmetal gray in color, fitting in nicely with the gray atmosphere of those war years.

The next fall Philo entered Fryeburg Academy and was living at one of the dorms. During the summer he become intrigued with making his own pipe bombs, which he had learned to make through studying chemistry. He was always careful to blow them up far from the house, so Phil and I were not aware of what he was doing.

One weekend he brought one of his dorm buddies (the son of a famous Maine poet) to visit. The boys took two of Philo's bombs down by the dam to set them off. Philo exploded one; then his friend wanted to light one. This one fouled up and just fizzled, sending out sparks, which started a fire in the dry grass. Since there was still danger of it exploding, Philo dared not approach it to stamp it out. They ran to the house and called the Fryeburg fire department, then took shovels and buckets to try to put the fire out.

It just so happened that Phil had chosen a spot near there to have his hardwood boards stacked to dry. When the boys returned, the fire had reached this cherished lumber. Skee and I were just returning from Fryeburg when the fire reached the "dud" bomb and exploded. We heard the blast and rushed to the scene just ahead of the fire truck, but by then it was too late to save much of Phil's hardwood. Philo was devastated. Seeing how pale and shaken he was, Phil decided he had been punished enough. We felt fortunate that he hadn't blown himself up by trying to save the lumber. Of course there were no more bombs, and we did save enough black birch for the dining room floor.

Philo shared his father's thirst for knowledge, and had been reading his father's technical journals. He had found his high school classes at Fryeburg Academy hopelessly outdated and boring to him. One day Phil received a call from the director of admissions of the Massachusetts Institute of Technology (MIT) in Cambridge saying he had a young man in his office wanting to enter the university. His name was Philo T. Farnsworth, Jr. Taken by surprise, Phil said he knew his son was bored with high school, but doubted he was yet ready for college, at least not a difficult engineering university such as MIT.

This gentleman said he had spent the last hour talking with Philo, and he seemed uncommonly advanced for his age. Further, he felt Philo should at least be given a chance to prove himself. If he could take a crash course at an approved college prep school and pass its examinations, he could be entered at MIT that fall. To everyone's surprise, Philo met these conditions and entered MIT . . . at age fifteen!

Phil could hear his sawmill going up on the mountain and was very anxious to see it in operation. A few days later he suggested we walk up there. I thought he was far too weak for such a jaunt, but he insisted. Stopping frequently to rest, we made our way up to the mill. As he was looking it over, he suddenly swayed as though he might faint. I put my arm around him to steady him, and he said he was having an unbearable pain in his groin.

Roscoe DuPlace, our bulldozer operator, had just dragged in some logs for the mill. His bulldozer was the only vehicle there. I asked Roscoe to take Phil to the house, but to be careful. Roscoe helped Phil onto the seat, and standing behind, he reached around Phil to the steering wheel. As they started down the hill, I heard Phil say, "Never mind being careful; just get me to the house . . . fast!" Roscoe took off, leveling everything in his path, with me running along behind, cringing every time they went over a bump.

By the time I reached the house, Phil had called Dr. Dore, who told him he probably had a strangulated hernia. He would be there in all haste to take Phil to Portland for an operation. He arrived with a driver, to allow him to take care of Phil in the back seat. He gave Phil a shot to help ease the pain, and they were off. I changed and followed them in our car. The road was paved, but narrow and bumpy, with many sharp twists and turns. Phil was in great pain when they arrived at the hospital.

Dr. Bramhall, the surgeon, was on his way to the operating room following a patient who was next on the operating schedule. When he saw Phil and heard his story, he told the nurse to prep him; the other patient was in no hurry. Dr. Dore, who witnessed the operation, told me later that when they began administering the anesthetic, Phil said, "Stop! What a relief; let me enjoy it a minute!" Dr. Bramhall told him nothing doing; he had other patients waiting. Phil, feeling guilty, said to proceed.

This operation prolonged Phil's recovery, and by the time he was on his feet again, he was thoroughly dependent on pantipon. He agreed with Dr. Dore that something had to be done about it. I accompanied them to an interview with Dr. Schlomer at his Baldpate Sanatorium near Topsfield, Massachusetts. Dr. Schlomer told us his treatment included some shock therapy. It was drastic, but very effective. After a thorough discussion about it, Phil decided the results would be worth it.

We arranged for one of the separate one-room cottages for Phil. I rented a room in Cambridge near Philo's dorm to be near both of them. This was a traumatic experience for all of us, and Baldpate was certainly a time we were all happy to put behind us.

As I drove Phil home a month later, Bing Crosby's voice came on the car radio singing, "Kiss me once, and kiss me twice, and kiss me once again; it's been a long, long, time."

"You can say that again," Phil said fervently. "We have a lot of time to make up for."

"Yes, we do, sweetheart," I agreed, "Bing should sing 'There'll be Some Changes Made' for us. After all this, we should have nothing but good times ahead. One thing certain is that you have to take it easy for a time and build yourself up."

"Let's take a cruise down through the Panama Canal and around to San Francisco," Phil suggested. This was a trip we had often talked about taking some day.

About a week later we took the train to New York City, not anticipating any difficulty in booking a cruise from there. We checked in at the Plaza Hotel as usual, only to find that civilian cruise ships were not allowed in the Panama Canal. They had been cancelled for the duration of the war. So we took in a couple of stage productions and returned to Brownfield. To take the place of a cruise, Phil made a suggestion.

"This might be a good time to take some flying lessons from Wiley Apt. Will you take lessons with me?"

"I'd rather you'd take Philo. He would love it."

"By all means, we'll take Philo, if he's home long enough, but I want you to have at least one lesson. You might just take to it," he said hopefully.

Wiley Apt ran a small airport in North Conway, eighteen miles northeast of us. Phil had hired him to fly us places in his Waco four-passenger cabin plane. He had flown us to Detroit when Phil received the Morris Leibman Memorial prize from the Institute of Radio Engineers. Actually, on that trip, he had turned the controls over to Phil, who flew us most of the way there.

Philo T. Farnsworth, left, father of electronic television, received the Morris Leibmann Memorial Prize for 1941 "for his contributions in the field of applied electronics" from Dr. F.E. Terman, president of the Institute of Radio Engineers.

Wiley had flown us also to New York for a Farnsworth Television & Radio Corporation director's meeting. In those days, few small planes were equipped with flight instruments. Wiley, a World War I fighter pilot, navigated by staying on navigational air beams and by using road maps. Geographical landmarks, such as rivers, lakes, and mountains were also a help.

One flying lesson was all I needed to prove that I would never make a good pilot. I told Phil he could be our air pilot, I would pilot our ground vehicles. Lincoln had taken flight training in California, and he now continued his training. Phil, Carl, and Lincoln's wife Iris all continued lessons. However, when the Farnsworth board of directors learned Phil was taking flying lessons, they said it was too risky. Phil was far too valuable to the company to be allowed to pilot a plane. Philo was able to make his first solo flight the next spring.

Carl and Lincoln bought land and made their own airport near Fryeburg. Then they bought a Luscomb and later two Cessnas and hired Joe Slovak, an accomplished pilot and airplane mechanic, to give them more lessons and to keep their planes in shape. Iris became a regular Amelia Earhart. After completing her requirements, she made her cross-country flight from Maine to Utah to take Vady and little Wendy to a special school for the deaf, then Vady returned with her. Carl and Lincoln found that flying saved them much time and money. Fryeburg was fifty miles from the nearest commercial airport, and there were only one train and one bus going to Portland daily. This left cars, but the roads were narrow, with many curves.

At one time, the entire boxshop was shut down because of a broken part. They were running on a tight schedule, and the nearest source for this part was one hundred and fifty miles away in Boston. Carl jumped into a plane and flew to Boston. Circling, he saw no airport near the city, so he brazenly set his small plane on the Boston Common near the river, hailed a cab, picked up his part, and left again before anyone was the wiser. At this time they were shipping three boxcars of box shook a week. Their only limitation was the lack of sufficient dry C-select lumber.

Throughout this time, Carl was having trouble keeping his woodcutters in line. The best men were French-Canadian, and they were a temperamental lot. Every payday they would head for the nearest bar and see how fast they could drink it up. On Monday, Carl would have to spend the entire morning rounding up his crew. Sometimes he would come up short and have to find new men to hire.

Zeline was also French-Canadian; her mother was a school teacher from France, and her father was a Canadian Indian. Zeline was a very special person and wise in many ways. She suggested we build a cook shack and hire a good cook, such as her cousin, who had cooked in hotels and resorts. This worked like magic. Carl now was able to hire the cream of the crop . . . and keep them. This new cook invited the three Farnsworth brothers and their wives for Sunday dinner. That was one of the most delicious steak dinners I had ever eaten, from the fruit cup to pie.

Many of our young men from the town went to fight in France. Many doctors were also called. When Dr. Dore got his draft papers, Phil called the draft board and told them if they took Dr. Dore, he would close down Farnsworth Wood Products. It was a hazardous business, and Dr. Dore was the only accredited medical man there.

Dr. Dore was excused, but now had an area with a radius of thirty miles to serve, and many of his patients were elderly, bedridden people requiring house visits. To handle this load, he and a friend bought a small plane, and Joe Slovak taught them to fly it. In the winter, they put skis on it, so they could land in a handy field anywhere. This was a big help and probably saved his life as well. On every emergency, he risked life and limb to get there, and those roads were not made for fast travel.

In the winter of 1944, Russell, now nine years old, was attending Eaglebrook Academy at Deerfield, Massachusetts, but he was very unhappy there. Phil had told him if he would stick it out for one year, it would be his choice whether he continued with it. The rules at Eaglebrook included no trips home during the first four weeks of indoctrination, with one exception: those students who earned two "A"s or better were allowed a weekend at home after two weeks. Russell was so determined to earn this weekend leave that he earned three "A"s, and all of his marks were high. He was allowed to call home with the news, and told me to meet him at the Boston train station. When I assured him I would be there, he said to be sure to wear old clothes he would recognize. He was afraid after those two long weeks he might not recognize me.

After that he was allowed every other weekend home, provided he kept his marks high. He never missed, and due to the transportation difficulties from Brownfield, we usually sent Joe Slovak to get him in a plane.

The next spring Phil and I went to Eaglebrook for graduation exercises. We had arranged for Russell to take piano lessons while he had the opportunity, so he was to play in the piano recital. He played one of his dad's favorite Chopin selections beautifully, and we were very proud of him. After the recital, his music teacher came to us almost in tears. She said she had just found out that Russell could hardly read a note of music. He had requested her to play his lessons so he would know how they should sound. She was very pleased that he had done so well until she found out he had memorized the pieces as she played, not bothering with the notes.

Skiing was a big thing at Eaglebrook. Philo was on the slopes at every opportunity, had taken Russell with him several times to the ski resort in North Conway, in the White Mountains of New Hampshire. When Eaglebrook had its big ski meet, Russell had looked at the carefully laid-out slalom trails for beginners and thought they were very childish. He took off and shushed straight down the mountain, stopping at the feet of the judges, who were obviously very impressed. Russell was given a first-prize ribbon for his performance and at the same time a mild reprimand for not following the rules. We were not surprised when Russell elected not to return to Eaglebrook. He later told us one of the reasons.

It seems the sons of many rich and famous people attended Eaglebrook, and one of these was the son of Frederick March, a well-known stage and movie actor. This boy said his parents only sent him to Eaglebrook to get rid of him, and perhaps this resentful feeling landed him often in trouble. Once when Skee stood up for this boy, but refused to tell who was responsible, he was punished along with the boy. They were required to kneel and hold their arms extended shoulder level for hours. Skee thought this very unfair, and decided to go A.W.O.L. He began hoarding food to this end. Fortunately, by the time he had enough food, he had thought better of it.

The next August (1945) saw the end of World War II, after the United

States dropped two Atomic Bombs on Japan, a sequence of events that plunged all mankind into an era of lost innocence.

It must have been about this time that I first heard Phil use the word "fusion." As he explained it to me, there are basically two ways to release the energy that binds atomic nuclei. In developing the atomic bomb, science had mastered a process called "fission," which splits the nucleus of heavy atoms such as uranium into lighter elements with an attendant release of energy.

Even as the bomb was being developed, scientists were busy devising a means to release this power in a less explosive manner, to harness this energy for more useful purposes. Fission is the process at the heart of every nuclear reactor in use around the world today. But fission is a risky proposition. The fuels involved are radioactive and highly toxic, and the waste products are even more so. The structure of the reactors is such that all the fuel is present within the reactor at once, creating the ever-present danger of a catastrophic accident.

Since the dawn of atomic theory, science has known that it might also be possible to release atomic energy by means of another type of reaction called fusion, which is the same process that powers our sun and all the stars in the universe. Fusion involves the binding, or fusing, of light nuclei, such as hydrogen, into a heavier atom, such as helium. Because the mass of the new helium nucleus is less than the mass of the two hydrogen nuclei which preceded, the difference is given off as energy, in a quantity expressed by Einstein's formula $E=mc^2$.

As is so often the case in the course of human history, mankind first learned how to harness these awesome forces in the form of weaponry. As fission is the process behind the atomic bomb, so fusion is the process behind the hydrogen bomb. But fusing atoms is much more difficult than splitting them.

Because the nuclei to be fused share the same electrical charge, their natural tendency is to repel each other rather than combine. This repulsion can be overcome only by heating the nuclei to extraordinary temperatures, like those found at the center of the sun. Scientists were able to trigger the hydrogen bomb only by building an atomic bomb around it, thus creating the conditions required to detonate the hydrogen fuel.

After development of the atomic bomb, it was only a matter of engineering to reduce the power of fission into a reactor that could produce domestic power. But harnessing the power of the hydrogen bomb into a useful reactor is an entirely different matter, and the problem is of a much higher magnitude.

Physicists have postulated since the 1930s that it might be possible to build a device that would harness fusion. If their speculation ever becomes reality, fusion could provide mankind with its ultimate source of energy. The hydrogen fuel that makes fusion possible exists in enormous abundance in the Earth's oceans; the reaction would be clean and safe and the by-products non-polluting. If the means can ever be found, mankind will literally be able to turn seawater into electricity.

But the problems inherent in producing fusion are extraordinary—a riddle of cosmic proportions. How does one create a container that can hold such extreme temperatures without melting the container? In short, how does one bottle a star?

This question has baffled scientists for over fifty years. The solution to the riddle of controlled fusion is the holy grail of modern science. Once achieved, it will alter the course of history and reform the condition of all mankind. It will, in short, be an achievement equivalent to the discovery of fire.

This is the quest that began to captivate the imagination of Phil Farnsworth at the end of World War II. Though he seldom spoke of it, the problem was very much on his mind. What was a mind-bending riddle to most scientists was precisely the sort of challenge that could stimulate the imagination of Philo T. Farnsworth. Phil thought of fusion in the same light as he had television twenty-five years earlier—as a difficult problem that he might be uniquely suited to solve.

CHAPTER 25

Forest Fire!

Having anticipated the end of the war, when box shook would no longer be needed, Carl and Lincoln were designing long laminated-arch beams to be used in structures such as airplane hangars. They also designed small two-bedroom homes to be prefabricated at the factory and assembled on the building site. For this operation they needed to stockpile various types of dry hardwood.

On September 8th, 1946 the brothers were returning in their plane from a lumber-buying trip to the southeastern states, when they spotted a violent storm ahead. They circled, looking for an emergency landing place. They found a farmer's field that looked suitable and circled again, looking for power poles to be sure there were no power or telephone lines in the way.

Carl, in the pilot seat, was making a smooth approach. Too late, they saw a power line directly ahead of the propeller. They struck this line and spun in, crashing the plane and snuffing the life from Carl instantly. They had not seen the power line because it had been run between two trees. Lincoln suffered a bad head wound, but mostly he suffered from the shock of seeing the lifeless, crumpled body of his beloved brother Carl.

The sudden and tragic death of Carl was a terrible shock to all of us, but especially to Vady and Phil's brothers. Lincoln and Carl had not only worked closely together the past few years but were married to sisters, their lives closely entwined. Phil and Carl were very much alike in both looks and temperament, and the bond of brotherly love between them was very strong. Carl's death struck Phil as a physical blow. He felt responsible, because he had influenced his brothers to come to Maine.

Lincoln made a heroic attempt to keep the Farnsworth Wood Products Company afloat. He had the help of two competent men, but they had a monumental job ahead of them. The WPB, having no further use for box shook, cancelled its orders. The lumber warehousing company and banks were calling in their loans, and there was no money to set the company up to manufacture the prefab houses and airplane hangar beams.

During the war, Phil had sold most of his Farnsworth Television & Radio stock to bolster the company and to finance his own lab and the two engineers he had working for him. His own payroll was over twice the small stipend we received from Farnsworth Television & Radio just to keep him on their rolls. He had also found it necessary to add a large machine shop to his lab, which was partly for the use of the boys for the Wood Products operation. All this and his medical expenses had reduced his stock holdings to almost nothing. The well was running dry. Phil told Lincoln to continue doing the best he could, and he, Phil, would be bound by his decisions. He would have to find another source of funds or close up shop.

All this stress was too much for Phil. He landed back in a Boston hospital under the care of Dr. Finesinger, a psychiatrist whom Phil had seen several times before. Dr. and Mrs. Finesinger had spent a weekend with us at Fernworth Farm. Phil was now advised to take a vacation and get away from his problems for a few weeks.

Phil, Skee, and I spent August of 1947 in a beach cottage at Cape Cod on the cool Massachusetts shore of the Atlantic. Philo was still in Cambridge, at MIT. Russell (Skee), soon to have his twelfth birthday, found friends on the beach.

One day toward the end of the month they were playing ball, when the ball rolled into some underbrush. Due to past experience with the poison ivy there, none of the boys would retrieve it. Skee not only went in after the ball, but to show his disdain for the timidity of the other boys, he took some of the ivy leaves and rubbed them all over his face and arms. This produced the proper amount of respect from the boys, but Skee was to pay dearly for this bravado.

That night Skee and I had little rest in our efforts to allay the horrible itching caused by the volatile resins left by the ivy. By morning Skee was one big blister. His face and hands were so swollen he was hardly recognizable. That ended this vacation. As I packed bags, Phil loaded the car. After stopping at the local druggist for calamine lotion, we headed for Boston and more serious treatment.

Since we had already decided to seek a more moderate climate for the coming winter, we leased a comfortably furnished house in Newton Center, near Boston, and registered Skee at the nearby junior high school. He was responding to treatment, and as soon as he could travel comfortably, we headed for Maine to close our home for the winter.

The previous winter had been quite severe in Maine. The thermometer had hovered around 50 degrees below zero for days at a time. As often happens in very cold weather, the aurora borealis was spectacular, especially in the wee hours of the morning. The sight was unforgettable, and Phil got the boys out of their warm beds to witness its splendor. The vivid colors flashing in broad streamers across the sky were breathtaking. The air was so cold it crackled and seared the lungs. Even bundling up and breathing through woolen scarfs, we could stay out for only brief periods. This and other beauties we witnessed during Maine winters failed to compensate for spending most of our time and energy just keeping warm.

Phil told Steve Bukata, who had been in charge of the two-man operation in his lab, to close the lab as soon as the current project was completed. Meantime, I made arrangements for the house. The furnace would need to maintain a minimum temperature. The circulator to the house would protect the Novachord, the circulator to the lab would protect the delicate instruments there, and the pool circulator would keep the pool from freezing and cracking.

Now, there was only one minor detail before we would be ready for our departure—we needed to upgrade our insurance coverage. We had maintained a continual building program, but had never increased the original twenty thousand dollar policy covering the old farm house. Over the years, we had added a large wing to the house, with a pool on the lower level and guest quarters on the second floor; a laboratory with a large machine shop was also added; and finally a two-car garage with an apartment above and a sizable farm-equipment shed had been attached. Yes, we were woefully underprotected. We made an appointment to meet with Ace Pike III, who had taken over his father's insurance business and was our present broker.

We had not worried much about our vulnerability. Western Maine was reputed not to have such catastrophes as tornadoes, hurricanes, or earthquakes—although we had lost a thirty foot wide swath of trees in a hurricane, and an earthquake had caused a crack in Phil's dam in the eight years we had lived there.

Two days before the scheduled appointment with Ace, a fire was started in the lumber yard on the east side of the town of Fryeburg, six miles north of us. The nearest fire engine was in Conway, New Hampshire, six miles beyond Fryeburg. By the time the volunteer firemen gathered and arrived on the scene, the fire had spread to the nearby woods and was out of control.

There had been a long dry spell, not uncommon in October, and a fire was also raging at Bar Harbor on the Maine coast and in two other widely separated areas. Work was suspended while every able-bodied man went to fight the fire.

By the second day, volunteers were arriving from all over New England. Phil had Joe Slovak fly him over the fire. We had surrounded ourselves with three thousand acres of woodlands. Two thousand of those acres were between the fire front and our home and lab.

Seeing how the fire had spread, Phil called and told Ace he would not hold him to their appointment under the circumstances, although the fire seemed to be headed to the east of us at the time.

The fire fighters had been battling the blaze now for two days and a night. To relieve them, I called the National Guard in Portland. They sent several trucks loaded with young guardsmen, none of whom looked to be over eighteen. When they saw the situation, they complained loudly, "You expect us to fight a forest fire in them woods? . . . at night? . . . these woods are full of wild animals!!!" Disgusted and ready to drop with fatigue, those in charge of the action told the Guard Commander to take his children back home. They were too busy to wet-nurse a bunch of city kids. So he did!

A Red Cross unit was set up at our home, since we were the nearest to the fire on the south side. Phil and I were taking turns on the night watch, with hot soup, coffee, donuts, and first aid at the ready. Philo, who had come home from Massachusetts with us, and his friends had been in the thick of the fire fighting front from the first.

On the third day a call came from George Everson in New York City. The Farnsworth Television & Radio Corporation was having a meeting of the Board that day, and they really needed Phil to be there. Phil told George he had planned to come, but for the past three days he had been fighting a forest fire. Just as George was telling Phil that those things seldom turned out to be as serious as they first looked, the friendly telephone operator (who knew more about town business than anyone) cut in to say that the wind had shifted and the fire was now headed our way. We would have at most twenty minutes to get out. Already the main road was cut off, so it would be necessary to take the back road to Fryeburg. At that moment the line went dead, leaving George still telling Phil how sorely he was needed in New York.

Our buildings were in the middle of a five-acre clearing. Earlier, Phil had taken his John Deere tractor out and plowed a ten-foot-wide swath, which he hoped was a firebreak, on all sides facing the fire. Friends arrived with trucks to try to save as much as possible. Phil and I told them to take out anything that looked valuable but not to distract us. We had to save Phil's papers, journals, and other records.

They loaded Lester, the piano from the Farnsworth Broadcast Studio in Philadelphia, on Garald Walker's truck. Garald, my step-sister Hazel's husband who had been one of Phil's employees, was also entrusted with Phil's papers, journals and other records. Skee insisted upon riding with Lester, so they drove off with Skee seated at the piano, playing and singing at the top of his lung capacity . . . his way of trying to bring some kind of sanity into this chaotic situation.

Robert Kennett and his Conway fire engine pulled into the yard at this point. He had promised to be there if our home was threatened. Making a quick decision, he ordered his men to run their fire hose out to the lake, a thousand feet away, to give them plenty of pressure.

At this moment, Philo and his friend, George Huffnagle, Jr., arrived, blackened by two days of fire fighting and completely out of breath. Wordlessly, they pointed in the direction from which they had come. To our horror, we beheld the broad front of a windswept crown fire bearing down on us. Phil refused to leave unless the fire department left also. The futility of the situation was obvious. He also warned the lab people, who were loading a lathe and shop equipment on a truck, to leave immediately before he consented to get in the car. Philo picked me up and put me in the car. I had been insisting I go bring my love birds. Saying we would do well to save ourselves, Philo took the wheel and headed for the back road to Fryeburg.

Not even waiting to retrieve their hose, the fire truck had pulled out. Steve Bukata, Harry Holt (the carpenter who had been building cabinets for Phil's study), and the men who had brought in the truck to help them came behind us.

A little way beyond the Fernworth Dam, Philo stopped the car and said, "Wait a minute." He and George ran back, and behind the safety of the dam, watched the fire. We could see that the fire front had narrowed and was headed straight for the notch road which ran between Frost and Perry Mountains and led to the town of Brownfield on the south side of the mountains. Our buildings were directly in its path.

The fire leaped the road, thumbed its nose at Phil's puny firebreak, and reached the sugar maples lining our driveway. The trees carried the flames straight to the house and the large tree in the center of the terrace. The tinder-dry shingles were aflame in seconds, and the wind carried burning branches the fifteen feet to the lab. There the fire ignited the small enclosure housing large cylinders of oxygen and hydrogen with their lines into the lab. The tanks exploded with a resounding bang, and it was all over. The entire place went up in a matter of minutes.

In shock from the horror of what he had seen, Philo raced us on, realizing that the delay had put us in more danger. Fire brands fell on the roof of the car in a continual downpour as we sped along the road through the woods. We all breathed a sigh of relief as we reached the highway leading into Fryeburg from the Conway side.

Our friends Gene and Rachel Martin opened their home and their hearts to us. Philo and George, stopping only for a hurried bite to eat, hailed a truck and headed back to the fire front to see how my father and stepmother had fared. Daddy had remarried and built a cottage down on the Portland highway about a mile and a half from our home.

The boys were brought in early in the morning, suffering from burns and total exhaustion. They reported that Dad and Mother Pearl, with their neighbors, had stayed through the fire-filled inferno of a night, breathing through damp towels and spraying their trees and homes with garden hoses. Among their neighbors were my other stepsister Muriel and her husband, Raymond Huntress, who was Phil's woods boss, Zeline McAllister, and her family. Fortunately, they had the paved highway in front and a wide open field in back. Their homes were all saved.

Later that morning we got word from Brownfield. The fire had come through the notch road like a giant blowtorch and leveled the town, catching all the townsfolk by surprise. Thinking the fire would come around the mountains, they had taken their belongings to what they thought were out-of-the-way fields and unloaded them, then gone back for more.

Garald and Hazel Walker, who were in the antique business, had a large barn full of antiques. While Garald was helping us, friends hauled all of his belongings out where they thought they would be safe. Garald took his load with Skee and the piano to Brownfield, but seeing the fire come through the notch, he took a roundabout way to Fryeburg, where he left his load, including Skee and the piano, with friends of ours. Then he went down the fire line to Brownfield.

The fire was very capricious. Garald found his home and barn empty. The fire spared his part of town, but destroyed all of his belongings which had been left in the open field. This happened with many of the people in that eastern part of town, along with our clothing and other things that had been taken there for safety. We were left, as many were, with only the clothes on our backs. The miracle was that the only life that had been lost was that of an elderly gentleman who died of a heart attack.

Later the next morning we drove down to check on my father. He and Pearl were taking a well earned rest after a harrowing night of fire fighting. Some kind soul had driven Phil's John Deere tractor as far as the turnoff to Brownfield center, where he had left it, still running, as he made a desperate dash to save his own home and family.

Heartsick, we drove up Farnsworth Road to what had been our home and lab. The sugar maples lining our drive would no more yield their sap for boiling down into the thicker than usual maple syrup we so enjoyed. Where the entry room had been was a pile of rubble that had been my cherished cedar chest made by Carl in his high school manual arts class for my birthday. It had been packed with my prized Haviland china, silver, crystal, and linens ready to be taken to Newton Center. Nearby the crumpled wire bird cage attested to the tragic end of my beautiful love birds.

That last night had been Phil's turn to stand watch. He had busied himself by taking the Capehart record changer apart to see why it was breaking some of his favorite records. The charred parts on the stone living room mantel attested to his good intentions. The Novachord was a melted mess of tubes and wires. There were no charred bits of wood, just fine ash over everything.

The massive floor-to-ceiling polished granite fireplace in Phil's study was now rubble. The intense heat had shattered the stone and melted the massive I-beam that supported it, letting the whole thing down into the swimming pool on the lower level. The greatest loss to Phil was his carefully collected library of over two hundred volumes. This was now ash, mingled with the rivers of glass from the plate-glass picture windows of his study. Many of those volumes were even then out of print.

As if in a dream, we went on to examine the remains of the lab and shop. All we found were melted globs of metal and glass. Phil picked up the only thing he could recognize, a twisted glob that had been a partially completed experimental tube being made to test a pet theory. The silver, gold, and platinum wire and sheet stock used in making tubes had become an integral part of the general mess and totally unrecognizable.

Pale and drawn, Phil said, "That's enough! Let's get out of here!" We left what had been our cherished retreat, not to set eyes on it again for over a dozen years. As we drove back to Fryeburg, Phil carefully averted his eyes from the black and charred remains of what had been our 2,000 acres of unspoiled woodland in which we had tramped looking for rare woods flowers, berries, and moss, always keeping an eye out for the wildlife who made this their home.

Phil had learned to recognize the kind of animal which had made its bed in the bent grasses or mounds of earth the previous night, whether it was a bear, a deer, or a Canadian lynx. We had many of these, as well as bobcat, fox, and other smaller animals. We had been concerned for their safety, but since no carcasses were found, they must have sensed the fire soon enough to find a way out. For this we were very grateful.

Phil turned our twenty thousand dollar fire insurance check over to Lincoln to use for the Farnsworth Wood Products Company, realizing, sadly, that it was insufficient to be of much help. Then we left for Newton Center, grateful for the kind providence that had inspired us to lease a lovely furnished home for the winter. At least we had a temporary haven.

CHAPTER 26

Rescue Attempt

The loss of our home and lab was hard for all of us, but coming so soon after the trauma of Carl's death, it was almost too much for Phil. He had tried to put television out of his mind. It was a taboo subject. When the Encyclopedia Americana requested him to write its article on television, he threw the letter into the waste basket, unanswered. This probably accounted largely for the deficiencies in his biography in that and other historical publications. For Phil, this was a time of deep soul-searching and pondering the futilities of life. He knew there were new areas to explore, and he continued to contemplate the riddle of controlling fusion, but he could not focus his energy. His spirits hit a new low. He was almost at the end of his financial resources, with the exception of his land in Maine, and he had vowed never to return to Fort Wayne and the television scene.

On the other hand, while experience had taught me to accept adversity with a certain grace, Phil had taught me to look to the future. I tried to point out the bright side. Our family and friends had all come through the fire physically unscathed. Fernworth Farm had been a heavenly retreat, but Philo could be right when he said it was time we returned to the mainstream; it might be time for a change. Fernworth pond was still there, and Mother Nature had a way of erasing ugly scars by covering the land with new growth. In a few years, everything would again be green, and we could rebuild. Devastating as this loss was to us, I knew we had the inner strength to override our mental scars. I reminded him that his early rule of learning from adversities still applied. As he used to say, we should look to the future and let the past take care of itself.

I called Dr. Benjamin Riggs, the psychiatrist who had helped Phil reorient himself at Baldpate. Ben made several visits to see Phil. They had some very lively conversations. Ben was intrigued with Phil's concept of the engram, or thought flow in connection with the here/now, which is the only reality, that split second between what has gone before and the uncertainty of the future. Ben's wife Norma and I sat mesmerized by their rapid-fire exchange of ideas. I am sure she realized, as did I, that this was good therapy for both of them. Ben was getting his furnace restoked with new ideas, and Phil was thoroughly enjoying the opportunity of expounding his ideas to one who not only was receptive to them, but had much to contribute as well. This was only one of the many esoteric subjects they discussed. These conversations put Phil's mind in another space and started him thinking more constructively.

As for our boys, after three months at MIT, Philo had decided he had no wish to be an electrical engineer. He had lived with creative electronics all his life and had seen his father ruin his health in the process. Also, he decided that much of his father's originality came from digging his education out of books of his own choosing. In so doing, he could come to his own conclusions. He was now attending a fine arts college to develop his painting skills and, on the side, studying the books wherein his chief interests lay.

Skee was enjoying the many advantages of junior high over grade school. When his science teacher began talking about television and mentioned Philo Farnsworth, Skee said, "You are talking about my father." There was some tittering in the room, and the teacher said, "He couldn't be your father. If he were, he'd now be sitting on top of the world."

"Well," answered Skee, thinking of the events of the past few weeks, "maybe he is sitting on top of the world, but sometimes the world can seem like a great big tack!" The next day, I sent a copy of George Everson's book, *The Story of Television, The Life of Philo T. Farnsworth* to the teacher. This changed Skee's status from object of ridicule to celebrity in a hurry.

Early in January 1949, Phil received a letter from George Everson saying he would be in New York the next week for a Farnsworth Company Director's meeting, and at his urgent request, we flew to New York. Phil came back from the meeting to the hotel, looking very glum.

"Farnsworth Television is in trouble," he told me.

"What about all the reports we've been getting about the E's (for excellence) the Navy has been bestowing upon them?"

"Oh, they have extended themselves for the war effort all right. That's the trouble; they have overextended themselves. The large bank loans they obtained for new plants and old plant expansion are now being called in. Rather than retiring the loans gradually from their income, they have expanded further. Now they are top-heavy and will have to sell off plants in a slow market. It doesn't look good."

"No wonder George wanted you here. How is George? Did you invite him to have dinner with us?"

"George looks as healthy as ever. I invited him to have dinner with us, but his commitments at the Lawrence Radiation Lab are pressing. He is taking the evening train for San Francisco. He said he would stop by to say hello to you, though. By the way, I agreed to fly out to Fort Wayne and get a firsthand look at things there. They are all urging me to go back and help them through this mess." His duty to the Farnsworth Company stockholders was overshadowing his vow never to return to Fort Wayne.

Our arrival in Fort Wayne was announced in the newspapers. We were greeted with open arms and more entreaties for Phil to stay. It was heartwarming to see what Phil's presence did for the morale of his men. He agreed to think about staying.

Phil was aware that RCA, Philco, and several other companies had been selling TV sets for over a year and now had their commercial broadcasting licenses. 'Nick' Nicholas and Ed Martin gave Phil the whole sad story. Unbelievably, it all came back to David Sarnoff, president of RCA. Despite the mutual cooperation of all the companies involved in television during the war, old animosities resurfaced when the war ended, and Sarnoff resumed his efforts to make life difficult for Farnsworth.

As the FCC began issuing commercial licenses, the entire television industry began frantically to tool up for making TV receivers. RCA now had the fate of Farnsworth Television in its hands. The industry, including Farnsworth, had licenses with RCA for its radio-type components, which were also necessary for television. It was a mad scramble to get parts and cabinets, and somehow the Farnsworth orders always found their way to the bottom of the pile. These delays slowed the Farnsworth assembly lines and made it difficult for the company to fill its orders.

In order to get top-of-the-line cabinets, Farnsworth had found it necessary to buy a substantial interest in a furniture factory. However, the first sets were now coming off the Farnsworth assembly line, and dealerships had been set up all over the country. Nicholas and Martin urged Phil to stay at least two weeks for the company's upcoming dealer's convention in Chicago. The first Farnsworth television receivers were being introduced. Pleased to see that the company had been broadcasting experimentally from its station at WGL, Phil agreed. He came back to the Keenan Hotel where we were staying and told me about the upcoming convention.

"Pem, we might yet get into the commercial television broadcasting business. I think Nick and I have a chance to save the company, and getting a license now would be no problem. How would you like to fly out to San Francisco to see the folks while waiting for the Chicago convention?"

"Are you serious?" We had not been West since leaving there in 1931, seventeen years previously. It had seemed a lifetime.

"You bet I'm serious! See what you can do about plane reservations."

We were on a plane that evening for Chicago to connect with our flight to San Francisco. Watching from high in the sky, I decided it was the most beautiful sunset I had ever seen. Venus, low in the sky, looked ten times larger than ever before. As we approached Chicago in the early evening, the crescent of jewel-like lights that were Chicago reflecting from the blue waters of Lake Michigan, made of it a fairyland. I suppose the magic emanated from my happiness at the prospect of seeing my family after all these years, but it was beautiful.

We were met at the San Francisco airport by Agnes and Claude Lindsay. Claude drove us up to San Francisco. What a thrill it was to see this magic city by the Bay after having been away so many years. Driving up the Barbary Coast, now the Embarcadero, Claude drove up to Sansome Street and passed 202 Green Street, our old lab where the work on television had started. Here Phil had made the first all-electronic television transmission in the world. What fond memories we had of those days. Claude said our home in the Marina district had had to be moved with others on Lyon Street to make way for the Golden Gate Bridge approach. We declined his offer to take us to see it, but going over Bay Street to the bridge approach, we passed the Yacht Harbor and Palace of Fine Arts Building, a mere three blocks from where our home had been at 3208 Lyon Street. I had often pushed Philo and Kenny down there in their carriage.

We soon had our first view of the Golden Gate Bridge. That magnificent, improbable monument to the ingenuity of man overwhelmed us. Phil had to stop and photograph it. When we left in 1931, engineers had been arguing about whether it would ever be possible to span the Golden Gate. Many difficulties had had to be overcome. The first anchor position had given way, killing a number of men, but they fought it through to completion. Such is the tenacity of men with an avowed purpose.

Agnes and Claude lived in one of the Lindsay Homes Claude had built in the Avenues toward the beach. We remembered this area as the sand dunes from which a glider club had launched their gliders. Laura and Lindy Player had purchased a Lindsay Home and lived nearby. We enjoyed getting acquainted with Linda, Steven and Gary, their three children. Agnes and Claude later adopted a baby girl and a baby boy they named Karen and John. We drove down to San Mateo to see my sister Rhae, her husband Wayne, and Hazel, Ralph, and baby Carl, their children; then on to Redwood City to see Verona and meet her husband Mac. Mac, musician extraordinaire, led an orchestra and also a band. Verona was now a successful interior decorator, and her daughter Virginia was now a grown young lady, and beautiful.

During the next week we had a wonderful time getting acquainted with my two other brothers and three more sisters and their families. Art and his wife Mary drove us from Las Vegas to St. George, in southern Utah, to the home of Mother Farnsworth and her new husband, Joseph Farnsworth (no relation to Phil's father Lewis). Mother and Daddy Joe drove us on up through Utah to my sister Lois's home in Salt Lake City, where we met her husband, Dr. Rees Anderson, and John, Susan, Sally, and Jim, their children. I was saddened to think of all I had missed by living such a busy life so far away from my family.

We flew back to Chicago in time for the Farnsworth Dealers Convention. I had reserved a suite at the swank Ambassador East Hotel to give us a place to meet with our friends and colleagues. The John Barrymore suite was sheer elegance, from the dining annex to the large combination dressing room/closet and bedroom with feather bed. Even though the January winds howled outside, it was all warm and very romantic inside. We recaptured some of our youth that night.

The convention the next day, professionally staged and managed, was a huge success. We and the Farnsworth management were pleased, and the reaction of the dealers—in the form of brisk orders—was most gratifying. Phil, feeling his responsibility to the company stockholders, announced that he had decided to return to Fort Wayne after Skee was out of school in June.

At first Phil's decision to return to Fort Wayne surprised me; he had been adamant that he never wanted to have anything to do with television again. But seeing that commercial television had at last arrived revitalized his interest, and he was quite excited to see the company getting ready to go into commercial broadcasting. I suspected he might have had an ulterior motive as well. New ideas were starting to simmer in his fertile mind, most notably ideas about fusion. After the lab in Maine was destroyed, he needed someplace where he could resume his research again. Besides, we had rented the place in Newton Center only for the winter, and beyond that our plans were nebulous. We had talked some of returning to Utah.

A few weeks after returning to Newton Center, I began having health problems. I was told by a gynecologist that either I had a tumor or I was pregnant. The pregnancy tests were negative, so that left me with a tumor and a frantic husband. Phil called Zeline, hoping she could come and help us, but she was caring for her daughter, who was gravely ill. He then called Alma Bean, who had helped us before. She agreed to come for two weeks while we looked for someone more permanent.

Neither Phil nor I could accept the diagnosis without a second opinion. This time the pregnancy test was positive. We were all greatly relieved and happy to contemplate another baby. Phil said, "We can thank our stay in the John Barrymore suite for this."

On the twenty-fifth of February, I celebrated my fortieth birthday. I had been born on my father's thirtieth birthday, and we had celebrated our birthdays together whenever possible. I was feeling sad because Daddy was in Maine and we would not be together this year. Unbeknownst to me, Cliff had met Dad's train the night before and spirited him away to his home in Waltham, then brought him to our place the next morning before going to work at Raytheon. This was the icing on my cake. I recalled my tenth birthday, when Dad had walked most of the thirty miles which separated us, so we could spend our birthdays together. Later that evening, Cliff brought his family over for birthday cake and ice cream and presented me with a dozen long-stemmed red roses. On the card he had written, "Congratulations! We're glad your tumor was a rumor."

By the time Alma had to leave, I was feeling well enough to take over my own housework. I had presented Phil with a membership in a men's health spa for Christmas, and he had reciprocated by giving me a membership in a women's spa. We were both benefiting from our twice-weekly visits. At Phil's insistence, I purchased a smart maternity wardrobe which did much to conceal my condition and made me feel more comfortable when I accompanied him (as I always did) to his various appearances. These maternity clothes were passed on to my younger sisters and served well through several pregnancies.

From time to time Philo had mentioned a girl, Ruth Skogsberg from Worcester, Massachusetts, a charming town to the northeast with a large Scandinavian population. One wild, stormy Saturday night, Ruth called Philo. Philo asked if he might borrow the Cadillac. When Phil said it was foolhardy to drive on such a night, Philo answered, "But Dad, this is a special girl, and when she says come, I come!"

He got the car. Phil recalled later that he remembered when we were dating. Many times he wished his dad were alive and had a car he could borrow, as the other fellows did. Several weeks later, Philo borrowed the car again and brought Ruth home for the weekend. She was moderately tall, with beautiful long blonde hair. This lovely, talented girl with a whimsical wit captured our hearts the first evening. The next day they announced their engagement and said they wanted to be married on March 18th.

Phil took Philo aside and had a serious father-to-son talk, pointing out that Philo was only nineteen; did he think he could support a wife? Philo, never at a loss for answers, reminded his father that he also had been married at nineteen, and, yes, he thought he was capable of supporting a wife. When all of Phil's questions had been answered to his satisfaction, they joined Ruth and me in the living room. Since they wanted to be married in our home, we began making plans. The next week we were invited to the Skogsberg's home to meet Ruth's parents, John and Hilma, and to attend a bridal shower for her.

We thoroughly enjoyed the evening with the Skogsbergs and all the aunts, uncles, and assorted relatives and friends. These were delightfully down-to-earth people, and I never saw so many delectable Scandinavian cookies and tidbits as were served there.

The next day we were talking over what we should give Philo and Ruth for a wedding present. Phil made a suggestion.

"What do you think of the idea of giving them the Smith Farm? The fire spared that area. They could fix up the farm house and at least use it for vacations."

"What a wonderful idea. That place has sixty acres, and I think Ruth will like living there by the Little Saco River. (The Little Saco would usually be called a creek, but the state had called it a river so it could be stocked with trout.) It's a charming location."

When we told Philo, he was delighted, and he came up with a good way to begin to support his bride. It seemed he had spent some time thinking about it.

"Dad, I walked through the Kennett lot (our 2000-acre wood lot which had been burned in the fire) and there's a lot of good lumber in those trees. I was thinking of going up and staying in the Smith house while I get Granddad Gardner and Raymond Huntress to help me log it out. You could give me a percentage for my work, and it would give Granddad a job. It will be great to have our own home; I'll bet Ruth will just love it."

On March 18th our house was overflowing with friends and relatives. At Ruth's request, John and Hilma Skogsberg brought their minister to perform the ceremony. Many of their relatives were also present, including Ruth's older brother Frank and his lovely wife.

Philo and his Fryeburg pals, George Huffnagle, Jr. and Willard Burnett, had invested in an antique touring car, which after all their changes had long since lost its identity. Philo wanted to buy the other boys out, but so much of themselves had gone into keeping it running, they could not face

Philo III and wife Ruth

letting it go. However, Philo could be very persuasive. He said since he was the first to get married, they should sell it to him. They finally agreed.

Sitting in their car after running through the hailstorm of rice thrown at them, they made quite a picture. Ruth was holding a registered cocker spaniel puppy, Philo's wedding present to her; Philo was at the wheel; and strapped to the top of the car was the mattress from Ruth's parents. Piled in the back were wedding presents, clothes, and other personal effects. While I took movies of them, Cliff, Skee, and George Huffnagle, Jr., were writing on the back of the car "JUST MARRIED" and tying tin cans to the rear bumper. The scene ended as they disappeared around the first corner.

In May, Phil and I made another trip to Fort Wayne. While Phil was at the plant, I did some house hunting. I thought our requirements were modest. We needed three bedrooms, two baths, and a study for Phil. There were many very nice homes with the required number of rooms, but lacking the extra bathroom. Then the desperate realtor said he had a house that fit our needs, but it was rather close in and would not be available until September. The owner, Georgia Mead, was spending her usual summer in Maine and would not consider returning until September.

This house was indeed just what we wanted. It was set on three-quarters of an acre corner lot. It had been designed and built by the founder of the Lincoln Life Insurance Company for his bride. When he died, the place was purchased by the succeeding president, Mr. Mead. The grounds were lushly planted, and in the center of the east side lawn was a birdbath with a Peter Pan statue. On the west side were a large lawn and a small fish pool with a cherub statue.

Inside, the house could not have been better suited to our needs had it been designed for us. It had four bedrooms, three baths, plus a half-bath off Phil's study. There were bookcases everywhere, even in the central hall. Despite this, Phil was building more bookcases in a few years. He had vowed to replace his library.

Fortunately for us, Mrs. Mead had been on a long waiting list for an apartment in the Fairfield Apartments, the town's only really nice apartment building at that time. A smaller apartment was now vacant, and she agreed to let us live there until she could come back and move her furniture. Then she would live there until a larger apartment was available. This was agreeable to us, since it would reduce my work to a minimum for the last few months of my pregnancy.

We returned to stay in Fort Wayne in June 1949. Whatever ideas Phil may have had about pursuing his own lines of research went on the back burner again, because he had to devote all his attention to fortifying the company's shaky financial footing. His first move entailed going to Washington, hoping he could fill the plant with high-paying research contracts. To his surprise and considerable pleasure, he found the man in charge of civilian contracts at the Bureau of Ships was Charles Stec, who had worked for Phil while he was at Philco. Charles was delighted to see Phil—he was just the man they needed, and Charles loaded him up with all the contracts he could handle.

Back at the plant, things really began to buzz. Phil, now back in his element, was a different person, and fired with his enthusiasm, his men gave him their very best effort. Phil sorted his men according to their capabilities and advanced the most capable men to positions of project supervisors to handle the contracts. This left him free to oversee them all to a better advantage. Mr. Nicholas and Ed Martin were astounded at the change Phil had wrought in the attitude of the personnel. When they told me that Phil had worked miracles there, I told them it wasn't the first time.

Now, with the research and development department in full swing and TV receivers and radio/phonograph combinations rolling off the assembly lines, the company's prospects began to look much better. The banks gave them one more year to clear off their loans. In the meantime, three of the plants that had been acquired during the war were sold off to tool up for the new contracts and make interim payments on bank loans.

Farnsworth Television & Radio (FT&R) was sponsoring the New York Metropolitan Opera Auditions of the Air program on Sundays at 4:30, and this continued for the present. The contests made an interesting program, and it was excellent prime-time advertising. Each winner was presented with a check for one thousand dollars and a silver medallion. The program was carried by sixty-two ABC stations nationwide, at a cost of six thousand, one hundred and fifty dollars a week.

As I approached the end of my term, Phil reminded me of his promise to go back to Boston with me to my doctor there for the delivery. However, I insisted I was quite satisfied with Dr. Bierlien, the Fort Wayne doctor to whom I had been referred. Besides this, Phil was too involved to leave the lab now. I think he was much relieved to hear my decision.

On September 4th, Phil took me to the hospital. Thirteen-year-old Skee had been very concerned about me, and Phil promised to come back and report. The hospital was only a few blocks from our apartment, so when Phil was told that nothing was about to happen very soon, he went back to tell Skee. He found our son in the manager's apartment. She had found him pacing the hall and had invited him in for a piece of pie to divert his mind.

By the time we brought the baby home, Skee had read my book on prenatal care and the handling of new babies. He insisted on being present when the nurse bathed little Kent, and to her amusement and also some amazement, he told her all the things she wasn't doing and what she did contrary to the book.

On September 15th, we moved into our new home. Our small down payment on the house had drained our accounts, so we were obliged to get along with a minimum of furniture until we could buy the pieces we wanted. Lester, our piano, along with Phil's walnut desk and two leather chairs, arrived from Newton Center, and with the breakfast-room furniture and a few other pieces purchased from Mrs. Mead, we needed only furniture for the bedrooms, the nursery adjoining the master bedroom, and the dining room. By some miracle, our cameras and photographic enlarger from our Maine darkroom had been saved. Phil set this up in the large powder room off his study.

Philo was doing very well in Maine. He had started to save the lumber none too soon; the wood worms were already at work on the fire-scarred trees. Given a start, they can do tremendous damage in a very short time. Soon our monthly checks started coming, and by Christmas time Philo had pretty well completed the job. Philo and Ruth drove out for Christmas in the secondhand Cadillac Philo had picked up "at a bargain." Since we still had no furniture in the dining room, it was a great place to put a large Christmas tree and conduct our Christmas activities.

All of the company executives belonged to the Fort Wayne Country Club and wanted us to join. We went with them once or twice, but declined their invitation to join. It seemed their main activities were golf, drinking, dancing, and more drinking, none of which appealed to us. I attended some of the Newcomers Club's monthly meetings and bridge luncheons, but I had lived in a man's world too long. I found it difficult to spend several hours in a room full of chattering women.

During all this time, Phil and his R&D department were operating at high efficiency. His input breathed energy into the men, and in turn their reciprocation kept him on his toes. It seemed as though the past dozen years had been obliterated. He was a new man. While the specter of the bank payments was still hanging over them, Phil knew he was doing everything in his power to save the company.

Although the government contracts Phil had brought in succeeded in putting the company operations in the black within a year, the income was not sufficient to clear off the wartime bank loans. The year's grace period given by the banks was up, and something had to be done. Phil was quite disturbed when the board of directors decided to sell the Farnsworth Television station, since he felt strongly that it offered the best long-term hope of assuring the company's future. But there was little he could do to avert this, and he focused his attention on what he could do, which was working in the lab.

Phil and Nick were aware that the research projects alone would not be sufficient to pay off the banks, and Nick did everything he could think of to step up the manufacturing output of the plant. They had an excellent sales division and distributors in all of the large cities. The Farnsworth name, plus the high operating standards of the company, sold sets as fast as they could be produced, but a session with the chief accountant painted a bleak picture about the company's ability to pay off the large bank loans.

CHAPTER 27

ITT Takeover

In an effort to refinance the company, John Wharton, of the legal firm of Paul Weiss, Wharton, & Garrison, filed a registration statement for a new stock issue for Farnsworth Television & Radio Corporation, on January 12th, 1949. However, the Federal Securities and Exchange Commission discovered some unexplained discrepancies in the financial statements, and the petition for a new stock issue was denied. All the executives and accountants were at a loss to explain this problem, which left the company with little recourse.

Ed Nicholas had hoped the new stock issue would enable the company to pay off the banks without liquidating any more assets. When the stock issue failed, Nick and Phil decided to put the company's furniture factory stock up as collateral for a loan of two hundred thousand dollars from the Lincoln National Bank in Fort Wayne. Now they were doing a juggling act while walking a tight rope, borrowing from Peter to pay Paul. All of the company's plants had now been sold. There remained only the original Capehart plant and the WGL radio station. The Fort Wayne News Sentinel owner had earlier made an offer for the station; now she made a higher offer which was accepted, leaving Farnsworth Television & Radio with only its original plant.

Now the International Telephone and Telegraph Company entered the picture with an offer to acquire the company, which was rejected. In a final effort to maintain the company's independence, Mr. Nicholas approached RCA, General Electric, and Zenith, inviting them to make a single royalty payment for the life of the Farnsworth patents, the oldest of which were due to expire in another five years. All three companies accepted the offer, which produced two million, five hundred thousand dollars from RCA, four hundred thousand dollars from GE, and two hundred twenty-five thousand dollars from Zenith, for a total of three million, one hundred twenty-five thousand dollars. Even this substantial cash infusion was soon used up in bank payments and other company obligations, leaving the company unable to pay off the two hundred thousand dollars at Lincoln National, so the furniture factory was sold to cover it.

In a last-ditch move to avoid bankruptcy, a letter was sent to all the Farnsworth stockholders, asking approval to sell the company to IT&T in a stock-trade deal. This was a sort of "one-horse-one-rabbit" deal, but they had unsuccessfully explored every avenue open to them, and they saw no alternative. Ed Nicholas asked Phil to write the stockholders' letter, thinking a letter from Phil might soften the blow.

This was by far the most difficult letter Phil ever had to compose. After days of struggling with it, he dictated it to me. We wrote and rewrote it several times before he took it to Ed. This is what he wrote:

Dear Farnsworth Stockholder:

Most of you know that my entire working life has been devoted to the development of electronic television, the last 11 years with this company which bears my name. None of you can be more deeply concerned than I have been by the bitter facts which our company has had to face.

I write to you now as a Farnsworth stockholder holding over 10,000 shares, which I am voting in favor of the IT&T plan.

With the stockholders' meeting scheduled to open today, I find that nearly half of the stockholders have not voted at all. We are in serious danger of losing our last chance to salvage anything for ourselves as stockholders.

The facts facing us are these: In January of this year, with working capital almost entirely gone, the company was faced with the immediate likelihood of shutdown and bankruptcy. I myself know that the management had tried long and hard to save this company. Nevertheless, the situation was so desperate that the President was authorized by the Board of Directors to file a petition under Chapter X of the Bankruptcy Act at his discretion. It was at this critical juncture that the management was able to negotiate an agreement with IT&T under which stockholders would receive stock in International, worth approximately $1,400,000 at present market value. Upon consummation of the agreement our company would become a wholly-owned subsidiary of IT&T.

It is important to note that the management could find no other offer at the time this agreement was made.

It is even more significant that no other offer from anyone anywhere has been presented up to the present moment, though a special committee of stockholders has been hard at work for more than a month. It now seems inevitable that the alternative to the consummation of the IT&T plan would be bankruptcy, with very probably a total loss for stockholders.

Under the circumstances I have been at loss to understand the bitter attack on this plan by some stockholders, as though it were an injustice to them. In all honesty, I feel obligated to point out that this plan presents the only way in which any return to the stockholders' investment can be guaranteed.

Let me ask what any stockholder can hope to gain by voting against this proposal or by refusing to vote at all. What advantage can any stockholder gain by declining to accept his share of $1,400,000 and, by that refusal, helping to force the company into bankruptcy, to the loss of all concerned.

Still many stockholders have not yet voted, or have voted against our agreement with IT&T.

There is still time within the limits of the present stockholders' meeting for those of you who have not yet voted in favor of the plan to do so by return mail. It is probable that a short adjournment of the meeting will be necessary.

Certainly I shall do everything in my power to enable stockholders to secure some partial repayment on the investment which they have made. I enclose another form of proxy and a return envelope for your use.

Sincerely,

Philo T. Farnsworth

No sooner was Phil's letter mailed than the whole house of cards came crashing down around us. First, a group of stockholders banded together to sue the company, demanding to know how their equity could have evaporated virtually overnight. In the meantime, the New York contingent of the Board of Directors, along with Jess McCargar, quietly sold all their stock and disappeared from the scene, resigning from the board one by one. Of the original investors, this left only Phil and George Everson, who was in San Francisco, as the angry stockholders began to converge on Fort Wayne. Finally, in the most suspicious development of all, Mr. Nicholas, the president of the company, and Ed Martin, head of the legal department, were suddenly called away on "urgent business" elsewhere. This left only Phil and Chester Wiggins, second-in-command in the legal department, to face the army of irate stockholders in court.

After the first day of the hearings, Phil came home so pale and drawn I was heartsick. When I learned that he and Mr. Wiggins had been left to represent the company alone, I was furious. Phil said simply, "I guess it's my baby, so it's my job to bury it." This statement conjured up painful memories of our sweet baby Kenny, lying cold and lifeless in the baggage car those four agonizing days from Philadelphia to Utah. I tried to change the subject.

"That's horrible, Phil, but now I want you to put it out of your mind for a while, and see what your real, live baby has learned to do today."

I had bought some toys which attached to the side of his playpen, a monkey, a clown, and a koala bear attached to little poles. From them hung a cord with a ring on the end of it.

"Now watch, Phil." I dangled the ring in front of little Kent, who was sitting in the pen. Laughing, he grabbed the ring and pulled, and the monkey climbed the pole. Delighted, he pulled another ring, and the clown climbed his pole. Phil pulled the last ring, and the koala bear climbed its pole. Then we all laughed. Phil picked his little son up and gave him a big hug. This was the most effective medicine Phil could have had.

"You boys go wash for dinner," I told them, "and tell Skee it's time to stop practicing the piano and get ready for dinner. I'll go dish it up."

Later, Phil told me about the hearing. It had been a traumatic day, and I encouraged him to get it all off his chest.

"These folks have a legitimate gripe, and I don't blame them for wanting some answers. They are entitled to answers too, but honey, I'm beginning to realize that I cannot answer some of their questions. There seem to be some missing pieces of this puzzle. It would be very helpful if Nick and Ed (Martin) were here."

"If you ask me, which you didn't, I think they planned to be away."

"It does look a little odd, but Nick called yesterday and apologized for not being here. He has worked very hard trying to save the company."

"I'd have liked it better if he had worked harder to keep the gate shut before the horse got away." (Some of the underhanded deals I have uncovered regarding RCA's tactics against Farnsworth have made me wonder about the war years' management of the company.)

The hearings dragged on for a week, both in the court room and in the newspapers. Eventually, the suit was dropped, and enough of the stockholders, realizing it was ITT or nothing, voted to accept the deal. Though business continued as usual, Farnsworth Television & Radio Corporation disappeared from the New York Stock Exchange and became a subsidiary of ITT.

New management was instated almost immediately, with the exception of Philo T. Farnsworth, who remained vice president in charge of research and advanced engineering, but for the first time, Phil was no longer a member of the board of directors of his company. E. A. Nicholas was given a temporary position as assistant to the president, and after a transition period, he was appointed to a position at the head ITT office in New York; Ed Martin was released and took a position in Washington, D. C.

The first president of the Farnsworth Company as an ITT subsidiary was Ellery W. Stone. The company continued to make television receivers and Capehart record-changer/radio combinations, and Phil's research department continued to work on space-age contracts, mostly for the Air Force. It soon became apparent, however, that the company was being phased out of commercial television. Manufacturing activities became limited to closed-circuit TV for surveillance and monitoring equipment for such places as atomic energy plants.

Years later, some of the mysteries surrounding these events were cleared up. In researching this book, I learned that ITT was engaged in an undisclosed agreement with RCA to stay out of the television field if RCA would not compete with it in telecommunications. This arrangement was parallel in many ways with RCA's long-standing agreements with the American Telephone & Telegraph Company. Phil was not aware of this arrangement when the deal with ITT was made, although he must have suspected it when Farnsworth was phased out of television. ITT wanted Phil's brain, the expertise of his men, and the Farnsworth Company facilities to assist them in obtaining a substantial role in the new space-age science. The company's involvement in television was of little consequence when viewed in this light.

But the most startling revelations regarding the company's troubles were revealed directly to Phil years later. One day while he was tending his rose garden, Phil was visited by a man he immediately recognized as a former employee of the company. This man told Phil he had something bothering him that he had to get off his mind.

The visitor then told Phil that he had been involved in a black-market operation during the war, selling company inventory "off the books." This unsolicited confession shed some light on those "discrepancies" in the company's financial statements that caused the SEC to deny the 1949 stock offering. The man had conveniently waited until the statute of limitations on such criminal conduct had expired before suffering his conscience to the point of baring his soul to Phil.

After listening in silence to the sordid story, and realizing the futility of the situation, Phil ordered the man off our property and told him never to return. Since two of the men involved in the operation were already deceased, exposing the scandal would only have hurt their families. Phil never did divulge their names, even to me.

As part of the ITT deal, Phil had agreed to stay on in his old capacity. The new contracts awakened his old yearning to travel in space, and he rose to the challenge. He became an expert on star tracking. He and his men developed a device for the United States early-warning system. Deployed around our borders, it could detect and explode a missile long before it reached our shores. An unidentified flying object of any sort could likewise be detected and destroyed.

Phil developed a new tube he called the Iotron, a memory tube able to retain an image for an indefinite period. The model 305c was the first unit (PPI Projector) to allow air traffic to be controlled from the ground. The model 310 was used in United States defense units. Another version of the Iotron was developed for telescopes, allowing astronomers to extend their vision by 50,000 times out in space. Phil had also planned to use this idea in a vastly improved television receiving tube. This would greatly enhance and stabilize the image on the screen, but this was not to be.

The collapse of his dreams for commercial television was a hard blow to Phil, but he continued to work at a feverish pace, leading his men in their new assignments. The military contracts the company was working on occupied most of his time, but it was apparent that he was setting the

stage for his next major line of research, whatever that might be. In the meantime, he still contemplated the puzzle of the mysterious blue glow in his multipactor tubes. That one just would not go away.

Working under the auspices of ITT turned out to be not so terrible. Colonel Sothenes Behn, who founded ITT with his elder brother Hernand in 1920, was still acting president. He was a tall, slender gentleman in his seventies, with an old-world courtliness in dress and manner. The company had grown from a modest telephone and telegraph company to a worldwide electronics manufacturing and telecommunication system of vast proportions.

Colonel Behn was well known for his elegant luncheon meetings, of which Phil attended several. Whether the menu included prime beef flown in from Argentina or crab flown in from Alaska, the food was always superb. At one time, Colonel Behn invited all of the Farnsworth executives and their wives to New York, the men for a meeting and the couples for a lavish dinner. Phil and I were seated in the places of honor. While those of us at the head of the table were being entertained with lively—but genteel—conversation, the folks at the other end of the table were entertained by the flamboyant, young Mrs. Behn, who regaled those seated around her with bawdy jokes and stories.

When Colonel Behn retired from the ITT presidency, he assumed the position of Chairman of the Board. There followed a succession of presidents, mostly retired colonels and admirals. With every change in the ITT presidency, changes were made in the Farnsworth Company management, until Phil was the only original officer left. The men at the plant were fond of saying that "presidents come and presidents go, but Farnsworth goes on forever." Phil gave them a sense of stability, an anchor around which to rally.

In 1950, while working on a submarine detection device, Phil was invited to be one of the civilian observers on board a destroyer in Navy maneuvers off Puerto Rico. Due to his poor physical condition, Phil at first found climbing the seaman's net ladders difficult. By the end of a week, however, he was handling them very well and enjoying the exercise. His presence most of the time was required either on the bridge or down in the engine room. He was very pleased with the performance of his equipment and the way it was accepted by the Navy officials on board. He came home in high spirits, and for the first time in years, he picked me up and whirled me around the living room.

Later that same year, plans were being made for the dedication of the TV cable link between San Francisco and Los Angeles. The San Francisco Press Club said it could not do this without the presence of Philo T. Farnsworth, who had started it all. At the club's special invitation, Phil and I flew out there. This was Phil's first official visit since leaving in 1930 to set up a television lab and transmitter for Philco. Warmly welcomed, he was interviewed over two television stations and gave a talk before a combined meeting of electrical and electronic engineers.

Some divisions of the old Farnsworth Television & Radio Company were sold off eventually, and Farnsworth Electronics was formed as a dummy holding company for the Farnsworth patents. Because of all the bad publicity connected with the Farnsworth Company during its unsuccessful efforts to preserve its identity, the ITT changed the name to Capehart-Farnsworth, an ITT subsidiary.

The growth of the company under ITT was phenomenal. Its operations expanded from the original Capehart plant to a second, and then a third plant. In 1957 the Boeing company chose the Farnsworth Electronics company to build prototype equipment for its seven million, one hundred nine thousand dollar contract with the U. S. Air Force for the Bomark IM99 interceptor missile. Farnsworth had been a pioneer in missile guidance systems since 1945, having subcontracts on the Bomark, Talos, Terrier, Sparrow, Meteor, Titan, Atlas, Rascal, and Lacrosse.

Left: Phil and Pem leaving to attend ceremonies in San Francisco for the dedication of the TV cable link between San Francisco and Los Angeles. Right: Philo Farnsworth lecturing to the Society of Electrical Engineers San Francisco chapter.

This latest contract would require considerably more space. In July of 1957, General Edmond H. Leavey, the current president and director of ITT, came to Fort Wayne. With Lawrence G. Haggerty, then president of Farnsworth Electronics, he announced plans to build a 160,000 square foot plant at a cost of three million dollars.

Phil's responsibilities during this period necessitated considerable travel, usually to ITT headquarters in New York or the Boeing plant in Seattle. He was beginning to tire, but the exhilaration of working again on the leading edge of discovery kept him going.

The next winter we took Skee and two-year-old Kent for a week on the beach at St. Petersburg, Florida. For the first time, Phil sat in the sun long enough to sunburn his legs. The next day, to protect them, he tied handkerchiefs around them. He usually walked the beach while I suntanned. He said I was a sun worshipper; I said he was a bumble bee, because he could never sit still for more than a minute.

This beach was a great expanse of white sand as far as we could see in either direction, and during this week, we had it mostly to ourselves. We really enjoyed our time with the boys there.

Despite all the activity at the plant, or perhaps because of it, Phil had a continual problem with his health. Although he seldom mentioned it, I felt that subconsciously the second dashing of his hopes to take part in commercial television was at least partly responsible. At this time he was refusing all invitations to speak or to make appearances. However, after the third invitation to appear on Garry Moore's "I've Got a Secret" TV show, he relented.

We flew to New York and were spirited off into a small hotel near the studio, where guests were concealed from the panelists on the next show. Phil was introduced only as "Dr. X," since using his real name would have revealed his identity and secret, which was "I invented electronic television in 1922—at the age of 14." The panel, which included Jane Meadows, Henry Morgan, and Bill Cullen, then asked questions, trying to guess Dr. X's secret.

Phil and Pem Farnsworth with Garry Moore after Phil appeared on "I've Got a Secret" television program.

The title of "doctor" took the panel off on a medical trail. One of the questions was, "Does what you do cause pain?" To which Phil answered, "Sometimes it does, yes." Another question was, "Does what you do have anything to do with psychiatric cases?" Phil answered, "No, not especially," but Garry Moore chimed in with, "In rare instances, it has been known to cause a few." Garry and the audience, who knew the answer, were having fun with this, but time ran out, and Phil was declared the winner and handed his prize—an eighty dollar check, a carton of Winstons, and Garry Moore's eternal gratitude: "We'd all be out of work if it weren't for you."

CHAPTER 28

Old Trails; New Directions

Even as he was working on military research projects, Phil's half-formed ideas lurked on the edge of his consciousness. His original thoughts were beginning to take him into territory that few men—if any—were capable of comprehending.

The original dimension of his thinking was manifest as early as 1937, in his Philadelphia lab, when he first witnessed that mysterious blue glow. The same phenomenon was observed in his Maine laboratory in a Klystron-type tube he had invented. The mysterious blue glow which had taken residence in the structureless center of his multipactor and klystron tubes in the 1930s and 1940s, those bright blue spots, persisted regardless of how high a vacuum he was able to maintain. This had been a puzzling phenomenon, since the usual glow associated with the ionization of the residual gas in a vacuum tube is equally distributed throughout the tube. After ruling out all possible explanations, he came to the conclusion that what he had created was a plasma!

Now he began to spend more and more time in studying this intriguing problem. By 1944 he was satisfied he had the answer. A virtual spherical cathode (negative electrode) was being formed in the volume close to the center of the tube, with an enclosing virtual anode (positive electrode) between it and the real cathode. A large circulatory electron current was flowing through the virtual anode (between the virtual (invisible) and real cathodes) which was ionizing the residual gas in the tube. These ions, which were oscillating through the virtual cathode, were being trapped between the spherical energy levels where they were created: the ions were being contained by inertia—thus the term "inertial containment!"

Phil's ideas gained solidarity early in 1947, when he engaged in a telephone conversation with the master himself, Albert Einstein. On one of our trips to New York for a Farnsworth Television & Radio Director's meeting, we stopped in for a visit with Frank and LuGuaria Reiber. Frank was a research scientist Phil had known in San Francisco. At their home, Phil and I were both captivated by an excellent painting on his wall of Dr. Albert Einstein. Frank told us it had been painted by his mother, and it was quite possibly the only time the venerable scientist had agreed to sit still long enough for a portrait.

Phil had been telling Frank about his ideas on controlled nuclear fusion; Frank asked if he had ever considered discussing them with Einstein. Phil said no; he had never spoken with Dr. Einstein and wanted to develop his math a little further before he did so.

"Well, why wait?" Frank asked, and without waiting for an answer added, "I can get Einstein on the phone for you now." With that, he disappeared into the bedroom, returning a few moments later to tell Phil, "I've got Einstein on the phone, and he'd be delighted to talk to you."

The better part of an hour later, Phil reappeared, his face aglow from the excitement of finding someone who understood what he was talking about. He said Dr. Einstein had told him his own thoughts had been going in this direction at one time, but he was so shocked that his work had been used to produce the atomic bombs dropped on Japan that he vowed never to contribute further. However, he strongly encouraged Phil to formalize and publish his math and pursue his ideas of harnessing the atom for peaceful uses. He said that after the bomb, producing controlled fusion would yield the beneficial side of his work.

This conversation was a turning point for Phil in more ways than one. Not only did Dr. Einstein confirm for him that his original conceptions were viable, it was a great psychological relief to find another human being who shared his increasingly unique perspective. Talking with Dr. Einstein provided the sort of boost for his self-confidence that can come only from finding a fellow traveler in the rarefied regions of the physical universe where his mind now dwelt. Phil resolved to refine his ideas and consolidate his math so that he could go back to Professor Einstein for further confirmation once he was more certain of the results. (It was not until 1953 that another piece of the puzzle forming in Phil's mind fell into place.)

Now back to the scene in Fort Wayne. Phil's rose garden was a great source of relaxation and a point of personal pride. The entire garden had an elaborate watering system of his own design. He planted a large variety of roses, from patented hybrid to miniatures and tree roses. Though he protected the roses with straw and burlap in the fall, he usually found it necessary to replace a number of them each spring. I remember his first bloom came on the first of June. He brought it in, presented it to me with a flourish, and said, "I wanted a rose garden so I could bring you a fresh rose every morning." How could I not love a man like him?

When his roses started to show mildew, Phil dug a trench across the driveway and ran a water pipe to his roses. Each rose had its own spray from holes he had drilled on one side of quarter-inch galvanized pipe caps, to keep the water off the leaves. This solved his mildew problem.

One day a man walking along the sidewalk over our picket fence stopped to watch. In the course of the conversation which ensued, he asked, "What sort of a person is Mr. Farnsworth?" Phil, noting he was assumed to be the gardener, answered, "Oh he's just an ordinary sort of guy." He enjoyed this brief moment of anonymity. His rose garden afforded Phil a welcome change from the daily routine at the lab.

Gordon Knight, then assistant to Fred Wilson, the current president of Farnsworth Television & Radio, came to Phil one day with a problem. His brother, a well-known surgeon in Texas wanted to know if Phil could design a lighted device that could be put down the patient's gullet to view the inside of his stomach. Gordon had heard of the one Phil designed for the Massachusetts General Hospital, but as far as we knew it had never been built.

Phil said he would have one constructed for Dr. Knight. When Gordon told his brother this was finished, Dr. Knight lost no time in coming to Fort Wayne. As they were all in Phil's office discussing the device, Dr. Knight asked Phil if he was sure it would work. Gordon spoke up and suggested they test it right there on Phil's conference table. He even volunteered his roommate Jim (not his real name) to be the subject of the test. Jim was not so sure he wanted to do this, but Gordon talked him into it.

The good doctor gave Jim some medication to deaden the nerves of his esophagus, and he stretched out on the conference table. With considerable difficulty they got the lighted instrument into the stomach cavity. Dr. Knight was delighted. He was actually seeing inside a patient's stomach!

"It looks very inflamed down there, young man; were you out on a party last night?" With a very pained expression, Jim gave a slight nod. "I thought so," Dr. Knight told him. "But otherwise your stomach is in excellent shape." Jim may never have forgiven Gordon for putting him through this, but he said at least he knew his stomach "was in fine shape." Dr. Knight was very grateful to Phil and told him he had a special patient who might now be spared a very serious operation. When he offered to pay Phil anything he wanted, Phil told him it was pay enough to know he was helping some poor, suffering person.

In the summer of 1953, we took the entire family, including Philo and Ruth, on a vacation to the Uintah Mountains in northeastern Utah. Driving from Indiana to Utah in the days before interstate thruways was slow and not all that pleasant. On the afternoon of the second day, I was driving, with Phil sitting in front with four-year-old Kent seated between us. Not a word had been spoken for some time. I thought they must all be sleeping.

Riding quietly in a car seemed to activate Phil's thought processes. Several times when he had a particularly difficult problem, he would ask me to drive him on the thruway. (He had disqualified himself as a driver since his bout with peripheral neuritis.) This was usually at night when traffic was light. Sometimes Phil would discuss his ideas with me, but he had taken a colossal step ahead of me with fusion, and about all I could contribute was to be a good sounding board. I was well qualified for that. When left to my own thoughts, I often wondered about the people in other cars. What kind of human drama was being carried along in this or that automobile? What would they think if they knew the magnitude of the ideas given birth on these quiet rides with Phil?

Suddenly, Phil sat bolt-upright, as though he had been stuck with a pin. Excitedly throwing his hands in the air, he shouted, "I've got it! I've got it!" The air was electric.

Philo and Skee must have been tuned to the same wavelength. As Philo told me later, his eyes met Skee's and they both knew what had happened. For a time, Phil was silent and contemplative; then, probably thinking he owed us some sort of explanation after that outburst, he told us.

"I've figured out a way to control fusion!" he said, with a note of wonder at the enormity of what he was saying. Then, as though to answer the unspoken questions we were dying to ask, he added, "If I can do this, it will be of tremendous importance to the entire world."

"More important than television?" Skee wanted to know.

"Much more, Skee, because it would furnish the world with a very cheap, almost unlimited source of power. Wells could be drilled deep enough to strike water in even the most arid of deserts, making it possible to grow food for starving nations. Since hydrogen can be made from sea water, it could be produced at very little expense. It would be like turning seawater into electricity. The possibilities are almost endless . . . but I'm going to have to be very sure of myself before I let this information out. I want all of you to forget you ever heard what I just told you. It must not go beyond those of us here in this car." With assurances that his secret was safe with us, he leaned back and closed his eyes.

Phil's outburst was a welcome relief to the tedium of the past two days. Our young people had found the trip very boring. The only moving thing we had seen this day was an occasional ground hog which disappeared down its burrow so fast we were left wondering if it had been real or imagined. Phil's words had given them something interesting to think about.

Driving across the flat eastern part of Colorado on the old U. S. Route 40, we encountered a severe electrical storm. Lightning was striking all around us, and the deafening claps of thunder shook us to the very depths of our beings. The sky was very dark and threatening from horizon to horizon. We had seen no cars for the past few hours. For a time it was as though we were alone on an unfriendly planet.

As we passed through the eye of the storm and left the black clouds and lightning behind, the clouds in the west parted, treating us to a most spectacular sunset. Ruth was taking her turn at the wheel, and the sight before her literally took her breath away. She had grown up in Worcester, Massachusetts, and had never been west of Indiana. The wide-open spaces she had been driving through, devoid of any sign of human habitation, were to her all but incomprehensible. Now her artist soul was pained that she could not stop right there and commit the scene to canvas.

We stayed that night in Denver and the next morning made the ascent to the 11,314 foot elevation of Berthoud Pass, the top of the great divide of the Rocky Mountains. Philo was having trouble breathing at this altitude, but Ruth and Skee took the gondola ride which climbed another thousand feet to the top. There they could see a great distance both to the west and to the east. Philo could think only of how soon we could get down where there was some air to breathe.

Phil was feeding quarters into the telescope provided to enhance the grandeur of the scene below. He wanted us all to see this and held Kent up to take his turn. That our sons should learn to share his own appreciation of the Rocky Mountains was important to him. To Phil and me it was coming home. I was driving when we crossed the Colorado-Utah border and announced we would soon be going through Jensen, the place of my birth. We crossed the bridge over Green River and entered the small hamlet of Jensen. Although my father's general mercantile store and the large white house nearby, where we had lived for a time, and even the post office across the road had all been replaced with more modern structures in the thirty years since we had left, I was able to point out where they had stood.

As we drove up the lane to our old home, I was met with an overwhelming wave of nostalgia. My father's brother Ira had married my mother's sister Mary, and they were still living in our old family home. I had written them we were coming. We could not have been greeted with more warmth had we been their own children. Aunt Mary had baked fresh bread and had a delicious dinner almost ready. They insisted we stay the night.

Although Uncle Ira was now crippled with arthritis, he was still the jolly uncle I remembered. When I was a child, he ran cattle on Blue Mountain, near the Colorado border. Each summer when he came home from the roundup, he would be riding a different wild stallion. These were beautiful animals, but no one could ride them but Uncle Ira. I presented him with the gift I had picked up at Berthoud Pass, a beautiful bronze horse, all saddled, bridled, and ready to go. Uncle Ira looked at it with tears in his eyes and said, "You know, Elma, I can't ride any more, but what a nice thing for you to do."

We left early next morning because the Utah Broadcasters Association was giving a banquet in Phil's honor in Salt Lake City. This dinner was a generous outpouring of friendship and acclaim for Phil and his family. At Phil's request, Arch Madsen, president of the association, arranged a reunion with Justin Tolman, the chemistry teacher from Rigby, Idaho, who had figured so prominently in the 1934 patent interference case with RCA. Mr. Tolman and his wife were seated at the head table along with Phil and me and many dignitaries, both local and national. Phil's all-time favorite teacher and mentor, Frances Critchlow, was in attendance. Also present were Dr. Franklin Harris, who had been the president of BYU when Phil attended, and Dr. Carl Eyring and Dr. Milton Marshall who had taught him chemistry and math.

July 2, 1953

Utah's Own Genius—Father of Television

Philo Farnsworth, the genius who made television possible, was back in his native state this week. Quite properly, he was honored at a public banquet by the Utah Broadcasters Association—incidentally, the first such honor that has been paid him in Utah.

That is understandable. Mr. Farnsworth has been absent from the state for a long time, working on his inventions and directing research for the Capehart-Farnsworth Television Corporation of which he is a vice president. And then, too, scientific achievement, while it is appreciated, never receives the public acclaim which it deserves. The applause goes to the extrovert—to the actor or politician or what-have-you who catches the public's eye. How many millions worship Arthur Godfrey or love Lucy who never heard of Philo Farnsworth?

But, no matter. Mr. Farnsworth can take pride in the knowledge that he has accomplished great things. And we, his fellow citizens, can be proud that he is from among us.

This was a heartwarming and memorable occasion for the entire Farnsworth family. My sister Lois and her husband, Dr. Rees Anderson, were there by invitation and gave an open house in our honor the next evening, attended by most of the above-mentioned people. This gave Phil the welcome opportunity to renew old acquaintances.

Lois and Rees had made reservations for us at the U-Bar Ranch at the foot of 11,000 foot Mt. Emmons, in the Uintah Mountain range. After giving us a few days to rest up and become accustomed to the altitude, Phil reserved horses for a trail ride up to the first of a chain of lakes, reserving the cabin there in which to spend the night. He planned to take Kent in the saddle with him. Kent had never been near a horse and was very frightened by this large animal. However, before long, Phil had gained his confidence, and Kent was riding the horse alone, with Phil leading it.

Skee liked to ride. My father had given him a little pony when he was a child in Maine. Both Phil and I had riding horses, but Philo had been more interested in canoeing or looking for turtles and snakes. He was not too happy about this trip, but was being a good sport about it. Unfortunately, he got off to a bad start. When he tried to mount his horse, the saddle turned. This was one of those trail-wise horses that had a way of blowing out his belly to prevent the cinch from being tightened. But, having made this statement, the horse maintained his attitude by giving

Philo trouble through the entire trip.

The trail was very steep, very narrow, and very rocky. The horses at times had to scramble over three and four-foot-high boulders on a narrow switchback trail. As we gained altitude, it was easy to see that one false step could send horse and rider tumbling down the mountainside. When we stopped for lunch half way up, I told Phil there was no way I was going to ride that horse down that mountain. Philo didn't have much to say, other than to complain about his cantankerous mount. He was stoically determined to stick it out, even if it killed him, which he thought it just might.

By the time we reached the cabin on the lake, all Philo could think of was to throw himself on a bed and try to forget the world. The rest of us were enjoying the scenery and the invigoratingly fresh, pine-scented mountain air. We gathered a large pile of dry wood, and Phil started a bonfire.

Soon Philo came staggering out of the cabin, gasping for breath and yelling, "What are you doing! Trying to burn up what little (gasp) oxygen we have up here?" Assured that we would let the fire go out as soon as we had cooked our dinner, he went back to lie down again. By the time dinner was ready, he felt well enough to put away his share of the food.

After dinner, Phil got out his fishing gear, and we all went down to the lake. This was a fantastically beautiful spot. The water reflected the deep blue of the late afternoon sky and the tall pines growing down to the water's edge. Phil began casting his dry flies out from shore, but those trout must already have had their fill of real flies; in any event, they would pay no attention to Phil's artificial flies. Not even his favorite royal coachman would lure them. When dusk started to close us in we gave up, with Phil promising to be up early to catch enough trout for our breakfast.

Phil had no better luck the next morning, so we breakfasted on the bacon and eggs I had brought along . . . just in case. As per instructions, Skee and Ruth led the horses up the mountain to a grassy spot and hobbled them so they could graze. The horses beat them back to the cabin, hobbles and all. The next day it took so much time to round them all up and get them saddled that Phil was concerned we might not make it down to the ranch before dark.

As we were mounting up, two men came down the trail. They had been fishing at a lake farther up the mountain. Asked if we had had any luck, Phil admitted he had caught nothing. They said their catch was more than their limit, so they would like to share with us. I was glad to have my sons witness some good, old-fashioned Western hospitality. This is what my father would have done. He always caught his limit and was generous to a fault.

As we started down the trail, we heard a "Helloo" from down by the lake. Phil answered and soon we saw a horseman coming up through the trees followed by two more. It was Richard L. Evans of "The Spoken Word" fame on the Mormon Tabernacle Choir television broadcast series.

We had met him and his family at the U-Bar corral the preceding evening. Richard had brought his sons up for an overnight and needed the key to the cabin.

When we stopped for lunch, Phil asked about my vow that I would not ride my horse down the mountain. I told him that after watching how carefully my horse placed his feet on that precarious trail when there was only one safe place to put them, I had decided I would rather take my chances with him than risk stepping on a rattlesnake if I walked. Besides, it was probably a two-day walk for someone like me.

Phil gave us only a short time for lunch. It was midafternoon, and the sky looked threatening. A little farther on it began to sprinkle, soon turning into a steady downpour. Dusk started to fall while we were still far up the trail. We rode the last part of the trail in heavy rain and total darkness. In the wet and darkness, I began truly to appreciate that horse; he knew these trails so well he could have traveled them blindfolded. I could hardly see the dim figure of Phil's horse dead ahead of me and knew the other three were behind me only by the sound of the horses' hooves on the rocks. Phil's frequent queries of "Are you all with me?" brought a prompt and welcome chain of response back along the trail.

I had not heard a sound from Kent, but he probably shared my confidence in his father to get us safely down the mountain. Phil had buckled him inside his own tent-like yellow slicker where he was warm and dry. Although Kent went on a number of western trail rides with us as he was growing up, this adventure at the age of four stood out above all the rest.

Arriving wet, chilled to the bone, and miserable, we found the worried stable boys waiting for us at the corral. We had been given the bunk house so we could all be together, and we ran for its beckoning, lighted windows. As we opened the door, I thought we had died and gone to heaven. Certainly, the smells that greeted us were out of this world. Mother Farnsworth and Daddy Joe had arrived laden with supplies. Mother had made hot rolls, beef roast, baked potatoes, and green vegetables. In the middle of the table was one of her specialties, a rich applesauce cake.

After joyful hugs and kisses, we changed to warm dry clothes and huddled around the hot wood-burning cook stove. By the time dinner was served, we had thawed out enough to sit at the table. Mother offered a heartfelt prayer of thanks for our safe return and a blessing on the food. During dinner we recounted our experiences and answered their questions. It was one of those very special family gatherings, a vivid memory to cherish for the rest of our lives.

A few days later, Mrs. Allred, who with her husband ran this ranch, called Phil to the telephone. It was hooked up to a park ranger's telephone line. His caller was a man in Boise, Idaho, whose company was dedicating its new television station, the first in Idaho. He wanted Phil to be there to help give it a big send-off.

Phil told the man he was here on vacation with his family and felt it would not be possible to accept the kind invitation. The caller persisted.

They would send a private plane to pick him up at Roosevelt, a small airport about an hour's drive away, fly him to Boise, and return him the same day. Phil finally agreed, provided he could bring Kent and me and stay over night at Idaho Falls for a visit with his old school friends in Rigby, a few miles to the north.

Meeting the pilot at the small Roosevelt airport, Phil had another request; could we fly over King's Peak on the way? King's Peak, rising to an altitude of more than 13,500 feet, was the tallest peak in the Uintah range. The pilot said we could do that, but since his plane cabin was not pressurized, we might become drowsy at that altitude. Kent did go to sleep, and I became very drowsy, but fought it off because it was such a thrill to see these mountains from this perspective. We had flown over them at a much higher altitude, but here we were almost low enough to touch them. Phil's excitement overcame any tendencies to sleep.

After enjoying the thrill of helping to launch another television broadcasting station, we paid a visit to the idol of Phil's youth, his cousin Kent Farnsworth, for whom we had named our son. He was now living in Boise. After a short but very pleasant visit, we flew to Idaho Falls, where we were met by many of Phil's Rigby schoolmates and their spouses. Phil had notified his close friend, now Colonel Vernal Sorenson, of our coming. To our surprise and great pleasure we found that eight or ten couples had come to meet us, and we were taken to a hotel where they had arranged rooms for us and an elaborate banquet in our honor.

Philo T. Farnsworth speaking to former
Rigby High School classmates.

After returning to Fort Wayne, Philo and Skee resumed their work on a radically new way of producing music electronically. They obtained backing from a distant relative of Phil's in Phoenix, Arizona, to develop a prototype of their instrument. Their benefactor was Joseph Farnsworth (apparently no relation to Phil's new stepfather). However, this connection failed to work out, and Philo and Ruth returned to Fort Wayne. Skee found the style of music for which he had been searching at the University of Arizona at Tempe, near Phoenix, and he enrolled there that fall.

It was not surprising that our boys had an affinity for music; they had always been surrounded by music of some kind. From the time Kent was six months old, I would set him in his jumper in front of our Farnsworth manufactured Capehart record changer. With the cabinet doors open, he could see the wondrous mechanism, which not only changed the record but could be set to turn the record over and play the other side. He was fascinated by this and loved to jump keeping time with the music. Before he was two years old, Phil taught him to recognize most of the frequently played records by their names. Since he could not read, he must have memorized the pattern of their labels. He also discovered for himself the little white record-reject button. He was delighted when he could walk and push it himself.

I think Kent was five when we gave him a small, newly introduced RCA 45 RPM record player. Phil demonstrated how to use it and warned Kent not to let the pick-up arm swing out too far because it would pull the small wire connection loose. That wire was always getting disconnected. The first few times, Phil fixed it; then he told Kent and me it was up to us. After a time, tiring of this, I turned it over to Kent. It sat on the closet shelf for a year or more.

One evening we heard music coming from Kent's room and upon investigation found he had reconnected the wire and was happy as a lark. He also learned to fix other parts of the player when they gave him trouble. A few years later, he and his friends were into CB's (Citizen's band equipment), and he was keeping all of their equipment in repair.

Phil had been thwarted in his plans to give Fort Wayne its own television broadcasting station. The nearest station to Fort Wayne was Kalamazoo, Michigan, and it required a serious antenna to bring in the signal. Reception was so poor Phil hadn't bothered to bring a television receiver home. Then Kent entered the first grade. One day he came home crying. He said the boys wouldn't believe that his father had invented television because he was the only kid in his class without a TV set. Phil gave in and had an antenna mast installed on our roof, then had a receiver brought to our home. Before long Kent took over the job of keeping the set operating.

After returning home from Utah, Phil resumed his duties at the lab with renewed vigor, but the real work took place after hours, at home. He was determined to prove his fusion concept mathematically before attempting to build an actual device that would reduce his theories to practice. Outside of the lab, he spent most of his waking hours in his study, running numbers on his big, cumbersome, top-of-the-line Monroematic calculator. This was really little more than a fancy adding machine, about a third again larger than an IBM electric typewriter, and a far cry from the calculators and computers in use today.

The Monroematic was adequate for Phil's purposes but only barely so. It had a memory bank, but offered only simple, common mathematical functions. Simple long division was a tedious and time consuming process. Phil's ideas were so advanced now, he was even inventing new mathematical symbols to express his new concepts. He was truly on his own.

There was only one man alive who would be able to understand Phil's ideas, and that was Dr. Albert Einstein. Phil's promise to present his math to him once it was formalized weighed heavily on his mind. He was aware that Dr. Einstein was getting on in years and in failing health; Phil fervently hoped he would be able to present his work while the professor was still alive.

Phil had some personal notebooks printed and bound and began keeping notes of his progress in October 1955. Since I was his only witness, it was my signature which verified the content and date thereof. I also made all but his simplest drawings (from his sketches).

As Phil's math developed into well-formed concepts, new problems emerged. Doubts assailed him as to whether he should continue this work. Phil was certain that fusion would provide a source of clean, safe, cheap, and abundant power to the world, but the realization began to dawn on him that it could also be developed into a formidable weapon. These were such uncertain times; did he want to place another atomic arrow into the quiver of a world seemingly hell-bent on nuclear annihilation? He thought of Einstein, who had virtually stopped working after his theories had been used to destroy Hiroshima and Nagasaki. Did Farnsworth dare continue where Einstein had left off? Could he be responsible for unleashing this kind of energy on a world where war and conquest were so rampant? These were questions that began disturbing Phil's conscience as the practicality of his fusion ideas began to materialize in his mind.

His work at the plant was taking most of his time and energy. However, I knew by the frequent chatter of his calculator at night before he came upstairs to bed that fusion was foremost on his mind. He became somewhat withdrawn, and although he seldom mentioned it to me, I knew these questions were eating away at him. I noticed he was making frequent use of Alka Seltzer, which he explained away by saying it was nothing, just a little sour stomach. We had no way of knowing what a terrific price Phil was soon to pay for his torment.

CHAPTER 29

Back at Square One

In March 1954, Phil awoke one morning at five with severe pains in his stomach. My frantic call to Dr. Hasewinkle, our family physician, brought him to our home very quickly. Suspecting a perforated ulcer, he had already called an ambulance. By the time the ambulance arrived, I had arranged to drop Kent off at a friend's home and told Phil I would be at the hospital as soon as possible.

This was a miserable day. The streets were covered with ice, and to make matters worse, a freezing rain was falling. After dropping Kent off, I was traveling on a through street, when a car approaching from the right was unable to stop and plowed into the side of my car. The driver, the owner of a local funeral parlor, listened to my frantic story, quickly wrote down the necessary information, and told me not to worry; he would take care of everything. Fortunately, my car was still driveable.

When I finally reached the hospital, I was greeted by Dr. Justin Arata, who calmly informed me that he had just removed two-thirds of Phil's stomach!

I was furious to think they had performed such a radical operation without my approval! It took some time for Dr. Arata to explain why such a radical procedure had been necessary and to calm me down to the point where I could begin to accept it. Dr. Arata turned out to be a kind and considerate person, and I cannot remember whether I ever apologized for my hostility at our first meeting.

After the operation, Phil experienced tremendous discomfort digesting food; and I felt for a long time that the operation had been more radical than necessary. However, this is what is sometimes called "Monday morning quarter-backing." I am sure it seemed the advisable procedure at the time.

In light of the terrific struggles going on in his mind, Phil again sought psychiatric help, from a Dr. Dunstone. At a conference with him and Dr. Hasewinkle in Phil's hospital room, we decided to take their advice and seek a warm, sunny place for Phil to rest and recuperate.

We ended up at the Papagayo, a highly recommended family hotel in Acupulco, Mexico. We reserved a small two-bedroom hacienda on the spacious grounds of the hotel and walked through plantings of banana trees, coconut palms, and assorted citrus trees to the hotel for meals.

Each morning by ten o'clock, Kent would prevail upon us to take him to the beach, a long, crescent-shaped expanse of sand ending in a huge boulder breakwater at one end. Far down the beach in the other direction was a tipsy-looking high-rise hotel. We were told the Hilton Hotel Corporation, had built it too near the water, and shortly after completion it had begun to settle on one side. We were fortunate to see this beach as pristine as it was, for I understand it is now lined with tall hotels and nightclubs.

My trusty English/Spanish pocketbook dictionary came in very handy; at the hotel the only ones who spoke English were Pepe at the front desk and a couple from New York we met at the beach. From noon to two was lunch and siesta time; then we were off to the beach again until four, when the air began to chill. Kent always kept us there as long as possible.

Once we returned from the beach a little early and caught our cleaning crew just finishing up. There were four or five laughing, bare-footed teenage girls. They had just splashed buckets full of water on the tile floor and were sweeping it out with brooms. It was easy to recognize their leader; she was the one who donned the single pair of shoes placed neatly outside the door—the rest went barefoot. She always left a small bouquet of fresh flowers on the table.

When we tired of the books we had brought, Phil produced a deck of Canasta cards, and we taught Kent to play. He became so good at it he was beating us both before we went home.

Just when I was feeling comfortable because I had not seen a single insect, I opened the medicine cabinet door in the bathroom one night, and a large chameleon-type lizard leaped out, frightening the living daylights out of me. The first night I turned the veranda lights on, I found the entire ceiling completely covered with these creatures. Phil said I should be philosophical about it. They had for the most part stayed out of sight and had certainly done a good job taking care of spiders, mosquitoes and other biting insects. I had to agree.

We spent one afternoon at the beach west of town, which was warmer in the afternoon. There we visited the hotel built into the cliff to give a good view of the cliff-divers, young men of great renown who risk their lives to dive from fifty to one hundred feet into the surf below.

The height of their dive is usually determined by the amount of money collected from interested onlookers. They can dive only at high tide, their leap carefully gauged to miss the rocks below and still strike the water at just the right time and place. Phil put a fairly large bill in the hat, not because he wanted the young man to climb higher, but because he thought he should be paid well for taking his life in his hands to entertain visitors.

One day as we walked from our hacienda to the hotel for lunch, a falling coconut barely missed Kent's head. I told Pepe at the desk I thought it must be time to pick these cannon balls. That afternoon we were entertained by watching the agile young boys shinny like monkeys up the coconut palms. At the top, each took the rope from around his middle and tied it to a cluster of coconuts, then let it down to the men on the ground below. At the beach, boys punched a hole in one of the eyes, inserted a straw, and sold the nuts to thirsty sun bathers. When the coconut milk was gone, the rest was discarded—I hoped they would find a use for the coconut meat.

After the first few days of lying on the beach, Phil was either playing in the surf with Kent or taking long walks on the beach. Kent loved to build sand castles and could busy himself for hours in this fashion.

Time came for us to leave, but due to my poor Spanish, I made absolutely no headway getting reservations over the telephone. I called a cab and went to town. I found the Mexican Airline office filled with yachtsmen, marooned by an offshore storm. When I began having communications trouble at the counter, a kind gentleman stepped forward and helped me make reservations. We had to change planes at Mexico City and planned to take a day for sight-seeing, but the best laid plans . . .

In Mexico City the next morning, both Phil and Kent awoke with fevers and a bad case of "Montezuma's revenge"—otherwise known as diarrhea—which we attributed to the fruit juice we had been served on the plane. We had come prepared for such contingencies, and they both got the proper medication. However, now our continuing flight had to be changed to the next day. Since Phil had lost all interest in sight-seeing, I took a cab and saw as many of the sights of the city as I could in one afternoon.

Arriving home and checking at the lab, Phil was very pleased to find how well the organization was functioning. Now he felt less guilty about taking so much time off. Phil made a valiant attempt to resume his work at the plant; however, his concern over world affairs and the feeling he should be doing something about fusion weighed heavily on him. His mental state, combined with his digestive problems, caused him to lose weight he could ill afford to lose. He requested release from the company, but was persuaded to stay on as systems consultant. This meant he could be called upon from anyone in the ITT worldwide system, but would otherwise be free to follow his own pursuits.

In September 1955, Phil received devastating news: Albert Einstein was dead at the age of 86. This was a crushing blow to Phil, as it came just when he was finalizing his math and getting it ready to share with

Einstein. Phil was very concerned that his ideas were so new only Einstein would be able to understand them, and he had been counting on Einstein's concurrence when the time came to persuade others. With Einstein gone, Phil was even more on his own.

Throughout the 1950s Phil continued to formalize his math and develop operative concepts for his fusion device, which now had a name if not a specific shape. He called it the "Fusor." In 1955 his work took a great leap forward when he solved Poisson's Equation for bi-polar charges (electrons and ions) in a spherical geometry, which was one of the most technically advanced mathematical concepts of the day. From this, he coined the term "Poissor" for the bright blue spot observed in the center of his structureless vacuum tubes. Suffice it to say that the reactive core of the "Fusor" began to take shape in the form of a hollow sphere.

In early January 1956, Rear Admiral Frederick R. Furth, U.S.N. ("Just call me Fritz"), a former director of the Naval Research Laboratory, retired from the Navy at his own request while serving as Chief of Naval Research. He joined the staff at Fort Wayne as assistant to the President of Farnsworth Electronics Company. Within a few months he was appointed vice president in charge of research and development. Having known Phil through their Navy contacts, he became extremely interested in Phil's theory.

Since Phil was again badly in the need of some sun and relaxation, we took Kent on a vacation to Arizona, where we could soak up some sun while preparing material for a disclosure of his theory. Phil wanted to ride horses, and Kent wanted to swim. We flew to Los Angeles, where we rented a car and drove to Camelback Inn, north of Phoenix. Skee was married by this time, and we had not yet had the pleasure of meeting his bride, the former Louise Wolff. We were happy to have them spend a few days with us at Camelback. Louise, a lovely girl, was in her last year as an art student. Skee was happy with the music department with which he was associated at Arizona State, especially his professor, Grant Fletcher.

We had the opportunity of attending their open-air concert at the Fifth Avenue Plaza in Scottsdale. All the music was composed either by the students or by Professor Fletcher. Speak of being carried away on the wings of a song, their music was ethereal; we were totally captivated.

We finally found what we were looking for at El Rancho Vista Bonita, fifteen miles north of Scottsdale. As an added bonus there, Kent found two boys near his own age. Ronny, son of the horse wrangler, was very good with the bull whip and very excited at being accepted at a school that taught trick riding. Robby, son of the couple who ran the ranch, was nearer Kent's age.

After a few rides with us over the desert and into the foothills of the Superstition Mountains, Kent preferred to stay at the ranch, where he could help Ronny take care of the horses. He confessed years later that he had taken lone rides into the desert. We had seen a rancher kill a large six-foot rattler by the road, and we knew snakes were out there. We had also been warned to watch out for scorpions and Gila monsters. Although he could not have convinced us of the fact, Kent was in little danger, for his horse Dot had a set of boundaries and rules of her own. No matter in which direction they headed, or how Kent tried to trick her by riding out through dry washes, she would go only a certain distance, never out of sight of the ranch house.

Scottsdale was a center for rock hounds. The gentleman who ran the largest rock shop in town also owned an interest in an opal mine. He displayed an opal crystal eight inches in diameter and over a foot long, with brilliant colors. It had come from a wet cave. He kept it in an aquarium to keep it wet, because when dry, the crystals fracture. He offered to give Kent one-fourth of his interest in the mine if Phil could find a way to prevent the stones from cracking, so they could be worked for jewelry. He gave Phil some small samples for experimentation, but Phil was soon to be so thoroughly occupied that there was no time for such things.

Phil had scheduled a business trip to San Diego and Los Angeles, so we invited Robby to go with us and on the way did some rock collecting. Kent had been spending his allowance on tools of the trade. He had a rock hammer, a tool to measure the angle of cleavage, strike plates for testing the hardness, and a book we bought him showing samples of all precious and semiprecious stones.

Driving along that first afternoon, Phil pointed to a nearby hill and said he thought that would be a good place to begin. He had been studying the landscape, and he really proved to us he knew his geological formations. This proved to be the most productive find of our entire trip. On the top of this hill, we found agates, jasper, rose quartz, and geodes, just to name a few. The boys were so excited we found it hard to pull them away, but Phil told them there would be other places.

Once more on the road, Phil told the boys if they were to be rock hounds, they should have a basis for this hobby. First they needed to know the basic rocks and their structure. He made them memorize these as we went. On the previous stop he had become weary of the constant question "What's this?" He wanted them to be able to identify their own finds. By the time we reached San Diego, we had many bags of rocks, and due to Phil's teaching ability, the boys had learned a great deal about geology and the structure of the earth.

We visited the famous San Diego Zoo and Mt. Palomar observatory, where one of Phil's Iotron-type high-vacuum tubes was in use, then continued on up the coast to La Jolla. We visited Dr. Claude Zobell, who had not only been a fellow school-wagon driver in Rigby, but had shared a double desk with Phil. He was now one of the leading scientists at the Scripps Institute of Oceanography. We were fascinated by the things Dr. Zobell displayed for us. We saw some of the samples that had been retrieved from depths of the ocean floor never before explored, by the use of some very cleverly designed apparatus.

Continuing on to Los Angeles, Phil purchased a small alcohol lamp, various chemicals and paraphernalia used for crystal identification. Then we circled around by southern Utah so Robby and Kent could see Zion's Canyon. Kent had been there with us in 1949, but of course he didn't remember this, since he was only ten months old at the time. Back at the ranch, Phil and I spent days helping the boys identify their large collection of rocks. Then Robby developed asthma from the dust, and his mother said no more rocks.

Not long after returning to Fort Wayne, Phil finalized his calculations until he had mathematically proven his fusion theory to his own satisfaction. The time for theory had passed, and while the issues that plagued his conscience continued to do so, he felt nonetheless that the time had come to reduce his theories to practice. Whatever reservations he may still have had were all but extinguished when the Russians became the first in space with the launch of Sputnik October 10th, 1957; Phil was quite certain that harnessing fusion energy would put the United States right back into the forefront of the space race.

Fritz Furth was now at ITT headquarters in New York City. As Vice President of Research and Engineering, he was in a position to bring Phil's fusion idea to the attention of Lieutenant General Ed Leavey, then president and CEO of ITT, and several other influential officers, and was also able to create a small separate budget for the fusion energy project. Phil had no idea what to expect from his superiors at ITT; and so complex and advanced were his concepts, he had little hope that anybody in Fort Wayne would understand them. So he wrote a paper describing his work and took it to New York, where he and Admiral Furth presented it directly to President Leavey of ITT, suspecting that only he had the authority to approve such a project.

As Phil feared, no one at the highest executive levels of ITT understood his proposal. Moreover, nuclear physics lay outside the realm of ITT's normal operations. It was common practice in those days to refer such work directly to the Atomic Energy Commission for evaluation. As luck would have it, the AEC's funds for this sort of research had recently been cut, and what they had left had already been allocated to the various research groups attempting by other means to solve the problem of atomic energy.

The Farnsworth method of controlling a nuclear-fusion reaction is quite different from any of those financed by the Atomic Energy Commission. He proposed to contain a plasma (a high temperature, ionized plasma-separated gas composed of positive ions and negative electrons) by inertia within a minute structureless volume, using a self-generating electric field. (Every other process makes use of magnetics for plasma containment!) Phil's approach required relatively inexpensive and simple equipment, whereas the others are very massive and expensive.

The various personnel at the AEC who were supposed to be expert in such things were called upon to evaluate Phil's proposal, but they didn't understand his ideas any better than the mathematical experts at ITT. They reported that while the Farnsworth idea looked like a good one, they doubted it could be made to work. When this opinion was passed on to ITT, its executives refused to back the idea further. When Phil learned of this decision, we sat down and talked about it.

"Pem, as you know, this isn't the first time the experts have said my ideas wouldn't work. I've proved them wrong before, and I'll do it again. It took Dr. Einstein years to get his relativity theory accepted. Well, I don't have years. I'm just going to have to make it work and put the burden of disproof on them."

"How much do you think it will cost?"

"It's hard to tell. Probably more than we can raise."

"We could put a second mortgage on the this place . . . and get a loan on your life insurance."

"That life insurance policy is for you, Pemmy; let's exclude that."

"Well then, if it's for me, I should have some say in how we use it. Besides, didn't you say the company has a seventy-five thousand dollar insurance policy on you? Were you thinking of working here at home?"

We had a large basement, the back end of which Phil had equipped with a wood lathe, table saw, etc. in order to make himself more bookcases for his ever-increasing library. On the lathe, among other things, he turned little two-inch balls to replace those cut from the front picket fence by pranksters. We had paneled the large front part of the basement for a family room, with built-in storage drawers and cabinets. Also, his metal lathe, drill press, and several other items had been shipped from Maine.

You guessed it; we tightened our belts, took a second mortgage on our home, took out a loan from Phil's life insurance policy, rolled up our sleeves, and went to work.

Phil began immediately to equip the basement for a lab and decided to convert the large front bedroom on the second floor to a tube lab. Where once this room had been filled with music from Skee's fervently practiced cello, it now offered enough space to construct the world's first live-in nuclear fusion reactor.

Sheets of cold-rolled steel, welding equipment, and insulation for a bake-out furnace were all brought into the house. A drill press from Sears and a custom-built transformer capable of turning the drill press into a spot welder for various tube components were set up in the upstairs front bedroom. On occasion, Phil secured help from friends in ITT's purchasing department in locating hard-to-find items.

Five half-inch copper pipes were threaded from the upstairs bedroom/ tube room through the walls of the house to a central storage space in the basement, where bottles of hydrogen, oxygen, helium, argon and natural gas were tapped to provide suitable flames for glass blowing and heliarc welding as well as the odd Bunsen burner or two. This was really starting all over again.

Phil hired Gene Meeks, a young engineer at the plant, to come in two or three evenings a week to help him with two-man jobs. Before we knew it, the money had all been spent, and we were not yet operational. Then came the day when we had neither money nor food in the house. I took Ruth and Kent up to the trunk room and told them my plan. We would hurry and pack up several boxes of National Geographic and science-fiction magazines and sell them to the secondhand book store downtown before Phil came home.

When Phil returned from the plant that evening, dinner was all ready. He never knew what we had done that day. In any case, that dwindled to insignificance when we heard the news he had for us. The Farnsworth Company and ITT headquarters in New York had put their collective heads together and decided that if Phil was so sure he had a good idea, perhaps they should put some money into it and give him a chance to prove it. It was on this day that I really began to feel the unseen force behind our "guided tour."

CHAPTER 30

Fusion

Harold S. Geneen, until recently executive Vice President of the Raytheon Manufacturing Company in Waltham, Massachusetts, replaced General Edmond H. Leavey as president of ITT in 1959. He had ambitious plans for the company. Despite the misgivings of the Atomic Energy Commission and his own senior executives, Mr. Geneen was very interested in Phil's ideas of harnessing fusion for domestic use. In 1959 he invited Phil to present his ideas to the ITT board of directors, and after considerable debate, the board agreed to provide nominal funding to allow Phil to prove the feasibility of his ideas.

In his talks with Mr. Geneen, Phil had stressed the utmost importance of keeping the project under tight wraps. His lab was to be tightly restricted to himself, his assistants, and those with a need to know. Also, because of the economic impact his invention would have on the country's economy, as well as that of the entire world, he wanted the right to have a say in how it was to be introduced. To begin with, he felt it should be restricted to space flight, as the power source could then be kept under wraps.

When the start-up plans were finalized, Phil and Fritz decided it was time to file a patent. Since this was a radically new approach to the fusion problem, they decided it would expedite matters if Phil prepared a paper to substantiate his patent claims. Fritz suggested Phil take a few weeks off and get some California sun while writing a presentation for the Patent Office in Washington, D. C. Meantime, his lab could be set up in a restricted section of the Farnsworth headquarters on East Pontiac Street.

A short time later, Phil, Kent, and I arrived in Los Angeles via the Santa Fe Railroad, rented a car, and drove to Twenty Nine Palms in the California high desert. We checked in at the Rancho Vista Delores Motel, and Phil gave Kent some ground rules.

"This is a working trip, son. You have your daily lessons. When they are done to your mother's satisfaction, you are free to swim or amuse yourself with your games. Hopefully, there will be other children to play with. I have a serious job ahead of me which will require much of your mother's time, so I want you to have fun, but stay out of trouble. We will be taking some trips into the desert later, but meantime you must stay close around. OK?"

"OK, Dad."

For the rest of the week Phil was engrossed in his books and papers. By ten in the morning Kent usually had his lessons finished, so unless Phil needed me in his research, I swam with Kent or sat by the pool just outside our door and suntanned. I had brought my portable typewriter to type Phil's paper. He was really handicapped without his calculator, but bringing that monstrosity was out of the question. (Oh, that Hewlett-Packard had been around then.) His slide-rule was of little help. He said he at least should have brought his abacus . . . this with a twinkle in his eye. Yes, he had one. It had been presented to him by a visitor from Japan.

"Hey, bookworm! How about joining us for a swim this morning?" It was Saturday and Phil had not so much as wet a toe in the pool. "I thought one purpose of this trip was to get you some rest and exercise."

"That will be easier once I get my ideas in order. Anyway, I was waiting for the pool to warm up. Motel swimming pools are never warm enough for me."

"The cool desert air of the night does drop the water temperature, but the sun soon warms it back up."

"Tell you what! Lets go have breakfast; then I'll wind up what I was working on last night and swim with you before lunch. This afternoon I want to take a drive in the desert."

"Sounds good to me!" I knew if Phil found the water to his liking he would really enjoy it. From then on he swam with us every day. Phil joined in our games, and Kent was delighted. These play times were becoming all too infrequent.

This was Kent's big day for another reason. There had been few people and no children at the Rancho Vista Delores—until today. A young couple checked in with a cute little girl named Susie, just Kent's age. We met them at the pool. They were taking advantage of homesteading rights. Our benevolent Uncle Sam had marked off a portion of his high desert property for homesteading. A responsible person could lay claim to own

two and one half acres of sand and cactus. Then, if within one year he
had erected a home (one room minimum) and produced a photo showing
the building and lot, all clear of trash or leftover building materials, he
could claim his deed. This couple had taken advantage of this benevolence
and had been building their home in the desert on weekends.

That afternoon we drove out to see the Cactus Gardens National
Park. There we saw everything from a forest of giant saguaro cactus to
the small cholla (choy-ya—and they would) and the "old man," a small
barrel cactus with a hoary white top. As we drove along, Phil spotted
something in the road ahead. He asked me to stop and got out of the car;
with a large paper bag, he advanced on the object. As I edged the car closer,
Kent and I could see it was a very large tarantula. It stood its ground,
and as Phil approached, it charged. Phil quickly swept his bag in front
of it and bagged it.

"What are you going to do with that thing?" I asked as he started
to tie the bag and get into the car.

"I'm going to take it back to the motel so Kent and I can study
it."

"Not with me in the car!"

"Oh, relax, Pem; he can't get loose. When I was nine I caught a
lot of tarantulas while herding cows near Fillmore (Utah). I won a prize
for the most unusual entry when I exhibited a two-quart jar of them at
the State Fair, but the judges said they doubted my wisdom in catching
them."

"Well, I should think so. Now turn that monster loose out here
where it belongs. I will not ride with it. I loathe any kind of spider."
Even though Kent added his plea to that of his father, I was adamant. As
the wife of a prolific inventor, I had become accustomed to strange objects
around the house—but I drew the line at dangerous live specimens. Phil
took it a short distance off the road and turned it loose.

Since it was getting well on in the day, and the magic of our outing
had been shattered, I turned around and headed home. Later, after the
air had cleared, Phil told me of his plans to find a location in this area
where he could set up a fusion lab and hopefully a manufacturing plant
as well, where he could be totally isolated.

The next day Phil arranged for a realtor to drive us out to the Apple
Valley area. At that time, it was largely uninhabited. This realtor was a
very colorful individual, a retired star of the rodeo circuits, as attested by
the photo of him on his silver-clad white stallion, which adorned his
windshield. He had put on weight, but still wore fancy silver jewelry with
his western attire. This was topped by a white ten-gallon western hat with
a rattlesnake skin band. He drove a white, leather-upholstered, two-seater,
open Cadillac with a two foot wide pair of long-horns on the radiator. His
flamboyance was reflected in the fancy prices he asked for the desert
properties he took us to see.

Twenty Nine Palms was a charming town. Taking the place of grass
and flowers were gardens of cactus, colorful semiprecious stones in the

rough, and exquisite "flowers" of fine crystal dishes and goblets turned into vivid shades of purple, green, amethyst, and gold by the heat of the desert sun. During the next week Phil contacted a down-to-earth local realtor, and the next weekend we explored a large area of untracted desert via dune-buggy. Far out in the desert we found an ideal location, about a thousand acres surrounded by hills on all sides. Phil said if he were able to tie up a township, he could plan a model town near the plant, where workers could raise their children and set up their own cultural surroundings, as had been done at the AEC's Livermore installation.

We were now down to our last week, which was spent in refining and retyping Phil's paper. On Saturday we said good-bye to Susie and her parents and were assured that they had completed all requirements for their deed. It gave us a good feeling to know we lived in a country where stories such as theirs were still being enacted.

We took a train directly to Washington, D. C., where we were met by "Doc" Salinger, Phil's mathematical expert, and George Gust, his patent attorney. While they were busy at the Patent Office, I took Kent to the Museum of Natural History. Kent was fascinated by a series of large photographs depicting the development of a human embryo from the time it began to form to its birth. I had not seen this in picture form outside of medical journals, and I was impressed with this wonderful way to teach a child how he came into being. In the Bureau of Statistics, a very large, lighted data board covered one entire wall section. Keeping up-to-date on the nation's population figures, the numbers advanced at every birth and declined with every death. It was disconcerting to see how rapidly these numbers changed.

Phil found us and on the way back to our hotel related what had transpired at the Patent Office. The head patent examiner had invited his top mathematical/atomic expert to sit in on this meeting. After Phil had finished his explanations, this man said he was sorry to say he didn't understand the concept. His superior said: "Let me remind you that never in all the patents filed by Mr. Farnsworth have we found it necessary to reject one. I think if he says he has patentable material, then he probably has. It is up to us to be able to evaluate it. I want you to take all the time you need to be able to give me an evaluation." Phil had anticipated difficulties in making his ideas understood and received some consolation in the reaction of the head examiner.

During the 1950s and 1960s, conventional wisdom maintained that the only way fusion could be attained was by heating the fusible materials to extraordinary temperatures, on the order of many millions of degrees. Even today, multi-billion dollar experiments are trying to duplicate the conditions at the very center of our sun, in order to strip the like-charged atomic nuclei of their natural tendency to repel each other. Only by overcoming this natural repulsion can fusion be attained. Scientists since the 1950s have attempted to produce fusion by a method called "magnetic confinement," which employs enormous magnets to contain and compress the fusion fuel. But heating the particles to high enough temperatures to achieve the intended effect requires inordinate amounts of energy, and the effect can be sustained only for tiny fractions of a second.

Phil's approach to fusion was very much analogous to his approach to television thirty-three years earlier. Where the well-funded "experts" were preoccupied with massive machines that produced very poor—if any— results, Phil had adopted an approach that was once again unique, simple, and elegant. As with his television work before, the problems and hurdles he faced were difficult and profuse. And as before, the experts all thought he was doomed to failure. However, this was the sort of challenge that energized Philo Farnsworth. He knew better than anyone alive that experts are well versed only in that which is already known. Phil excelled in blazing new trails and expanding the horizons of human knowledge.

The analogy to mechanical-versus-electronic television cannot be ignored. As Phil recognized instantly the futility of mechanical scanning, and thus devised electronic scanning, so he had recognized the futility of magnetic confinement. He never wasted a moment of mental energy contemplating magnetic confinement—he went straight on to something much less complicated.

Back in Fort Wayne, Phil was delighted to have a working lab. He was now equipped, once again, to explore the territory he most cherished— the invisible frontier, where he had nothing but his own instincts and his God-given genius upon which to rely.

He had already chosen Gene Meeks as his special assistant and George Bain, an electronics engineer, as project chief under his direction. Since he had access to the most able technicians in the many departments of the plant, he had no need for a large crew. Thus the nature of his work could be kept within the tight bounds he had set. I could see his energy growing as his work progressed.

Now that he had the go-ahead, Phil plunged into the task of building an actual fusion reaction tube which he called a Fusor. To produce the fusion reaction, he would need tritium and deuterium, which required a special permit from the Atomic Energy Commission. While this order was wending its way through the AEC's red tape, preliminary experiments in electron optics—a field which Phil had pioneered—and other areas pertinent to their project were being conducted.

In experiments with tritium and deuterium, a great deal of caution was necessary to protect the workers from accidental exposure to radiation. Phil was above all a cautious man. He and each of his assistants wore badges which registered the amount of radiation to which they were exposed, and the badges were regularly monitored.

By the end of 1959, Phil had made and discarded several Fusor models. He then progressed to a design that appeared to have considerable merit. This was a spherical metal enclosure with six pairs of opposing electron guns, arranged in the form of a dodecahedrin with a hollow spherical anode having twelve conical orifices interspersed radially between the guns and an "electron-collection" system.

To test the electron optics, and as a preliminary test of this design, a simplified version of the two-electron gun was built and tested. This gave Phil valuable data to continue with the more complicated design. Meanwhile, George Bain was designing and constructing a vacuum-pumping system capable of maintaining a vacuum of better than 10^{-7mm} (millimeters) of mercury. Gene Meeks was assigned the task of constructing a high-voltage power supply.

On Friday, October 7th, 1960, in a small basement room, the Fusor was assembled with its bell jar and hooked up to the vacuum and power systems. Making a vacuum-tight seal between the lower half of the Fusor shell and the bell jar was quite difficult. The indium metal used as a sealant formed bubbles which were breaking and preventing a vacuum from being obtained. Eventually (at about 10:00 p.m.), this problem was solved. At sufficiently high vacuum, power was applied and gradually raised until the power supply's maximum was reached. A bright glow within the Fusor increased in intensity as the voltage was increased. When a magnet was placed against the bell jar in line with the orifice of the Fusor, a gas-like flame was drawn out of the center of the structure to a length of about one inch. This proved beyond a doubt that a plasma had been formed, as a natural gas would not have been affected! Phil, Fritz, George, and Gene were witnesses to this major achievement.

The next morning, Saturday October 8th, 1960, deuterium was admitted for the first time, and a run was started. Soon after voltage was applied, a Geiger counter placed adjacent to the bell jar began registering counts which increased progressively as voltage was increased until the counter pointer was driven off its top scale! Just what was causing the intense radiation—x-ray, gamma radiation and/or neutrons—could not be determined.

The following Monday, when the plant's supply room was opened, a sheet of lead was obtained to shield the Geiger counter, preventing x-ray and gamma radiation from entering the counter and permitting only neutrons to register. A deuterium-charged run was made and a small neutron count recorded. The neutron count increased as the voltage increased. As the power-supply voltage was quite limited, the neutron count was also limited. Regardless, this was considered a major breakthrough! The Mark 1-Mod.0 was declared a huge success. (A major change in the geometry of the Fusor was designated as "Mark" with a Roman numeral, and minor modifications as "Mod" followed by an Arabic numeral.)

To delve into Phil's "electrostatic inertial confinement" would entail explaining the details of the Fusor's operation, but such terminology as "virtual cathode, "permeable anode" and "force-fields" would only confuse the reader. Suffice it to say that Phil intended to employ the special properties of atomic particles in effect to contain themselves. These were the very properties that he had first discovered when he learned the source of the mysterious glow in his multipactor tubes.

It seems that only Phil had a special insight into these properties, so it was no wonder that he faced enormous difficulty convincing his peers of the viability of his approach. This is often how it is when men of great vision attempt to push back the horizon of man's understanding of the universe. But Phil's forty years of experience on the very leading edge of discovery had prepared him for the struggles ahead. More importantly, it seems Phil recognized that he had been chosen for a very special role.

By January of 1961 Phil was obtaining very encouraging results. Word of what was going on in his lab began to leak out. The ITT switchboard started getting calls from alert newsmen, like bird-dogs sensing the scent of a pheasant. Finally, Phil agreed to give a New York Times writer, Gene Smith, an interview. A front page article in the late evening edition on January 3rd took the AEC to task for spending so much money on fruitless research when Phil Farnsworth had put his "Fusor" together from "spare parts" in his modest laboratory in Fort Wayne, Indiana. Indignant calls came in to the Times and ITT headquarters in New York. The next morning, the following, somewhat watered-down version of the article appeared, also on the front page of the Times.

Phil also promised Ernest Williams of the Fort Wayne Journal-Gazette a scoop on the story, and his article came out about the same time. This article included some of the material omitted from the Times article.

Once reported in the New York Times, the rumors of "some new process developed by the company" had brought the ITT stock up to the sixteenth most active stock on the New York Stock Exchange for the year, a turnover of 4,116,100 shares.

At this point Phil demanded and succeeded in getting a new contract with ITT. Consequently, in 1962 ITT reorganized the ITT Farnsworth Research Corporation, which had been left as a holding company for the Farnsworth patents. Phil was named a director, president, and director of research of the company. For the first time in his life he had a salary somewhat commensurate with his contributions. To this was added a Christmas bonus of anywhere from four thousand dollars to eight thousand dollars, plus fifty dollars for every patent that was filed for him, a company policy which applied to any employee. Added to this was a seventy-five thousand dollar life insurance policy, payable to me.

Also, Phil was given an option to purchase 7,500 shares of ITT stock at the going price of thirty-nine dollars a share, to be exercised in three lots of 2,500 shares each, and at least a year apart, but within a five-year period. Admiral Furth arranged for us to go to New York, where we were introduced to an executive of the Chemical Bank. Within a few minutes we had obtained a signature loan in the amount of one hundred thousand dollars to buy our first 2,500 shares.

Back at ITT headquarters I was given the honor of writing a check to ITT in the amount of ninety-nine thousand, two hundred fifty dollars. I had been handling our bank accounts, and as Treasurer of the Farnsworth Wood Products Company in Maine, I had handled fairly large amounts of money, but this was big business. I was quite impressed. That Phil was similarly affected was evidenced by the slight trembling of his hand as he was given the envelope containing the stock.

Early in 1961, Phil's fusion project was moved to an improved

I. T. ████ Hopeful on Experiments To Harness the H-Bomb's Power

By GENE SMITH

"Encouraging promise" of a "low-cost nuclear fusion process" was reported here yesterday by the International Telephone and Telegraph Company.

The company gave no details of its experiments, but said they had been conducted "for a number of years."

The problem of producing a controlled and sustained nuclear fusion, and thus harnessing the reaction of the hydrogen bomb, is the goal of many experiments being conducted both here and abroad.

Temperatures of millions of degrees Centigrade are necessary to produce the reaction, and these have been obtained in laboratories for only thousands of a second at most.

The company made no claim to have either achieved or sustained the temperatures necessary for the reaction.

The Atomic Energy Commission in Washington said that it had been aware of work on the fusion process since 1956. The commission also said that it had been told last year that the company was constructing a device to experiment with nuclear fusion.

The commission emphasized that it did not have enough information to evaluate the company's research.

Present nuclear power reactors utilize the fission process, or the splitting of the atomic nuclears. This is the atomic bomb reaction.

Virtually all the thermonuclear experimental work to date has been under Project Sherwood, an Atomic Energy Commission program.

The commission spent $32,148,000 on this program last year. This was described as the equivalent of 515 man-years of scientific effort. The 1960 outlay ran some $4,000,000 more than was spent in the preceding year.

In a formal statement, which he termed "preliminary," Harold S. Geneen, president, said that the experiments were being conducted in company laboratories in Fort Wayne, Ind., under direction of Dr. Philo T. Farnsworth, a pioneer in the development of television. Mr. Green said that the announcement had been made because of "continually circulating reports" on these experiments.

In recent weeks the company's stock has been extremely strong because of rumors of some new process the company had. It wound up 1960 as the sixteenth - most - active stock traded on the New York Stock Exchange, closing the year with a gain of 9½ points at 48. The year's turnover was 4,116,100 shares. It reached its high of 48⅞ in the final week's trading.

Company spokesmen would give no details of Dr. Farnsworth's process, expect to describe it as "an electronic process" that "represents an entirely new approach to fusion experiments."

However, Dr. Farnsworth's work is said to involve an electrostatic process in which clouds of electrons would confine the hydrogen atoms in a small area for the actual fusion process. Most efforts to date have involved the use of magnetic fields to contain the fuel and produce the intense heat—tens of millions of degrees centigrade—necessary for a sustained reaction.

The heart of his unit is a metal ball about half-way between the size of a basketball and a softball. The fuel itself, reportedly tritium, a form of heavy hydrogen, is located in the center of this ball and measures no more than a teaspoonful. Yet once in action it is said to produce tremendous power. An installation about th size of a standard swimming pool reportedly could produce enough power to light for almost two months the area from Forty-second Street to Fifty-ninth Stree between Fifth and Eighth Avenues.

WORKING WITH ATOMS: Dr. Philo T. Farnsworth, who is conducting experiments for the International Telephone and Telegraph Corporation on a low-cost process for nuclear fision.

The actual cost of the device is not known, but it was built at Fort Wayne with spare parts that could be assembled from regular I. T. T. operations.

A. E. C. Visit Expected

The commission emphasized that it was not in position to evaluate the research by the company. It is reported, however, that a delegation would soon visit Dr. Farnsworth in his Fort Wayne laboratory.

He reportedly is ready to explain his basic theories and submit them to cross examination. He may also be able to demonstrate a working model of the unit.

Mr. Geenan's Statement said: "It is true that we have been working for a number of years on a low-cost nuclear fusion process and that our current experiments indeed show encouraging promise. •

Farnsworth's A-power Unit Near Reality

By ERNEST E. WILLIAMS

"Encouraging progress" on a low-cost nuclear fusion process—based on experiments conducted in its Fort Wayne Laboratories by Dr. Philo T. Farnsworth—was reported today by the International Telephone and Telegraph Corp. at New York City.

In its statement, ITT gave no details but indicated Dr. Farnsworth had been conducting experiments for a number of years on the problem of producing a controlled and sustained nuclear fusion energy release.

In the company statement, Harold S. Geneen, ITT president, said:

"Continually circulating reports on a nuclear fusion process we have under experimentation in our laboratories at Fort Wayne, under the direction of Dr. Farnsworth, prompts us to make a preliminary statement at this date in advance of our normal announcement.

"It is true that we have been working for a number of years on a low-cost nuclear fusion process and that our current experiments show encouraging progress.

"However, the final results of these experiments may not be known for some time. But if the conclusions do confirm the present results, they would be important to the future of the company. It is desirable to point out that even these successful results, if confirmed, would be several years in being reflected in the products and earnings of ITT."

While a company spokesman would give no details on Dr. Farnsworth's process, he did describe it as an "electronic process" that "represents an entirely new approach to fusion experiments."

Philo Farnsworth

However, Dr. Farnsworth's work is said to involve an electrostatic process in which clouds of electrons would confine hydrogen ions in microscopically small volume for the actual fusion process.

Most efforts to date — and the major experimentation has been carried on under the Sherwood Project of the Atomic Energy Commission at a cost of some $60 million over the past two years — have involved the use of magnetic fields to contain the fuel to produce the intense heat — 10's of millions of degrees centigrade-necessary for a sustained react⁻¹.

The heart of Dr. Farnswo⁻¹ unit is said to be a metal tu⁻ containing the area of a good-sized grapefruit.

The fuel itself, reportedly, is tritium or deuterium — forms of heavy hydrogen — located in the center of the tube, containing a very small quantity of the fuel.

Yet, once in action, it is said to produce tremendous power.

Dr. Farnsworth, speaking before the Central Lions Club here last September, gave his audience a preview of just how tremendous that power could be.

He visualized a high-energy power pack, capable of being housed in the average-sized living room, which could generate enough power to supply the energy requirements of a city the size of Fort Wayne.

He mentioned an average home with a power plant capable of producing more electric energy than the Grand Coulee Dam. He said it would be a completely noiseless power plant, with no moving parts to wear out.

He described cars with a built-in power pack, capable of running them for the life of the machine.

The actual cost of the device Dr. Farnsworth has built in the ITT Laboratories here is not known, but it is known that much of the equipment was assembled from precision parts made in the ITT plant here.

location on the first floor rear of the Farnsworth Plant. An exhaust hood with blower was installed over the Fusor, and a power supply purchased capable of providing up to 100,000 volts (100 kilo volts). Also, the AEC now issued a license to obtain and store a modest amount of tritium. Runs charged with both deuterium and tritium gave much higher neutron production.

On Friday June 29th, 1961, a strange casualty occurred during some minor adjustments to the experiment. At a time when the Fusor was charged with a mixture of deuterium and tritium, and when no direct current was on the anode, with about 2,000 volts on the electron collector and 100 volts of radio frequency between dynodes and anode, the device suddenly glowed with a very intense blue light which persisted for a few (two or three) seconds. The crew, Phil, Fritz, George and Gene, made a rapid retreat from the room! It was observed that the vacuum had been lost and that tritium was present in the atmosphere, indicating a hole in the cathode. Also, gamma radiation in the vicinity of the tube was quite high!

Since the annual vacation shut-down was to begin at the end of that day, the Fusor was hermetically sealed, and the exhaust blower left on during the two-week vacation. What was at first diagnosed as a secondary electron beam striking an internal arc was later thought actually to be a fusion reaction! We spent two weeks at Estes Park, Colorado.

ITT wanted Phil to move his lab to the east coast. He was presented with an architectural drawing of a large modern plant designed by the Bechtel Corporation (which had constructed the Dresden nuclear-power plant) in the Connecticut River Valley with his name in large letters at its top. We were taken to see the site and were greeted with open arms by the local Chamber of Commerce.

However, news stories began to appear about the range of Russia's long-range missiles and the vulnerability of Washington, D.C., and New York City. Phil, fearing that his project would be targeted, decided he should pursue his plans of hiding his plant away in a remote area in the West. Fritz Furth suggested California, where he would have access to Stanford, where Dr. Chodorow was doing research on particle acceleration.

Phil asked his brother Lincoln, then living in that vicinity, to have a realtor begin a search for a fairly large isolated area, preferably near the ocean. They found such a place in the Half Moon Bay area. Phil and Fritz Furth flew out to see it. It looked very promising except for its location on a hilltop where water might be a problem. This is rolling hill country, and everything from homes to colleges was built on the top of hills. The deal fell through, however, because the property was part of an unsettled estate, and the heir was in Europe for an indeterminate stay.

However, ITT now decided that the work should continue where it was until further progress was made. "Further progress" meant the ability to produce not just a momentary fusion reaction, but one that would self-sustain. This is the ultimate goal of all fusion research—the reaction which, once started, would continue indefinitely under its own power. Phil had certainly succeeded at this point in producing short bursts of fusion and was confident that the ultimate goal of sustained fusion was nearly within

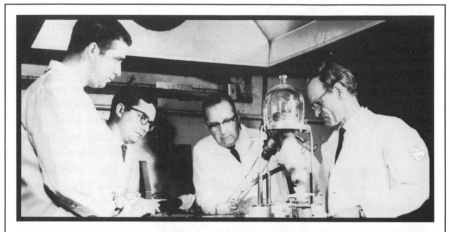

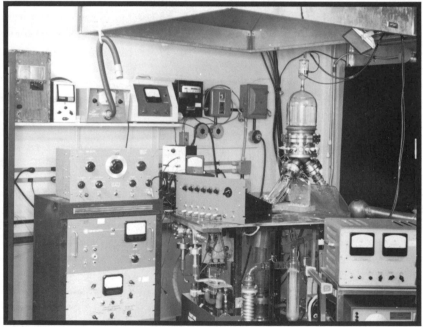

*Top, left to right;
Gene Meeks,
George Bain,
Frederick R.
Furth, and Philo
T. Farnsworth,
inventor with
1962 fusor;
Center: the Mark
II; Left: Proposed
site for the
Farnsworth Lab.*

reach.

By September 1962, Phil was making good progress with the Mark II-Mod.0. Although he had not achieved his goal of 10^9 (or 1,000,000,000) neutrons per cubic centimeter per second, he was completely satisfied that he had proved without a doubt the validity of his concept, and that on more than one occasion he had observed that order of neutron count! He believed that this and other goals would be reached primarily by development and engineering, rather than by any major breakthrough.

Phil felt it was unsafe to run the input energy up sufficiently to reach the sustaining point in such a confined area. Since his desire to move the entire operation to a less-confined location was postponed, he had a fourteen-foot-deep well dug and insulated in the middle of the floor of his lab. The Fusor could then be lowered into this "fusion pit" during tests.

Once when Phil was testing the "Mark II," the second model of the Fusor, he created some excitement that verged on panic. He had heavy, well insulated cables leading from the Fusor to large oil vats designed to dissipate the energy. They had gauges and controls to regulate the amount of tritium and deuterium being used and also to control the amount of power required to trigger the reaction.

One day in 1962, as Phil put the equipment through its paces, he increased the power input beyond the levels of previous tests. The degree of nervous tension present in the lab was already high, as it always was whenever the Fusor was being tested. Phil sat at the controls, slowly adding power to the Fusor, watching all the gauges intently. Steadily the power increased; 75 kilovolts . . . 80 kilovolts, then 90 and 95. Not a word was spoken, and all eyes turned anxiously toward Phil as the power went past 100 kilovolts. Suddenly, there was a terrific power surge, a loud crack like a high-powered rifle, and a lightning-like electrical discharge in the pit. Fearing the worst, all hands abandoned their posts and bolted for the door— except Phil, who sat calmly watching all his gauges, quite certain that everything was under control. Upon examination, it was found that the sapphire support rod in the tube had been melted by the surge of power.

By June 1963 they were working on a sophisticated half-scale Mark II-Mod.O with concentric-sphere optics. This half-scale model could be operated for longer periods and at neutron counts far exceeding those of the Mark I. Phil had observed once in April and another time in May an output exceeding his goal of 10^9 neutrons. One important measurement included the approximation of the quantity of helium and tritium produced by the deuterium-deuterium reaction. These results were indicative of the desired reaction.

It was found that ion guns in the half-scale Mark II-Mod.0 would greatly increase the current inside the tube, thereby enhancing and maintaining the poissor and the fusion reaction. The half-scale model experiments also demonstrated that the Mark II-Mod.O operated as its own vacuum pump! The decision was made to add more ion guns.

The Mark II-Mod.I was designed to permit a maximum count in

the order of 10^{12} neutrons per second for short bursts, without overheating. This device consisted of two concentric hollow stainless-steel spheres assembled in a fifteen-inch bell jar.

During the out-gassing of the half-scale Fusor on October 13th, when only two of the six ion guns were activated, it was noted that one of the neutron counters consistently showed the equivalent of about 10^9 neutrons per second when the applied voltage was in the 35 to 50 kilovolt range!

On the following day, with all instruments carefully calibrated, one instrument did record a small neutron count normally associated with that voltage range; the other registered abnormally high. Phil concluded that the device was generating an extremely high radio-frequency field which was affecting that one instrument. That phenomenon was a reduction to practice of the type of very high-power, high-frequency microwave multipactor he had envisioned.

On February 7th, 1964, a run with the Mark II-Mod.2 reached the full-scale stop. This reading was calculated to indicate a neutron count of at least 1.35×10^9 neutrons per second—the milestone Phil had been striving to reach for so long! This level was reached with a cathode voltage of 80 kilovolts and a current of 30 milliamperes! The upper limit was fixed not by the capability of the device, but only by the radiation tolerance of the personnel in the vicinity. The operation was completely stable and could be controlled and repeated.

The presence of field emission, along with the occurrence of corona, again made modifications necessary. This was completed the last week of May.

In June 1964, Robert Hirsch, who had just completed his doctorate in nuclear engineering, joined the fusion staff. He was assigned the task of making diagnostic measurements and developing an improved ion gun.

Because of the hazards from optimal operation of the Mark II-Mod.3 in an unshielded laboratory and the need for making diagnostic measurements with that device at higher neutron and gamma levels, a four-foot-thick solid concrete-block maze was erected from floor to ceiling. A high-capacity blower system was installed in a hood directly over the Fusor to evacuate any traces of toxic gases.

On December 15th, 1964, the Mark II-Mod.3 Fusor was operated in the shielded room at 80 kilovolts and 30 milliamps with deuterium fuel-gas. On one ten-second run, a neutron count of 5×10^6 neutrons was obtained. On the following day approximately 5×10^7 was recorded.

Having made a real breakthrough at the end of 1965, Phil had high hopes that 1966 could be the year for another major achievement. Experiments with the Mark II-Mod.7 were continued. The goal now was 1,015 neutrons per second—a region where modest power extraction becomes a possibility. New calculations had been made on the top neutron production that could be tolerated in the Fort Wayne Laboratory if the pit were covered and metal tanks of water as a moderator were placed on the top. A sectional hatch cover was constructed for access to the unit.

Experiments on the Mark III-Mod.7 were continued during the summer of 1966, but these produced no significant progress. Many changes were made, but none produced the expected results. These disappointments probably contributed to Phil's ever-worsening health situation.

CHAPTER 31

Ultimatum

During the mid 1960s, Phil's usual reluctance to speak in public began to fade, and he accepted some of the numerous invitations to give talks about his life, his work, and his philosophy. He accepted these invitations because he was concerned about the potentially staggering impact fusion might have on the world, and he wanted to do whatever he could to prepare people for the changes to come. I went with him on most of these occasions, and even I was amazed with the scope of his vision. When his fusion work was finished, the world was in for some big changes indeed.

By 1962, I am sure that fusion was every bit as real in Phil's mind as television had been during 1926 and 1927. There was simply no question in his mind that the Fusor was going to work, and he talked frequently of the breakthrough that was only a few steps away.

In his public addresses, Phil would begin by saying that in the future, historians would look back on the 1960s as the point of demarcation between the high-energy era we were about to enter and the low-energy period that preceded it. He spoke of the enormous energy that would be at the disposal of every man, woman, and child on the face of the earth— and he always spoke in terms of how much fun it was going to be.

Phil's vision for the future could best be divided into two fields of view—his vision for life on earth, and his vision for life in space.

On earth, Phil predicted that fusion power would soon replace every source of energy presently in use. The most obvious benefit of this development would be the end of the pollution that fouls our skies from the burning of fossil fuels, and our streams from human waste. It would also eliminate the dangers of nuclear waste from the fission reactors in use today.

The energy contained in even a small quantity of fusionable material is so vast only a tiny amount would provide the power needs of an entire city. He often cited some calculations performed by Fritz Furth with engineers at Con-Edison, the New York City power company, indicating that all the power necessary to run a city the size of New York for an entire month could be produced by Fusor fuel at the cost of about a nickel; accounting for inflation, that amount is probably up to about a dollar by now.

Phil predicted that all forms of transportation would be radically altered. Fusion engines would replace the internal combustion engine, and all forms of ground transportation would become electrically powered. New cars would come not with a refillable fuel tank, but with a small energy unit which would probably last longer than the rest of the car.

He predicted weather control and talked of "unwinding" tornadoes and diverting hurricanes. He envisioned a Fusor-powered ship that could meet a hurricane at sea and erect a force field in its path that would divert it harmlessly out into the upper atmosphere. Similarly, tornadoes could be tamed by a fusion-powered airship. He also had plans for localized climate control by the creation of "water domes" that would permit the recreation of all four seasons regardless of the actual time of year.

At home, Phil expected that individual dwellings would all be fusion-powered, eliminating the need for power lines. He once stated that a 50,000 kilowatt power plant would sell for around four hundred dollars! Given the vast power at our creative disposal, our homes would be vastly different from what they are now—we might not even recognize them as homes. Phil stated more than once that homes might cease to be built of brick and mortar, and would instead be formed from high-energy force fields, modeled after the poissor phenomenon which formed the heart of his Fusor.

On a subject closer to his heart, Phil predicted that one day the same technology would be used to create free-standing television images with no visible tubes or screens.

He predicted the end of waste-disposal problems, suggesting that each fusion-powered home would be equipped with its own sanitation facilities that would convert human waste into ash that could serve as fertilizer for home gardens.

Phil described how fusion-era metallurgists would discover a whole new range of materials, made possible by foundries that could cook their molten brew at temperatures of up to a billion degrees. The new materials that would result would enable great fusion-powered cities to rise from the deserts and oceans.

On the international front, Phil believed that fusion energy could make warfare obsolete. With vast energy at everyone's disposal, the political and economic barriers that divide nations would soon disappear. Barring that eventuality, all the nations of the Earth could be protected from nuclear attack by virtue of a fusion-powered defense system capable of destroying incoming missiles before they could reach their targets.

But Phil saved his grandest vision for the future of man's exploration and colonization of space, which he believed would one day exceed the predictions of even the most imaginative fiction writers.

At the heart of Phil's vision for space travel was a fusion-powered starship. Once the Fusor was perfected, he figured it would be a relatively simple matter to employ it as a star drive. He said that a fountain pen could hold enough fuel to fly to Mars.

Phil was very critical of the contemporary methods of space travel. He considered modern rocketry quite antiquated, since most of the fuel involved is consumed just getting the rest of the fuel off the launch pad, leaving very little room for an actual payload. With fusion power, he predicted the ratios would be reversed—the propulsion system reduced to the size of a space capsule and the payload the size of the booster rocket.

On a more theoretical note, Phil was equally convinced that our concept of distance would soon be replaced and that man would discover the means to cross the vast emptiness of space. He summed it up in the simple question, "Why do we have to spend so much energy to cross something which is actually nothing?"

There was no question in his mind that fusion would give us the power to colonize other planets and perhaps other solar systems. He predicted that space flight would become as common as a jet flight to Europe. And he predicted that interstellar ships would take the form of a giant fusion "ram jet," hurtling through space at awesome speeds and gathering all the particles in its path, feeding them directly into the fusion star drive as fuel.

And finally, if the population on earth ever got out of control, Phil believed that the Poissor technology he was developing inside his Fusor would one day be used to create whole new planets, by gathering asteroids and other space debris and compressing them in its force field.

Phil's vision may sound utopian, fantastic, and unachievable. But one must remember that his was a unique perspective. He knew all these things were possible because he knew what he was about to create in his own laboratory. Thus, his vision was a window on the future through which only he could see, and he did everything he could to share that perspective with all who cared to listen to him. Phil firmly believed that all this was possible. All he had to do was sustain his fusion reaction, and the future would be at our doorstep.

Early in 1963 Phil completed some investigations to determine the potential field bounded by two concentric spheres, with particular attention to the distribution inside the inner cathode sphere. These investigations, completed in March 1963, demonstrated rather conclusively that a concentric-sphere Fusor with the outside sphere as the anode not only was practicable but also might be the preferred method for producing the controlled nuclear-fusion reaction using the inertial containment principle.

Accordingly, during the third week of March, 1963, Gene Meeks was assigned the task of constructing a rather crude wire-skeleton model of a Fusor with outside optics. On March 26th, 1963 there occurred what was considered to be a major breakthrough and advance in the art of nuclear-fusion energy conversion. Using this model in a bell jar, the actual formation and development of a poissor was observed visually for the first time! In the words of Fritz Furth in a recent interview, "It was a thrilling experience to watch the poissor start forming a spherical, bluish-colored cloud which almost completely filled the volume within the cathode and see the cloud decrease in size progressively as the voltage was increased. When the poissor was somewhat smaller than a golf ball, it became necessary to enclose the experiment in a shield to protect the personnel against gamma radiation. It appeared that with but minor modifications in the optical system and the admission of fuel gas, a substantial neutron count should obtain."

"The indicated modifications were made," Fritz continued, "and just one week later, deuterium was admitted into the bell jar. As voltage was applied, the Geiger counter began to register the presence of neutrons, which count increased as the voltage was increased. When the spherical cloud became somewhat smaller than a golf ball and the radiation became hazardous, the experiment was shielded. At some 60 to 65 kilovolts, the maximum the structure could tolerate, a neutron count of approximately 3×10^6 registered! This operation, importantly, was repeatable. If tritium had been used, the count would have been increased by a factor of 50 to 1.5×10^8."

Phil was certain that his goal of a sustained operation was tantalizingly close.

In October I wrote a birthday letter to Phil's sister Agnes which pretty well summarized the current state of affairs:

"Phil is on the home stretch now, and he has the bit in his teeth. Two years ago I wouldn't have believed he could survive a pace half as strenuous. The next week will be the most hectic yet—because people have begun getting in his hair. The company has had it under wraps—but the time is coming soon when they won't need to or indeed want to. Agnes, I marvel at the drive Phil exhibits. We both feel strongly that he has unseen help. Almost singlehandedly he has solved not one but a dozen of the most pressing problems. Our fight is not over yet. We expect the AEC and other factions on whose toes we are about to step to put up a fight as long as they can—then they will try to prove they did it!"

As the Fusor evolved, the equipment and materials involved became increasingly exotic, and in one instance I became the direct beneficiary.

The Lindy Air Reduction Company was producing man-made sapphire boules for commercial use. These were claimed to be the very strongest insulation available, and Phil had the Lindy Company make long sapphire cylinders to support the inner structure of the Fusor. Even these had to be replaced a number of times after power surges burned them out.

When the representative from Lindy arrived with one of his special orders, he brought with him a jeweler's case full of beautiful cut star sapphires and rubies of all sizes, some of the very first artificial sapphires and rubies ever made. One of Lindy's beautiful ten-carat star sapphires was taken to Tiffany's in New York City for appraisal, where it was appraised at fifty thousand dollars. The jeweler said he had never seen such a perfect star; he was incredulous when told Lindy had made it.

When Phil showed me these stones, I could hardly contain myself. "Honey, I've never seen anything so gorgeous!"

"Believe it or not, these are man-made stones, Pem. They were made by Lindy Air. I was allowed to bring them home so you could choose the one you like. Don't worry; my price for even the stars is only ten dollars a carat. This is my chance to replace some of your costume jewelry." He disliked my wearing costume jewelry, so I had told him it was only until the real thing came along.

I chose an eight-carat star sapphire. Phil insisted I take two six-carat baguette-cut sapphires for matching earrings. These were only eight dollars per carat! I later had the ring and earrings made from my own design.

Though he was very much energized by his work, Phil's schedule was exhaustive, and he was still in constant need of physical buildup. To fill a need for weekend relaxation, he purchased a used twenty-one-foot Trojan cabin cruiser, a beautiful, sturdy mahogany-trimmed boat with two 35 horsepower Johnson outboard motors and two bunks in the bow. We put it on Lake James, at Lanky Dye's Landing, fifty miles north of Fort Wayne. This was an easy one-hour drive on the thruway.

This turned out to be a very good investment. Behind the wheel of the Mary Ann, Phil was a new man. He would shed his worries as a snake sheds skin. Once clear of the dock, he would start to sing, usually "Sailing Down the Chesapeake Bay." We often went up Friday after work, taking our camping gear. We would anchor off shore for two nights, and explore the lake during the day. There we became avid fans of the Detroit Tigers from listening to the games on our Zenith ship-to-shore radio. At first, Kent enjoyed going with us, but he and his friends were into water-skiing, and the Mary Ann lacked the necessary speed for that.

We decided to get adventurous and put the Mary Ann on Lake Michigan at Holland, north of Chicago, and from there make our way to the north end of the lake to Frankfort. My Aunt Agnes and Uncle Harry Russell could meet us and drive us to their cottage at nearby Crystal Lake for a visit. From the Coast Guard, Phil ordered maps of the entire eastern shore line of Lake Michigan, with detailed information of all the marinas, harbors, and other necessary information for our safety. The motors each ran off a ten-gallon gas tank, and we carried spare tanks which he always kept filled.

We had a trailer-towing ball attached to the rear of our car and packed everything we would need for the trip. Kent and his girlfriend (and future wife), Linda Douglass, were to accompany us as far as Holland. Arriving at Lanky's Landing, we asked Lanky to assist us in getting the Mary Ann out of the water. I backed the trailer into the water. They thought they had the boat securely tied down, but she was a heavy boat, and half way out of the water, she slipped and rammed a post on the pier, making a hole the size of a softball in the bow.

"Of all the dumb luck!" I was upset. We had been planning this trip for months, and now it looked as though I would have to cancel our reservations for accommodations at Holland.

"Whoa! Not so fast!" Phil said as he assessed the damage. "I can repair this! The hull is fiberglass. We'll pick up some materials on the way and repair it in Holland. It won't hurt us to stay there an extra day or two. My repairs will need that long to dry and set; then I'll want to put the boat in the water for at least a day to check whether my repairs are seaworthy." Lanky told us of a place in the nearby town of Angola where we could buy our materials, so we secured the boat and started out. I had trailed small vacation trailers, but trailing the Mary Ann was something else. However, by the time I got her in town to the boating shop and out again, I had the situation fairly well under control.

While we waited for Phil's repairs to dry in Holland, our host at the inn took us all out on the trawler he had converted to a fishing boat. To the delight of Kent and Linda, he made us all part of his crew. He was a most interesting chap, and we learned from him much about seamanship on the big waters.

Since we were going to be there several days, we called Philo and invited him to bring Ruth and their son Mark (now five years old) up for a day or two. By the time they arrived, Phil had pronounced his repairs seaworthy, and took us all out for a practice run on the lake. Mark wanted to go on the trip with us, but having been told that Lake Michigan could be a challenge to small boats, Phil invited him and Ruth to go with us only to the next yacht harbor on our map, which at our speed of twenty knots was about three hours away. Philo was to drive up with Kent and Linda and meet them there.

Until we reached deep water, Mark had amused himself with the sonar depth-gauge equipment and other features of the Mary Ann. Then Phil put him on his lap and let him help steer the boat. After he tired of that, he curled up on one of the forward bunks in the bow and went to sleep. We had been traveling about two hours when the wind suddenly began to blow. Ruth and I went back to fasten down the canvas cover over the rear deck, but the wind had increased so rapidly we had to stow the canvas to keep it from blowing away. We sought the shelter of the cabin, because by this time it had begun to rain, and the boat was pitching badly.

"You'd better sit down and hold on," Phil was fighting the steering wheel. "I've been trying to head into the wind, but it's coming from all directions. The waves are getting higher and very choppy. I'm thankful for the sturdy construction of this boat, but it should be ten times larger for this sea."

The visibility worsened until we could barely make out the front of the boat. The commotion had awakened Mark, who was sitting with me. We were all very much concerned that we might collide with another boat. The windshield wipers were no help. Then a small voice piped up, "Grandpa, why don't you wipe the inside of the windows?" Feeling very foolish that we hadn't thought of this, I complied. We could see again! Mark was the only one who was keeping his cool.

Boats were soon approaching from every angle, all headed for the narrow channel leading to the harbor. Once we were safely tied up inside the harbor, we discovered the Mary Ann had taken on a considerable amount of water. After delivering his family to a very worried Philo and seeing them on their way, we formed a two-man bucket brigade to relieve the Mary Ann of the bulge in her bilge. That out of the way, we took our aching backs to the club house for a hot and very excellent dinner. As we came back, the Mary Ann looked so small on the far end of the long crescent-shaped jetty, it could have been the launch used to carry passengers to and from the surrounding yachts. Back on board, we waited only long enough to hear the evening news and get a weather report before seeking our bunks for a well earned night's repose.

It took us four more days to reach Frankfort. We were met by the Russells and spent a delightful evening at their charming home on Crystal Lake. Agnes played her new organ and Harry sang for us. It was a treat to hear Harry's rich, operatic baritone voice again.

The next day we bade these special people good-bye and began our return trip to Holland. We had a good run that day, but the next morning the radio announced "small craft warnings" for Lake Michigan.

Phil was uncertain whether to chance the trip back to Holland in rough conditions, finally deciding to attempt the run by staying close to shore, even though that meant a longer course. The water became increasingly choppy as the day wore on, and by the time we reached our day's goal we were once again in high waves and a driving rain.

Since there seemed no immediate break in the weather, Phil arranged to leave the Mary Ann in port; he had no stomach for further jousting with the unpredictable waters of Lake Michigan. We took a Yellow Cab the sixty or so miles to Holland to pick up our car and drove home from there. For the next three weekends we had small craft warnings. On the fourth, we started out to get our boat. When we had almost reached the east-west thruway, I-80, the radio announced small craft warnings. At the thruway, Phil asked me to take the on-ramp heading east. Once under way, I asked where we were headed.

"To Detroit; the Tigers are playing the New York Yankees there today."

Back at the lab, Phil continued to be immersed in the fusion project.

While considerable progress was made and valuable data compiled, the ultimate goal of a self-sustained reaction still remained tantalizingly out of reach. The work had been going on for almost five years now, and there was little question but that Phil was able to produce fusion, as evidenced by the prodigious neutron counts the Fusor could produce. These neutrons were proof that atoms were being fused together, since the extra neutron was one of the by-products of the reaction. After one test run of the Mark II, Phil reported that "a neutron count of 1.3×10^9 per second (1.3 billion neutrons) was obtained for more than one minute. The operation was stable and could be controlled by the operator."

Despite these astounding numbers, far surpassing the results produced anywhere else in the world, Phil's superiors at ITT were beginning to object to the considerable costs involved and began to express doubts that Farnsworth would ever bring his Fusor to the point of a controllable sustaining conclusion. Phil was aware of the growing unrest in the executive suite, but his faith in the correctness of his concept remained unshaken. He decided that the geometry of the Fusor was at fault. He suspected that even an infinitesimal variance could make the difference. So Phil turned his attention to building a new model, the Mark III.

Fritz Furth told Phil that ITT's Nutley, New Jersey, labs had just purchased a lathe that was claimed to be the absolute pinnacle of man's precision. To get it for a week, it had to be sent air freight . . . with its operator. On this modern marvel, a miniature model of the internal components of the Fusor was made. This small model was a work of art. After Phil had made his tests with it, he brought it home to me, saying, "Here is a thirty thousand dollar piece of jewelry for you, Pem." (At my request and in honor of Phil's contributions to space flight, this was later taken on one of the shorter space missions.)

In the fall of 1965, ITT planned a convention of all of the executives of its world-wide subsidiaries and their wives at the prestigious Hotel Waldorf in New York City. Despite all attempts to build him up, Phil's health continued to be a problem. Fritz, George, and Bob Hirsch were now carrying most of the load. They had worked hard with the company comptroller and accountants to compile a realistic budget for 1966, which they were to present at this time along with a report of results of their previous experiments and a business plan to and including 1969. Phil and I took a plane for New York, and as we approached La Guardia Airport, Phil said he was feeling a little light-headed. I had noticed a paleness around his mouth which had concerned me, but I had not mentioned it.

Later, while dressing for the formal banquet, he suffered some kind of a seizure and fell to the floor unconscious. Frantic, I called for the house physician. By the time he arrived, Phil was regaining consciousness. The doctor said it looked like some kind of seizure and gave him an injection. After I told him what had happened on the plane, he reassured us that it was probably brought on by stress. No sooner had he left than Phil suffered another seizure. I again summoned the doctor, but Phil had regained consciousness by the time the doctor arrived. This time he left some medication which he said would prevent any further trouble. After the doctor was gone, Phil complained of numbness all along the left side of his body. Fortunately, this soon left him.

Phil still felt obligated to attend the banquet, but I would not allow it. I called Fritz and told him to offer our excuses, and we took a plane back to Fort Wayne the next morning. Phil seemed to be recovered, except for a tired, weak feeling. However, the next Sunday at the family dinner table he had another seizure. We were all very concerned about him.

ITT required all of its top executives to have a complete physical once a year at the company's expense. This was arranged in the country-club atmosphere of the Greenbrier Clinic in West Virginia. It had everything from golf and swimming to riding. This was very convenient for those on the east coast, but involved three plane changes from Fort Wayne. Phil told Fritz it was just too much bother. So Fritz arranged for ITT's Beechcraft plane to pick Phil and me up on October 9th, then swing by Washington to get Fritz and his lovely wife Page. We landed at the White Sulphur Springs Airport, where we were met by the hotel's limousine.

At Greenbrier, the resident physician, Dr. Crumpacker, examined Phil to see if he could determine the cause of his seizures. Dr. Crumpacker found no changes since his previous physical, when he had pronounced him fit but in need of rest. He did, however, note that Phil had a large gallstone, but said it should cause him no trouble as long as it was in one piece. He thought it would be a good idea for Phil to put on some weight and take it a little easier. He also suggested that Phil check in to the Mayo Clinic in Rochester, Minnesota, where he could be examined by the head of Mayo's neurological department.

At the Mayo Clinic, Phil went through a mill of humanity seeking help. The Mayo clinic had earned the reputation of a clinic-of-last-resort for thousands of people suffering a variety of illnesses. Phil said it reminded him of his days in Navy boot camp. It was all I could do to persuade him to go back the second day. After three days, Phil was given an anti-spasm medication and told to come back in three weeks for the results of his tests. He had not yet seen the doctor with whom he had the appointment.

When we returned, he finally had an interview with the doctor he had originally come to see. He was told that he had probably had a petit mal, and would need to take the anti-spasm medication for the rest of his life, especially in times of stress.

During this period, ITT came under even more intense pressure to drop not only the fusion research, but the entire Farnsworth subsidiary. Various Wall Street investment analysts were now criticizing the direction of the company, and the Farnsworth operation was at the heart of their jibes. In December 1965, an article appeared in the business section of the San Francisco Examiner, which praised the company's rapid growth, but went on to say:

"Several mistakes have been made, one being the acquisition of the Capehart/Farnsworth radio and electronic concerns. So there were differences in the board and the management which resulted in the decision to diversify into the fastest growing field, service."

To understand ITT's position regarding fusion, it is necessary to see the broader picture of the fusion race at that time. Billions of dollars had been spent overall, and funding had been withdrawn from many of the groups who had failed to reach a continuous power-sustaining reaction. Billions are still being expended in most countries of the world, where scientists are competing for the honor of being the first to make a breakthrough on producing fusion power. It was hard for us to understand why the ITT directors were beginning to lose faith in Phil's project when it looked so promising, but they were.

Despite the controversy surrounding the ITT/Farnsworth relationship, ITT continued the lucrative Farnsworth research group under the name of the Aerospace/Optical Division of ITT, and probably due to the urging of Fritz Furth, Mr. Geneen prevailed upon his board of directors to continue the fusion research for one more year. Fritz came to Fort Wayne with the news that ITT had accepted the laboratory's budget for 1966.

All of his doctors had stressed the need for Phil to slow down. How could he comply, with a deadline to meet and everyone depending upon him? He was determined not to let Fritz down, and he was also determined to prove his detractors wrong; the Fusor would sustain.

Phil had collected a large file of reprints of scientific papers by researchers in the field of nuclear physics. He now went over this material in the hopes of shedding new light on his problems. With a creative mind such as his, sometimes a seemingly non-related item will focus ideas in an entirely new light.

He had jotted down a list of subjects in which he was most interested. I was still scanning the twenty scientific journals he received each month and highlighting articles in which he might be interested. These were noted and placed in a card file for him to read when time permitted.

Robert Hirsch was proving to be of considerable help, especially when Phil was unable to be at the lab. Gene Meeks was exhibiting an uncanny ability to follow Phil's way of thinking, and George Bain had come up with some very good ideas. Phil hoped to find in Bob a person who could follow him through his mathematical path to the final conclusions leading to his fusion equations. To this end he gave Bob access to his reference files and gave him specific pointers to guide him.

On October 5th, 1965, the Fusor Mark III-Mod.5 was finished and tested to determine the effectiveness of the new design. It was finally made stable at 100 kv, but in making a run for a neutron count at 100 kv, with 1 to 5 ma, field emission developed, and a hole was burned through the anode shell. Mark III-Mod.6, completed and tested on October 25th, produced 10^6 neutrons per second at 20 kv and about 1 mm amp. This was about 1,000 times higher than any previous measurements made for that power level. This reading was repeated once but could not be duplicated on succeeding runs, although several times they reached 10^5 nps.

One of the principal problems in the magnetic containment program, the method used by other research teams, was plasma instability. Instabilities represent the major roadblock to controlling the nuclear fusion reaction. In Phil's experiments, random noise pulses were evident over much of the spectrum, but they were few and far between. Therefore, at that stage of development, the inertial containment system did not appear to be troubled by significant instabilities.

On December 28th, 1965, the stability of the Fusor encouraged them to admit tritium and go for a high neutron count. On the first run, a new high of 2.6×10^9 nps was reached at 105kv and 45 ma. When a high voltage run was attempted, field emission developed at 130 kv.

The next morning after the unit was dismantled and cleaned, the power was advanced to 170 kv at a vacuum of 10^{-6} mm of hg, with a mixture of tritium and deuterium as fuel. On the fifth run, a new high neutron count was established of 6.2×10^9. Thereafter, new highs were recorded as the operation continued to improve:

7.25×10^9 (140 kv and 50 ma)
8.85×10^9 (150 kv and 30 ma)
1.55×10^{10} (150 kv and 70 ma)

In addition to breaking the 10^9 neutron-count barrier, the neutron production per watt-second (joule) was increased by a factor of 6! Thus the year of 1965 ended on a very high note.

In May 1966, ITT called another conference for executives of its worldwide subsidiaries. This began with a banquet at the Waldorf. Then the entire group was taken on three reserved trains on an overnight trip to Boca Raton, Florida, where the entire resort had been reserved for a week of meetings, entertainment, and sunning on the beach.

While the gentlemen were attending meetings, the ladies were royally entertained. One day we were taken on a day-long cruise on the Mississippi Queen paddle boat. We were also invited to tour the plantation mansion of a wealthy man up the coast.

On the last night we were treated to a gala party and banquet. This happened to be May 27th, our fortieth wedding anniversary. All five couples at our table were serving, or had served, in Fort Wayne. They were aware of the importance this day held for us, but we had no inkling of what was about to happen. After the last course was served, the master of ceremonies went to the mike on the orchestra stage. Calling for quiet, he announced that a couple in the audience were celebrating their fortieth wedding anniversary, and would Philo T. Farnsworth and his bride of forty years come up on the stage and be recognized? Phil hated this sort of thing, but we were persuaded to be good sports, so went on stage. When asked if there were other couples celebrating a wedding anniversary, two more couples joined us. We took our bows to enthusiastic applause.

Phil and Fritz felt all summer that they were on the brink of a breakthrough, but this coveted success stayed tantalizingly just beyond their grasp. I warned Fritz that Phil was dangerously near the breaking point. He was having so much discomfort after eating he ate less and less. The only thing keeping him on his feet was his tenacious willpower and grim determination to succeed before Fritz reached the age of retirement.

Even as his determination increased, so did his mistrust of ITT and its intentions. Phil harbored great hopes that fusion would be used for the benefit of all mankind, but he doubted that the directors of ITT shared his humanitarian intentions. ITT being a highly profit-oriented organization, it was naive of Phil to expect them to go along with his philanthropic ideas. Despite his reservations about ITT's ultimate intentions, Phil continued to try to solve the problems in the Fusor.

Meanwhile, Bob Hirsch, George Bain, and Gene Meeks were trying some of their own ideas on the Fusor, but their results were no better than Phil's. The problem was of course one of the highest technical order, but perhaps it could be explained in simple terms: in producing a fusion reaction, Phil had created what amounted to a miniature man-made star, around which formed a multi-layered electrostatic force field. The problem was that, once the reaction was started, the force field prevented more fuel from getting into the center of the reactor core. Without additional fuel, the star simply burned out.

Phil wrestled endlessly with this problem. He had come so far and solved so many problems along the way he just could not rest until he found his answer.

One day, Phil came home from the lab early in the evening with a look on his face such as I had never seen before. After dinner I asked him what was on his mind.

"We made a run today. I didn't dare take it up as far as I wanted to, but I want you to see this."

I drove Phil down to the lab, which was dark and empty. The facility was still off limits to all but those involved in the project, but was guarded only by a single night watchman. The guard was surprised to see Phil at that hour, but had me sign in. Phil guided me to the back of the building and unlocked the door to his lab.

Indicating a stool where I should sit in front of a row of meters he wanted me to observe, Phil took his place at the controls. There was one meter in particular he wanted me to watch. I was to report on the meter's response as he started applying power to the Fusor, which was still resting at the bottom of the pit where it had been tested earlier in the day.

It took just a minute or two, as Phil applied the power, for the Fusor to begin coming to life. Not knowing what to expect, and with chills running up and down my spine, I kept my eyes glued to the needle Phil told me to watch, reporting its position to him as it climbed the scale. At first, the needle settled in a position about three-fourths of the way up the scale. All at once, the needle shot all the way up the scale and stuck there, pegged against its highest value.

"It's gone off the scale!" I called to Phil. Immediately, he turned off the power. And then the most amazing thing happened: The needle just stayed right where it was. All power had been cut to the Fusor, but that needle just stayed stuck . . . for a period of at least a half a minute after Phil had shut it off.

When the needle finally started settling down, I turned to Phil, who was now staring at the needle as intently as was I. I waited for him to tell me what this meant. I could almost hear his thought wheels turning. Then he broke the silence by saying,

"That's it. I've seen all I need to see. Let's go home!"

CHAPTER 32

Back to the Woods

Phil usually turned down invitations from scientific journals to write about his work. However, late in the summer of 1966, his friends from the Franklin Institute in Philadelphia came to Fort Wayne to see what he was doing. This time, he accepted their invitation to write a paper for the *Journal of the Franklin Institute*. However, he had one important detail to take care of first.

Phil was working with Fritz Furth, Hans "Doc" Salinger, and George Gust, his patent attorney, on his second fusion patent. He was happy in the belief that at last Hans and Fritz had finally grasped an understanding of his new math. Together they worked for the better part of a week on the patent claims. Finally, at a critical point concerning one of Phil's pivotal equations, he realized that they had completely missed the vital point of his concept.

With this disheartening realization, Phil closed his briefcase, arose from his chair and announced, "I have given you all the material you need to finish this patent. Now I am going home and get drunk!"

On the way home, he bought two large cases of beer and went home to see how fast he could drink it. To see his pale, pain-racked face made me heartsick. He told me he was all used up; he had nothing more to give. He prayed God to let him die.

I wanted to call his doctor. He said he would not see anyone, least of all a doctor. He had no more faith in the medical profession. Also, he asked me not to contact his sons or his family; neither would he see or talk to anyone from the lab or the New York headquarters.

Fritz called to inquire about Phil. When I told him of Phil's orders regarding talking to or seeing anyone, he said he knew Phil would like to get the Franklin Institute article written. He offered that if Phil could dictate it to me, and I typed it up, he and Bob Hirsch would put it in shape to publish. Fritz thought this could be done, even if it was only a page or two at a time. I told him I held little hope, but promised to let him know whether this were possible.

Phil had refused any kind of food. When his two cases of beer were used up, he ordered four more cases from the neighborhood liquor store. Now he left his bed only to walk to the adjoining bathroom and back, still praying to God that he could be relieved of the burden of this life. Sure of a negative reaction to Fritz's suggestion, I approached it carefully. Suggesting he might enjoy hearing some of his favorite records, I brought in a record player. Then I suggested it would be a good time to put these on tape, a project we had long talked about. I set up our large Sony reel-to-reel tape recorder by his bed.

He seemed to enjoy this. When I put on some of the old numbers we used to play, he even asked for his violin. I was encouraged.

The next day, I brought up the subject of his Franklin Institute article. When he said it was out of the question, I said perhaps it was not. He could dictate his ideas into the microphone, and I could transcribe them. Then I told him of Fritz's offer, and said he could at least give it a try. When I had a half-dozen pages ready, I called Fritz, who sent Hugo, the company driver, for them. By the time these pages came back revised, we had six more ready to go.

I was feeling pretty good about all this until Phil read the revised pages. He was very upset. He said they had revised them all right. They had revised his math so it would fit into the accepted grooves of their own ideas. He changed it back to his equations and sent it back to the lab. No doubt thinking it would not be accepted that way, they changed it back. Phil gave up and refused to have anything more to do with it.

A week or two later, Bob Hirsch appeared at the door with an article he had written for the *Physical Review* on Phil's work. He wanted permission to add Phil's name as co-author. I asked him to wait while I asked Phil. Phil took one look at the math and said, "I can't put my name on that; it is not my ideas. It is Bob's version of my ideas. He completely misses the mark." Nevertheless, Bob published it in the *Physical Review*.

Through the winter of 1966-67, Phil clung doggedly to his determination to die. It was torture to see him gradually waste away, in spite of anything I could do. His doctors had said unless I could instill in him some will to live, there was nothing they could do.

Our son Philo had divorced and remarried by now, and had moved with his new wife Diana to San Francisco, where their baby girl, Maya Aum, was born March 11th. By early June Phil was very weak, and after these long months of twenty-four-hour nursing days, I was very near to complete exhaustion. Then Philo called. He caught the note of desperation in my voice when I told him his father was very ill.

That evening they arrived in Fort Wayne, after catching the next flight east. We all went upstairs, and Diana laid little Maya down beside Phil on the bed.

What happened next still moves me deeply. Phil considered little Maya, and little Maya looked back at her grandfather, and suddenly their eyes met and locked in a mutual gaze which went on for many minutes. There seemed to be a silent, profound merging of mortal souls taking place before our very eyes. The baby just stared, and Phil kept staring right back, both silent and still; their hushed exchange was a wonder to behold. It was as though this tiny babe, whose soul had so recently communed with her heavenly Father, had brought a message to her emaciated grandfather. The solemn stare between these two held so long I glanced at Diana and Philo in wonder. Tears filled their eyes, and I could hardly see them for the tears in my own eyes. We were all sharing in a most sacred moment. At that moment, Phil decided life was worth living after all.

Since Phil still refused medical treatment, I suggested we go to Maine, where we had built a cabin on our old property the previous year. I secretly hoped our old friend Dr. Ken Dore could help him. This presented a problem. Phil was too weak to stand the trip by car, and to fly entailed two transfers and a fifty mile ride on the other end by automobile. In any case, I wasn't sure he could even withstand the trip by air.

In the end, Phil agreed to let Philo and Gene Meeks get him to the private clinic of Dr. Arata, the surgeon who had performed his gastrectomy, for a check up. To my great relief, he was pronounced fit enough to make the trip by chartered plane, which Philo arranged. Philo's son Mark and I accompanied Phil, while Philo drove his wife and baby and our collie, Thunder. Kent and Linda (Kent's wife and the daughter we never had) were living in Fryeburg and continuing the research on Phil's vacuum-drying of lumber project.

The plane landed at the regional airport, which included a four-hundred-acre strip of land formerly belonging to us. We were met by our good friends Dotty and Harold Kiesman, who delivered us to our cabin. Harold had been overseeing our property, and Dotty was keeping the books. There we found a cheerful fireplace and a hot dinner waiting in the oven. Kent and Linda soon arrived with their lovely little daughter, Jennifer. Later that evening Dr. Dore paid us a visit. The next day he returned and presented to Phil a schedule whereby he could regain his health and strength, and Phil eagerly accepted it.

I felt as though a tremendous weight had been lifted from my shoulders. Now the long weeks of strain, worry, and sleepless nights began to take their toll. I had been holding myself together by sheer necessity and willpower. I was taken to the hospital with acute appendicitis. This was a close call. Actually, the appendix ruptured as they opened me up, requiring extra time in the hospital to clear the infection. Soon after my return home, a blood clot caused a bilateral infarction in my heart, taking me back to the hospital.

Philo was needed back in California. He had located Zeline McAllister, our former housekeeper, but she felt duty-bound to stay with the elderly bedridden gentleman for whom she was working. However, the morning after my return to the hospital, Zeline called to say she would go and cook for Phil and be there to care for me when I came home.

This was a great relief to Philo, because now he could return to his work. Concerned that housing costs in California had gone beyond the reach of low-income families, he had devised a do-it-yourself modular house to be built for under thirty thousand dollars. To save our life-giving forests, he designed his house to be constructed from space-age plastics. These plastics, now used in space shuttles, are stronger than steel. Since he lived in Bolinas near the San Andreas fault line, his house was designed to withstand earthquakes up to eight on the Richter scale. Also, its spherical shape could withstand winds of hurricane strength.

Later, Philo helped Diana get elected to the Bolinas School Board, then went with her to Sacramento, where they convinced the State Board of Education to put up funds for replacing the dangerously old and outdated school complex in Bolinas. Then he assisted in designing the new buildings.

My own problems had come as a shock to Phil. For the first time, he realized that I was, after all, not quite invincible. He determined to get himself in shape so he could take care of me. On the third day he was able to be driven to the hospital in Bridgeton, approximately eighteen miles away, to visit me. As soon as I was out of danger, he began thinking of ways to get me home.

Dr. Dore offered the hospital bed he had acquired for his father's last illness. Phil called a local family friend, Barbara Harmon Tyner. She had retired from nursing when she married, but said she would be glad to make a daily visit to take care of nursing routines. I was then brought home in an ambulance. My homecoming was a great relief to Phil; the strength of the bonds between us had made the very thought of losing me very distressing to him. Our faithful collie took up his stance by my bed. He would rest his head on the edge of the bed and gaze at me with eyes expressing his love and concern.

The presence of dear, devoted Zeline hovering solicitously in the background was a great comfort to us both. That night dinner was an epicurean delight, such as only Zeline could prepare.

Later Phil took up his violin for the first time in many months. He went out into the solarium adjoining my room and serenaded me, pouring out his love in his music. At the end, he played our song *Always*; then as though to close in prayer, he played the well beloved Mormon hymn, *Oh My Father*. This act of love and the progress Phil had made on his road back to health did me more good than any medical help.

On my third day home, I felt so well I forgot the warning not to raise my arms, especially not to brush my hair. This thoughtless act unfortunately sent me back to the hospital. This time I stayed in the hospital for four weeks. Phil came every day with flowers, a gift, or some dainty tidbit Zeline had baked.

On December 15th, I was given permission to ride in a car for the first time. Phil asked Harold Kiesman to drive us to the nearest serious shopping center, which was in Lewiston, where we visited the best women's clothier. Then he told me, "I want you to pick out your Christmas present, and I suggest you start with the mink stole you've always wanted."

"Don't you think that's a bit extravagant?"

"No, I don't. In fact, I want you to get an outfit to go with it. When you first went to the hospital with a heart attack, I realized I might never have the opportunity to do this for you."

We decided to spend the winter in Florida, so we reserved a cottage on Sanibel Island, offshore from Ft. Meyers, for January and February. Dr. Dore told us the first of January should be a safe date to make the trip to Florida. Phil chartered a Boston-based plane to pick us up. Zeline was going along to take care of us. To avoid the New Year's rush, we planned to stay in Boston the first night, catch the early flight to Ft. Meyers, spend New Year's Eve there, and arrive on Sanibel Island the next day.

All of these reservations were made—then the day before departure it began to snow. By the morning of the day we were to leave, there was nearly a foot of snow on the ground. Phil called Harold to see if the flight were still possible. Harold called back with word from the man who operated the airport snow plow. He was standing by, but could not plow the landing strip until the snow stopped falling.

That was a nerve-wracking game of suspense, with frequent calls to and from Boston and Fryeburg. The runway had no lights, so it would be necessary to take off before dark. At the last possible moment, the snow stopped. The snowplow went to work, and the pilot took off from Boston. Kent, Linda, and Jennifer were among the well-wishers who came to see us off. With a sigh of relief, we cleared the runway and headed for Mt. Chocorua, New Hampshire, and Boston. Thunder had been left to keep company with Lotta Dog, Kent and Linda's St. Bernard.

Sanibel Island is a beautiful spot and one of the world's best beaches for gathering shells. Zeline and I could hardly wait each morning to get out and see what treasures the waves had washed on shore during the night. Phil searched with us the first few days, but then said he was "shell shocked" and refused to take further part. He enjoyed walking along the smooth, wet sand near the water or just sitting in the sun looking out to sea and thinking.

When the cottage next door became vacant, we rented it for a month. Phil had the Kiesmans drive down for two weeks to chauffeur us around. When Harry and Agnes Russell returned from a visit with their son in Puerto Rico, they spent several days there. Ken and Dorothy Dore, spending the winter near Ft. Meyers, were also frequent visitors. I was not yet allowed to drive, so Kent and Linda drove our car down to relieve the Kiesmans. Phil chartered a fishing boat, and we took Kent, Linda, and the Dores out fishing. The captain and his mate knew these waters; we always came home with a load of fish. Zeline was top angler.

Arch Madsen, the president of KSL-TV in Salt Lake City, sent a man to interview Phil for a documentary on his life, at the suggestion of LDS Church President, David O. McKay. To complete the filming, Phil promised to be in Utah on May first. In April we arrived in southern Utah.

My sister Lois and her husband Rees met us at Cedar City, in south central Utah. They were on their way for some fishing at Lake Powell, with their boat in tow. Lois had thoughtfully driven her own car down for us to use. We spent a few days with Philo, Diana, Maya, and their new baby Matthew at the Driftwood Lodge at Springdale, at the mouth of Zion's Canyon, before going on to Salt Lake City. While at Zion's Canyon, Phil slipped, and in saving himself from a fall injured his wrist on a large boulder.

At the famous old Hotel Utah in Salt Lake City, Phil struck his wrist again in the shower. When Lois and Rees arrived that morning for brunch, Rees's trained physician's eye noted the angle of Phil's wrist, and upon examination, he told Phil it was broken. Brunch was delayed while Rees and an orthopedic surgeon met at the hospital to set the bones and put a cast on the wrist. This was to add greatly to Phil's problems in the coming days.

Ted Capener, who was to make the documentary for KSL, wanted to film part of it in San Francisco. KSL offered to fly us down there, but Phil wanted one last ride on the scenic vista-dome train, which was soon to make its last run. This was not entirely selfish; he knew I would enjoy it and he wanted Zeline to see some of the western scenery. These were the good old days, when travelers by rail expected good food and good service and got both.

The present occupants of 202 Green Street were gracious hosts to us and to the cameraman; then after interviews with Provost Fred Terman at Stanford University and Dr. Leonard F. Fuller, formerly of UC-Berkeley, at his home, the film was finished on the viewing area atop Telegraph Hill by the Quoit Tower. In the beginning days of television, we had often climbed the western side of the hill from our flat on Vallejo Street to feast on this view. In those days there was no tower or railed viewing area. Now, instead of the many ferry boats, there were two bridges, the beautiful Golden Gate Bridge and the long Bay Bridge, linking San Francisco, via Treasure Island, to Oakland.

After a short visit with our families in California, we flew back to Salt Lake City. Zeline attended LDS church meetings with us there. She was greatly impressed with the friendliness of the members and the ability of the young people to get up and give talks before the congregation. We explained that they were given this opportunity to be heard as children, to prepare them for more responsibilities as they grew older.

When she was a child in Canada, Zeline's family had belonged to the Catholic Church. Her mother, a genteel French lady, had come to Canada to teach school. She married a Canadian Indian and raised a family. They were very poor, so when her dear mother died, the priest refused to let them have her funeral in the church. He did condescend to come and administer her last rights on the church step. Zeline never attended church after that. Now she wanted to know more about the Mormon (LDS) Church.

We had the unexpected pleasure of an audience with LDS Church President David O. McKay. Due to his advanced age and failing health, we hadn't thought this would be possible. Arch Madsen had arranged this meeting and went with us. This was one of our most treasured experiences.

When we got up to leave, with great difficulty and finally with considerable help, President McKay got to his feet to bid us good-bye. In the foyer, his secretary told us with tears in her eyes, "That was to show his esteem for you folks."

Since we planned to stay for the BYU commencement exercises in June, the Hotel Utah offered us its vacant motel manager's apartment on the top floor of the motel, where we enjoyed the picture window overlooking Temple Square. We had an inspiring view through the glass-fronted second floor of the Temple Square Visitor's Center of the beautiful large statue of our Savior Jesus Christ, which was always lighted. Always up before the sun, Zeline loved to sit by the window and gaze at this statue. Then she would watch the wedding parties come in on their way to receive their endowments and be sealed to each other for time and all eternity in the Temple. This impressed her deeply.

We drove to Provo to pay our respects to Ernest L. Wilkinson, president of BYU. Phil was to receive an honorary degree of Doctor of Science. We also met several of the faculty, including Dr. John Gardner, head of the Physics Department, and Dr. Andrew Gardner, who headed BYU's atomic energy research. Though I was a Gardner, as far as we could tell neither was related to me nor to each other. There are many Gardner families.

On the way back to Salt Lake City from Provo, Phil was thoughtful. Suddenly he broke the silence.

"How would you like to come back to Utah to live?"

"Do you mean that? You know how much it would mean to me to be close to my family."

"Would you think I meant it if we bought a home while we're here? I think I'd like to finish fusion at BYU. This would add considerably to the university's world prestige. I've been thinking about it. My fusion group in Fort Wayne has been left more or less rudderless. I think they would come out. We would have to form a research company to raise money for the fusion project. Besides, I think it's high time we carry out our plans to get married in the Temple . . . Why are you crying?"

"B-because I'm so h-happy."

We found our dream home, a rambling stone house at 5166 Cottonwood Lane, situated on Cottonwood Creek in Holladay, fifteen miles south of the city. Phil wanted two riding horses, and this was horse country. We met again with President Wilkinson of BYU, the Doctors Gardner, Ben Lewis, assistant to the president, and several others. Excited about having

Phil finish his fusion project there, they greeted us with open arms. As a matter of fact, Phil was not so sure he liked the hug-and-kiss greeting I always got from President Wilkinson.

On the big day of the commencement exercises, Agnes and Claude were there, since their son John was graduating. Lois and Rees were there, and we were waiting by the entrance for the long procession of graduates to march past. Phil was following the university officials with the other honorees. As soon as he came in sight, we could see he was having trouble keeping his "mortarboard" on his head. It was windy, and even two-handed graduates were having difficulty. Phil still had one arm in a cast and a sling. Then Phil's mortarboard was lifted from his head by the wind. Fortunately, William "Bill" Edwards, a fellow student at BYU back in the twenties, now a leader in financial circles, was directly behind Phil and caught it. He managed to help Phil put it back on without breaking step with the others.

As he sat on the stand with the other dignitaries, I could see Phil's headgear was still not very secure. When his time came to arise and receive his elegantly framed diploma, his mortarboard fell off again. He carefully put it on his seat and went to the podium with wind-tousled hair. Agnes and I shed tears of compassion for him, but the entire audience rose as one and cheered him. Asked to say a few words, he told the graduates that theirs was a tremendous responsibility. They and other graduates around the nation would one day be the leaders of our country, and "I hope you will be able to do a better job of it than we have." He returned to his seat amid another standing ovation.

We flew to Fort Wayne—for the last time—to list our home with a realtor and arrange for movers to pack and ship our belongings. Philo met us there to see what he could do to help. I was told I could have only two days to sort and pack. On the second day I told Phil this was an impossible task; a week would be a great deal easier on me. He was in no condition to help, and I would trust it to no one else, so he called the movers and told them since we would not have time to sort our belongings, they should just pack everything in the house and ship it to Utah. They did a good job of it, though even Phil agreed they were going too far when they boxed up the contents of waste baskets.

While in Fort Wayne we talked to Phil's former fusion group, George Bain, Gene Meeks, Jim Heiney, Edy and Harold Heastan, all of whom agreed to come to be part of our company to be known as Philo T. Farnsworth Associates. Gene was to take his family to Utah in time to get his children enrolled in school. Jim Heiney and his wife Eleanor would come after we arrived. The Bains and Heastans would come when the company was organized.

We picked up a new Cadillac Coupe De Ville with all the extras. Phil said that since I had to do all the driving, he wanted to make it as easy as possible. However, he thought I was not yet strong enough to drive to Maine. He invited our daughter-in-law Linda's parents, Eugene and Jean Douglass, to go with us. We enjoyed their company, and Linda was of course delighted to see them. We planned to stay in Maine until September.

To our great delight, Zeline had agreed to return to Utah with us. Knowing how much Phil disliked eating in restaurants, she came up with a plan. She would take an electric coffee pot and a hot plate. Then with a minimum of food supplies, she could cook our breakfast plus any other meals we required.

Neither Phil nor I were in very good shape, so we planned to take as long as needed for the trip. Phil had set three hundred miles as a maximum day's drive. However, by the time we reached Kansas City, I was getting anxious to get to Utah and our new life. When I thought he wasn't looking, I would slip in another hundred miles, but he usually caught me.

I always found driving fast exhilarating. Early one morning on an open thruway, Phil and Zeline seemed to be dozing, so I decided to see what the 472 cubic-inch, 300+ horsepower V-8 engine under the hood could do. I was up to ninety before I knew it, so I just kept pushing it. I had reached my goal of one hundred mph and was gradually bringing it down when Phil opened an eye and said, "Don't you think you're going a little too fast?" I was then down to eighty and agreed that perhaps I was. I brought it down to my usual setting.

We arrived in Salt Lake about the second week in September. My sweet sister Lois and her daughters had washed and relined shelves and drawers. They had even unpacked and stored dishes, utensils and supplies. Lois had also bought pink towels to match the color of our bathroom. Phil said using pink towels made him feel like a sissy, so I bought blue towels with "IIIS" embroidered on them. I could always put them in a drawer when we were entertaining.

We were happy to be again involved in church affairs. After Phil was ordained an elder, we were married in the Salt Lake Temple May 27th, 1969, our forty-third wedding anniversary. As we drove into our driveway, Kent was ready with his camera. Inside, there were two wedding cakes, one with fancy decorations and a replica of the Temple from Robert Stone, who worked for us; the other was a four-tiered cake Zeline had made and iced; Linda had covered it with tiny fresh roses.

Zeline joined our church, and at her request, Phil baptized her. He also baptized Bill and Linda Cramer, friends of the family. Bill had come from Fort Wayne to work for us, and they had been investigating the LDS Church since they had arrived in Utah.

Phil was on medical retirement from ITT and had been advised to take at least a year to get back on his feet. One day we were talking of how to get our new venture started.

"Pem, I figure I have somewhere between three and five years to live." Holding up a hand to stop the protest I was about to utter, he continued, "Within that time I want to give the world three things."

"I know you want to finish fusion, which would supply cheap, safe, and almost unlimited power. That seems to me to be monumental in itself, for one in your condition. What else?"

"I want to get the company organized so the men can take in contracts; they are well qualified for that. Meanwhile, I will put Gene Meeks in charge of setting up a lab at BYU so we can resume work on the Fusor. When George Bain arrives, he can take charge of setting up a lab to fill contracts. Meantime, I'm going to add to the back of this house a glass-enclosed swimming pool. This will be made large enough for my other experiments."

"Swimming will be good for both of us. Can we afford a Jacuzzi somewhere in a corner?"

"I'd planned on one, but let me go on. I have a couple of ideas

Front and rear views of Farnsworth home
on Cottonwood Lane, Salt Lake City, Utah

that will solve two growing problems in urban communities. I can remove unfilterable viruses from culinary water and solve the ever-increasing problem of human wastes."

"Is that all? Phil, I don't mean to sound sarcastic, but I think you are taking on too much."

"The last two projects can be carried on simultaneously with my other work. I will add eight more feet to the length of the pool addition for this and add six feet to the width for hydroponic gardening experiments. This will have to be carried out to a fine art for deep-space exploration."

"Surely, Phil, you're not still planning on going into space!"

"With a lot of luck and an east wind I just might make it. There is no place I would rather die and be buried than out there among the stars and galaxies."

"If you accomplish all this, honey, you will need a lot of help."

"I'll have a lot of help. You know that Edy Heastan is a registered nurse; she can help me on the microscopic studies on the virus project. She was in charge of our clean room in the tube department in Fort Wayne. When Dr. Arata saw it he said he wished his operating room were as clean. In making our tubes, we had very little tolerance for dust of any kind."

"Yes I know. Edy and Harold will both be great as two of our associates. How are we going to finance all this?"

"True, we have to raise a lot of money, but these things are so badly needed, we should be able to sell them to someone that can see their potential."

"Phil, you think so big, sometimes it frightens me. If you were thirty years younger . . ."

"But I'm not. We will have to train young people who can take over. I want to build a combination lab and university. Students will conduct hands-on experiments along with their studies. When they complete their experiments they will have finished a worthwhile and useful product. Knowing why they need to know will make learning fun. My engineers will need to be able to double as teachers and continue to guide through the experiments."

"All this sounds great, honey, but it will be a tall order to put together."

CHAPTER 33

Philo T. Farnsworth Associates

After 1966, the fusion project at ITT had been suspended and Phil placed on medical retirement, which entitled him to a modest monthly benefit check. However, feeling his time was running out, he started making ambitious plans for the new company, Philo T. Farnsworth Associates. Each of the associates was capable of heading a department in his field of expertise, and so could function with minimum direction from him. Phil reasoned that by taking in research and engineering projects, the company could finance itself, and when he was able, he would be in a position to complete those projects that were so important to him.

Wanting to pick up the fusion work where he had left off at ITT, Phil chose Gene Meeks to oversee the early stages of the project at BYU, and with Dr. Andrew Gardner to conduct preliminary experiments. Dr. Gardner was in charge of the BYU atomic energy research. While they did this, Phil hoped, by the therapeutic use of the pool and Jacuzzi, to build himself up to the point of being more active on all fronts.

Knowing the propensity of his creative mind to push his frail body to almost inhuman achievements, I was very concerned. However, my efforts to persuade him to take another year to regain his strength before implementing these plans fell on deaf ears. Phil said he had no choice.

His time was very limited, and he felt duty-bound to solve these three last problems for the world: as the population grew, virus control, waste disposal, and a cheap source of power would become ever more urgent. I had no doubt of this and hoped his plan would work out the way he had visualized it. Certainly, he would find it hard to take it easy with all these ideas urging him on.

We engaged the services of my nephew, John Anderson, an attorney connected with the firm of Beaslin, Nygaard, Coke, and Vincent, to form our company. Meanwhile, Gene Meeks and Jim Heine located a place for a laboratory in Draper, fifteen miles south of our home in Holladay, just south of Salt Lake City. They began making preliminary plans for adapting it to our use.

Soon, George Bain, our vice-president and technical director, and his wife Eva arrived; then Edy and Harold Heastan and Raymond "Ray" and Tony Bart joined us. George had been second in command through the Fort Wayne fusion project. Edy, a registered nurse, had been in charge of the clean room where electronic tube components were fabricated under the most stringent sterile conditions. It had been Edy's capable hands who had turned drawings of fusor components into beautifully crafted, workable elements. Harold was a capable electronics man. Ray had been with us since our Philadelphia days. After Cliff left, Ray had been put in charge of the glassblowing tube department. Ray was not only an artist with glass; he did marvelous paintings in oils.

I gave a welcoming party for the group. Our new home's lower level, with its large family room with fireplace and snack bar, complete with stove and refrigerator, was a wonderful place for entertaining. Everyone seemed to enjoy getting together, though once the ball got rolling we had very little time or energy for such pleasures. Between the family room and the guest room was a hall which opened through sliding glass doors onto a terrace and lawn, which were later sacrificed for our swimming pool and jacuzzi.

In late 1968, we called the associates together for our first meeting. Phil, as president, outlined what he expected to accomplish by getting this group together. Then all of those assembled were invited to express their opinions on what they saw as our potential. A consensus arose that we needed three more people to make this a fully functional operation: Earl Keiser, a model maker; Cornelius Hart, whose specialty was welding the difficult metals needed for the vacuum tubes we would be making; and Kenneth Crow, an expert in the chemistry connected with these vacuum tubes. These people were still in Fort Wayne.

This was something of a surprise to Phil and me. The expense of moving this group to Utah had already far exceeded our estimates. Phil could see there was merit to what they said, so he acceded to the decision of the associates. He warned them, however, that he would soon come to the end of his resources at this rate. While in Fort Wayne he had invited Wayne Frame, the machinist who had performed miracles of precision for the fusion project, to join us. He had also asked Fred and Irene Haak, who had so ably assisted with the fusion work. These people had been a part of the Farnsworth group for years, but their commitments in Fort Wayne were too strong to break at that time.

Phil had delegated George Bain to contact the National Aeronautical Space Administration (NASA) and other concerns that might be in need of our capabilities and research.

Long range financing for the company was discussed and a vote taken on the advisability of contacting an underwriter to take a stock issue through the red tape of the SEC. This passed unanimously.

Gene Meeks and Jim Heine gave a report on the building in Draper and displayed drawings with their suggestions of what had to be done to make the building functional. With certain changes, the plans were approved. Now all we had to do was find the money. Phil had sold most of his ITT stock to cover initial expenses, except the shares he was holding to pay off the Chemical Bank in New York. He said he would do well to carry the company for another month, but if it became necessary, he would put a second mortgage on our home.

When John Anderson heard about Phil's plans for an underwriting, he suggested he turn us over to a partner of his firm who was more experienced in these matters. This was Bruce Coke, who said he thought he knew a man who could link us up with an underwriter. That person turned out to be John Turner, and the underwriter was Lloyd W. Sahley, President of Midwestern Securities Corporation, members of the National Association of Securities Dealers, Inc., operating out of Chicago and New York City.

Mr. Sahley came to Salt Lake and met with Phil and me; then Phil called another meeting of the associates and presented Mr. Sahley. Mr. Sahley outlined the situation to us and confirmed his offer in a letter of intent to Mr. Coke.

To fill the gaps in our group, we first approached Ken Crow, since the associates felt he would be helpful in making our initial plans. He accepted our offer and managed to move to Salt Lake within a month. Hart and Keiser liked the idea, but would not be able to make the move so soon. Since their services were not yet required, this was well suited to our purposes.

On March 12th, 1969, we called our first official meeting of Philo T. Farnsworth Associates. Phil brought everyone up to date on the two projects he felt the company was ready to take on.

Phil suggested our first project might be an ore separation project, which was intended to remove valuable minerals such as titanium, chromium, and vanadium from land along the Union Pacific Railroad's rights of way in Montana. He felt this project was one the associates could jump into with a minimum of tooling-up and without waiting for funding from the stock issue. He also considered the titanium of special interest and had other plans for projects employing its unique qualities.

The second project Phil outlined was an infrared-sensitive surveillance device that the Salt Lake City police department needed in its efforts to compile evidence on drug smuggling and other illegal activities. They wanted a tube with special memory capabilities, so the images could be retained and recorded long after the actual activity had taken place. Phil felt that the associates could produce a device that would sell nationwide, but Ken Crow expressed reservations about conflicting with ITT's patents in the field. Phil was less concerned with the potential patent complications than he was with just stopping dope traffic. He suggested that ITT would be happy to cooperate if it were guaranteed manufacturing rights for whatever device the associates developed.

"I like the idea of working with ITT," Ken said. "I think that would be the quickest way, to let it have some of the . . ."

He was cut off in mid-sentence by Phil, saying, "They might go along with it as a public service."

Hearing this, Jim Heine interjected, "They don't strike me as being 'public service' people."

"That's a sad commentary on ITT," Phil said.

"But I think it's very accurate," Ken added, concluding the discussion.

On the subject of financing, Phil announced that he soon expected to have two hundred thousand dollars in front money available from the underwriters. "I will have to reimburse myself for sixty thousand dollars in order to keep my credit rating high. If, toward the end, we find the remaining one hundred and forty dollars inadequate, I will have either sold my property in Maine or mortgaged it so I can carry the company again for a little while."

There followed a discussion of the underwriting process, particularly as it related to the underwriter's cut and how much stock would be left for the associates to purchase. Each associate was required to own at least one share of stock, although Phil said he would just give the stock to them if need be.

Our son Kent had designed a corporate seal for the company, and this was accepted with a minor amendment. Then a recess was taken so Phil could call Bruce Coke for an update on Mr. Sahley's activities on the underwriting. In particular, Phil was anxious to learn if Mr. Sahley had sent some of the stock that was to serve as collateral for a bank loan.

Phil reported that there was still some disagreement over the number of PTFA shares Mr. Sahley was to receive. The matter was still being negotiated, so the collateral stock had not yet been delivered to the bank.

Following some discussion about the criteria for hiring a receptionist and the appointment of Edy Heastan as head of quality control, the meeting was adjourned.

Although the ore separation and police surveillance projects were essential for the operating health of the company, the project closest to Phil's heart was fusion. BYU had agreed to build a lab for the Fusor, but before he could proceed, he needed to reach some accommodation with ITT, since ITT still owned his two fusion patents.

Phil's first move was to write Mr. Cornell Ramsen, Jr., head of the ITT patent department, with an offer to buy the fusion patents. He thought since ITT had lost faith and, apparently interest in them, they would be willing to sell them.

Mr. Ramsen was in Europe when Phil's letter arrived, so the letter was acknowledged by an associate, saying an answer awaited the return of Mr. Ramsen. Weeks passed. Finally Mr. Ramsen replied that it was not ITT's policy to sell patents. However, he felt a non-exclusive license might be to the advantage of Phil as well as ITT, due to the high cost of yearly fees to keep the patents active in foreign countries. The patents had been filed in every country with a patenting system, of which there were many. Mr. Ramsen said that ITT might or might not maintain these patents in all countries.

This arrangement would mean that Phil would have to finance the research, but ITT would have complete control of the results of his work. He would not have any say in how fusion power was introduced, which presented him with a serious dilemma.

However, we now had more immediate and pressing problems. Mr. Sahley had not sent the stock to secure our interim loan, and even worse, Mr. Coke was unable to reach him by telephone. Only after threatening legal action did the associates receive a promise by one of Sahley's assistants to send the stock to secure the bank loan.

In order to keep the company operating, we had taken a second mortgage on our home and mortgaged a ten acre lot where we had ambitious plans for building a new concept of a combination laboratory/university complex. We had also cashed out Phil's matured life insurance policy and finally, assured he would shortly be reimbursed, Phil pledged the remainder of his ITT stock for a fifty thousand dollar bank loan. When the stock arrived from Mr. Sahley, the bank insisted that Phil and I sign the loan as guarantors.

Despite the tight financial situation, the company was beginning to take shape. George Bain had secured a lucrative contract from NASA, but although we had been able to lease furnishings and some equipment, we still lacked some expensive equipment to complete this contract. Ken Crowe was working on the ore separation project. Jake Garn (later mayor, then U.S. senator), who was married to my niece Hazel, was at the time a city commissioner in charge of the water department. He brought Phil some water samples from the various sources serving Salt Lake City. Edy Heastan was doing microscopic studies of the water, as Harold had procured a small ruby laser as a light source and set up the necessary equipment. Kent, now a commercial photographer, was setting up to do microphotography of her slides. The other men were working on various other jobs.

Under Kent's direction, the pool addition to our home had been completed, and Phil was making use of the pool and Jacuzzi for daily therapy. A virus removal setup had been built from Phil's sketches and was ready for testing in the extension to the pool.

We had most of the family with us the Christmas of 1969. Philo and Diana were now the proud parents of three: Maya Aum, Matthew, and Philo Krishna, just four months old. Kent and Linda were there with their four-year-old ballerina, Jennifer. Russell and Louise had parted company after the death of their sweet little daughter Ruthie. Russell's newest love was a talented artist/writer, Rose Kaplan. Russell's musical career was now keeping him very busy, particularly during holidays. He had found that making a living with a piano or cello was very difficult in New York, but good bassists were in great demand. He shifted to bass and teamed up with the Recordo Ray Latin orchestra. They were very popular, especially in Latin America, where they won a popularity contest against the other leading Latin orchestras, including the tzar of Latin music, Tito Puente. We sorely missed Russell and Rose, who were unable to be with us.

It was good to hear the patter of little feet in the house. Mark Willem, Philo's oldest son by his first marriage, now nearing the advanced age of twelve, was granted permission to use Grandpa's riding lawn mower. When he learned how to handle it, he was all over the place. His father had to remind him it wasn't a motorcycle. This was a family gathering I will always remember.

At Phil's suggestion, BYU built an underground testing lab for the Fusor in an old root cellar in an on-campus hillside. They had given Phil a small office in the nearest building. ITT had sold us some power supplies and other equipment from the Fort Wayne operation, and Gene Meeks was beginning to run fusion experiments there.

The underwriting now seemed indefinitely delayed, further aggravating the company's financial position. In a last-ditch effort to raise money for the company, Phil and I flew to Maine. There we learned that New England banks do not lend on undeveloped property, so we put the now fourteen-hundred-acre woods lot up for sale and returned to Salt Lake in a very depressed state of mind.

All the PTFA business had been accomplished almost entirely by the associates. What energy Phil had was used in trying to get funding. The contracts and projects in-plant, given the equipment with which to work, could have made us self-supporting. But this was not to be. At this time another bombshell was lobbed into our camp.

The Travelers Insurance Company, carrier for ITT's employee medical insurance and payer of Phil's disability checks, sent a man out to check on him. The investigator reported back to Travelers that although Philo Farnsworth was in very poor health physically, there seemed nothing wrong with his head. Since he had essentially earned his living before through his thought processes, there seemed nothing to prevent him from continuing to do so. So Phil's monthly payments were cut off.

At this time our close friend Vern Hobson of BYU came to our rescue. Hearing of our dilemma, he reported to President Wilkinson, who authorized Phil to be put on the BYU payroll for his fusion project.

This was July 1969, and the biggest story in the news was the flight of Apollo II to the moon. The journey was scheduled to climax with Neil Armstrong and Buzz Aldrin setting foot on the moon's surface on July 20th. Zeline was watching with Phil and me as the Apollo was circling the moon.

"I just can't understand how we can get a television picture to earth all the way from the moon," Zeline said, her eyes glued to the screen.

"I can tell you the reason the picture is as good as it is. They are using a miniature version of my Image Dissector tube," Phil said, the tremor in his voice betraying his emotion at seeing the mission so near to completion and knowing his part in it.

"Phil's Image Dissectors still give the best detail to the picture because of their direct scan operation," I told Zeline.

"This will be the first big step," Phil said. I could imagine the thoughts that must be in his head, as he continued. "If this all goes well, there will be no holding us. The natural curiosity of man will take us out, one planet at a time, until we break from our own solar system into the universe beyond. I wanted so much to be a part of this exploration." There was a note of wistfulness in his voice. Knowing how much and how long he had planned for this, I was filled with compassion to hear the hurt coming through what he said.

Fascinated, we watched the preparations for the landing, and Neil Armstrong's perfect execution of this operation which had been so long and carefully rehearsed on earth. As Armstrong's foot touched the surface of the moon, Phil expelled a long sigh and said, "Pem, this has made it all worthwhile."

CHAPTER 34

Curtain

Phil was always fond of saying that our lives were a "guided tour." But if that were the case, then it seemed by now that our guide was determined to keep us from reaching our desired destination.

Although we watched with millions of people the world over each phase of the return trip of Apollo II to earth and rejoiced in its recovery, our hearts were heavy. Philo T. Farnsworth Associates was in serious trouble. Bryce Wilhite, a professional corporate troubleshooter, was hired. During this time, Bruce Coke had been burning the continental wires up in an attempt to learn what was happening to our stock issue. His efforts succeeded eventually; however, before locating Mr. Sahley, he found through another source that Mr. Sahley had cut too many corners on a previous stock offering, and the Securities and Exchange Commission had suspended his license. We'd been taken in by a sharp operator.

Now, due to the delays, PTFA was in such a precarious position no one would take over and underwrite us. Bruce Coke, who was to receive a large block of stock for his services, now bowed out of the picture. Except for the choice of underwriter, he had performed very well for us.

Then a letter came from the president of the American Sony Company wanting a conference with Phil. We named a time, and three gentlemen arrived. One, carrying one of the first Sony video cameras, asked if he might record the interview. They offered Phil anything he wanted if he would go and set up his research lab in Japan. Thinking their chief interest was in his fusion energy project, he politely refused the offer. Our new attorney, David Gillette, George Bain, and our son Kent were present at this interview. Zeline served one of her delicious luncheons to the group, and when they left, Phil was so weak he required my help to get to his bed.

We were unable to meet our payroll, and Nellie Downey, our very capable secretary/accountant had all she could do to hold things together. When the lease payments on the lab and our payroll withholding taxes became delinquent, we were locked out of the lab by the IRS. Those were indeed dark, desperate days. We could see no way out of this crisis. Were all of Phil's unselfish efforts to cure some of man's most serious ills to be for naught?

It was not much longer before PTFA came tumbling down around our ears. The bank loans were called, erasing the last of Phil's ITT stock. Bryce Wilhite and the associates found it necessary to find employment elsewhere. Edy Heastan took a nursing job with a local gynecologist. Harold went into business for himself and Neil Hart was hired by a local nationally known electronics company. The others took employment in various parts of the country.

In order to keep the fusion project going, we gave Gene Meeks a deed to a hundred-plus acre lot adjoining our property in Maine. The Draper Bank gave him a mortgage on this to pay his salary. We had recently purchased this land to help the owner who was seriously ill in the hospital. We had not yet had it surveyed, but were familiar with the boundaries claimed for it.

At this point we had a visit from Mr. Glen Young, a business consultant. He offered, for a certain percent of the action, to connect us with people who could, and very probably would, bail us out of our situation and fund Phil's projects.

Some prominent local business people were brought to interview us. In each case they seemed very interested in working with us. Several of these appeared to be people with whom we could make a reasonable agreement. However, after our hopes rose, the decision was always the same: it would take too much money to pay off our debts, or what we had was a "bag of worms" they did not wish to be entangled in. I began to feel this "bag of worms" was gnawing at my innards.

I could see beyond what they were saying. Their real concern was Phil's health. He was obviously not well, and since the real assets of the company were the products of his brain, they feared that without him, we had nothing. This was especially true of fusion.

I had seen Phil bring himself out of serious health problems twice before and was convinced that, relieved of his financial worries, enabled to devote his energies to his pet projects, he would yet achieve his goals. It was breaking my heart to see how his fading dreams were sapping his will to live.

At the request of the Draper Bank, Gene Meeks had his Maine lot surveyed. The surveyor found that the larger part of the lot we thought we owned had been sold to another buyer, prior to our purchase. Investigations by our Maine lawyer revealed that the former owner was now deceased and had left no estate. It seemed that no matter what we did, we were doomed to failure.

Gene came to me with his problem. I told him to file a "friendly" suit against us. Suits had already been filed by the IRS, the plumber, electrician, and several vendors who had worked on the laboratory. To give us some breathing room, our attorneys suggested filing for Chapter 11 of the bankruptcy code. Phil bristled at this. He said absolutely not. His Maine property would cover all claims. I told Gene he had better get in line with the rest of them. BYU was paying Gene a small salary, but this was inadequate to keep his family. Not long after this, because of the state of Phil's health, the fusion project was cancelled, as was that source of income for Gene as well as Phil.

John Anderson came to our rescue. Presenting our case but getting nowhere with Travelers Insurance Company, he finally entered a suit against them on our behalf. He eventually obtained a settlement from them of forty thousand dollars to be paid to Phil in monthly payments equal to the amount of his former checks.

In January 1971, Phil became very ill with pneumonia. I wanted to call an ambulance and get him to a hospital. He flatly refused and said if he ever went to another hospital, he would not come out alive. He was given massive shots of penicillin. On the fourth night, his temperature shot up to 104.8 degrees, and he became delirious. I kept cold cloths on his forehead.

About 4:00 A.M. he opened his eyes and calmly told me not to worry; it would be all right now. He said his guardian angel and another personage would now keep watch, so we could go to sleep. He then drifted off into a deep peaceful sleep for about six hours. When he awoke, he told me these "personages" said he was on the brink of death, and it was his choice whether to return to his earthly life or go on. He told them he still had work to do on earth. They then said, "So be it." He felt the fever begin to leave him. It was then he spoke to reassure me, then drifted off to sleep.

Phil had told our good neighbor A. Ray Curtis about his wish to acquire Arabian horses for us to ride. Mr. Curtis advised us to start with a gentler breed. Arabians require a strong hand. He wintered his horses on his ranch in a high valley; the previous fall he had told Phil he would leave his horse Major for Phil to ride if he would feed and care for him.

There had been no time or energy for riding. Major had been saddled only once that fall. Now as Phil began to gain strength, he wanted to ride. In February we were treated to an early thaw; the sun was warm, and we decided this was the time to saddle Major. Kent and Linda came over with little Jennifer. They brought Major to the house. Phil needed assistance to mount up, because he was still very weak and shaky. After riding up and down the lane just once, he was tired and gave us all a chance to ride. Even little Jennifer took a turn with her mother. Phil looked forward to many more rides as the weather warmed and he gained more strength.

With Phil's renewed interest in the life around us, the world took on a little brighter hue. However, as the days passed, he seemed to grow weaker. I managed to get him down to the Jacuzzi a few times, but as this became more difficult, he finally just refused to make the effort.

As our situation became more widely known, we had more processors at the door. I just signed the receipts and mailed them to our attorney. To save us money, our account had been handed to Stephen D. Swindle, a junior member of the firm of Van Cott, Bagley, Cornwall, & McCarthy. Stephen made court appearances for us when possible. When necessary, I represented Phil and myself. This was not the first time I had found it necessary to shoulder our burdens alone, but never before had I faced a situation such as this.

We welcomed a visit from Dr. Ken and Dorothy Dore, enroute from Maine to California to see Dorothy's brother. Ken agreed with Rees that medical science would be of no help to Phil unless he had a will to live. It was becoming evident to me that rather than willing himself to live, Phil was willing himself to die. Nothing I could do seemed to make the slightest difference.

About this time, Zeline was called back to Connecticut to help her daughter Mildred, who was desperately ill. She had been very discouraged by her inability to tempt Phil into eating. Phil had reached the point where he was unable to retain anything he ate.

With my parting hug, I told Zeline that no one in the world could have come close to equalling her in all the delicate dishes she had prepared for Phil. She had our never-ending love and appreciation for everything she had done for us, but now she must go to Mildred. We had been blessed to have dear, faithful Zeline with us, and we sorely missed her sweet, gentle presence.

Phil had been making payments on his cousin Arthur Crawford's Farm in Lehi for some experiments he planned to make. We had been unable to continue the payments on Crawford Meadows and had turned this property back to cousin Arthur Crawford. My sister Rhae's husband, Wayne Thompson, who had been helping Arthur, took a night job at City Hall and stopped in every afternoon to chat with Phil.

Wayne was a remarkable man, and we welcomed the opportunity to become better acquainted with this brother-in-law of mine. His down-to-earth philosophy, dry sense of humor, and broad range of knowledge were just what Phil needed. Wayne could converse on almost any subject. If Phil brought up something that stumped him, he would go home and bone up on it, then bring it back into the conversation the next day. Phil thoroughly enjoyed talking with him. Wayne had gone through the horrors of the "Battle of the Bulge" in France, a subject he never would discuss, though he did talk about his time as field secretary and driver for General Dwight D. Eisenhower.

At this point, Phil had no interest in television or music, but he enjoyed hearing me read. This had long been our favorite way to spend an evening. It now took fast moving adventure stories to capture his attention and take his mind off the depressing problems plaguing him. He often requested poetry. He liked everything from the homespun philosophy of Edgar A. Guest, to the sometimes morbid poetry of Edna St. Vincent Millay. He preferred her lighter work and had memorized some of the poems from *A Few Figs From Thistles.*

It was no secret that I planned to write the truth about Phil and his contributions to mankind. I wanted the world to know this remarkable man as I did and had been collecting documents and making notes for some time. He often talked about his early life, and we frequently discussed the times we had shared. As he often dictated to me, I usually had pen and paper handy. However, I was beginning to feel inadequate to write a book worthy of him. I suggested hiring an experienced biographer to write his story. Phil brought me up short with, "You can write it if you really want to, but you can't write about me without writing about us. We are one person, inseparable." Little did I dream this would be our last such conversation.

Dr. Rees Anderson had dropped in every few days. He warned me the day after Zeline left that Phil's life forces were getting very weak and I should be prepared for the worst.   The following day, Phil departed this veil of tears and went on to his next estate—the life beyond.

Philo T. Farnsworth display at Fort Wayne, Indiana Historical Museum

Later, in Phil's study, I noticed the small plaque he always had on his desk, which read, "MEN AND TREES DIE—IDEAS LIVE ON FOR THE AGES." "Oh, Phil, how true," I thought, but he had taken so many unfulfilled ideas with him to his grave.

Addendum

The morning after Phil died, I awoke to a feeling of profound despair. For nearly forty-five years we had been an integral part of each other. How could I go on as this half-person, with no purpose ... no direction ... no future? We had lived all of our married lives for the future. Just as Phil told me on our wedding night, we had lived our lives on the leading edge of discovery, always for the future. I had been caught up in and had become a part of Phil's dreams, which became our dreams, and those dreams had died with Phil. In my despair, I saw no reason to keep on living.

My loving family gathered around me. With their help, that of my sisters Lois and Rhae and that of Bishop Brimhall, I managed to get through the viewing and funeral services. Our good friend Arch Madsen gave a heartwarming eulogy, and Richard L. Evans, of the Tabernacle Choir/Spoken Word, gave an inspirational talk, his last "spoken word" for Phil and his family. Phil's mortal remains were laid to rest in the Provo Cemetery, near the graves of his father, his brother Carl, and our sweet little Kenny. The grave of his half-brother Ronald is nearby, and the graves of my dear mother and father are in the same cemetery.

I awakened the next morning at dawn with a strange feeling. In recent years Phil and I had experimented with mental-telepathy to a small degree of success. I had a feeling that he might be attempting to reach me mentally. I concentrated all of my thoughts on Phil. My intense efforts began to cause pains through my eyes and temples.

As I was about to give up, a voice spoke to me in my mind. There was no sound, but the clear and distinct words had a calming effect on me. The voice told me this was a very important time for Phil, and I must let him go ... The voice went on to say that I still had important work to do on earth. Suddenly I knew without a doubt the nature of this work, and I was at peace.

I felt my first obligation was to write Phil's story, but it was not until five years later after his estate was settled that I was emotionally calm enough to begin. In the meantime, I concentrated my efforts in serving my family and my church.

In June 1977 I was visiting my eldest son Philo and his family in California. Philo was assisting me on some of the more technical chapters of the book. He had driven me to Los Altos, in the lower Bay area to see my brother Cliff and his lovely wife "Bo." Cliff had built the first operational television tubes for Phil, and was chief of our tube department for the next ten years.

Cliff told us that the nearby Foothill College had a very interesting historical museum. He, along with many other scientists, inventors, and innovators, had contributed their papers and artifacts to this museum, and they were most anxious to have something from Phil. He suggested we stop in on our way home, and this we did.

We were greeted warmly and soon found ourselves with a group of administrators around a conference table. As we talked, the thought struck me that this September 7th would mark the fiftieth anniversary of the first transmission of all-electronic television, and it was done in Phil's Green Street lab in San Francisco. When I mentioned this, Philo said of course we would have to celebrate this momentous occasion.

The assembled Foothill people were enthusiastic and suggested we have the celebration there. They would do anything they could to help. Philo said we could reenact that first transmission. We had the very tubes used on that occasion, but they would need to be rebuilt because they had lost their vacuum over the years. We retraced our steps to Cliff's home and asked if he would help us do this.

Cliff was skeptical. In the first place, he had not made a tube for thirty years, he was now much too shaky to handle glass, and he knew of no facilities where hand blown tubes could be made. Tubes were now made on automatic machines. Furthermore, even should we overcome these obstacles, there was not time in which to achieve a demonstration.

Obviously Cliff had been away from Phil too long, but Philo was undaunted. As he talked I was reminded of his father fifty years ago. He asked Cliff if he would supervise the project provided all other obstacles were overcome. Cliff said of course he would be happy to do what he could.

That evening we called Tobe Rutherford in New Jersey. He was delighted with the idea. If we could pay transportation for him and his wife Helen, he would take his vacation time to come and help us. He was the vice president of the company where he worked.

Our first hurdle was to raise the necessary money. Philo and I drove to Salt Lake where I obtained a personal loan for four thousand dollars. By the time we returned to Bolinas where Philo lived, his friend, Kirby Ferris, had located a place where the tubes could be made. Ironically, this was on the University of California Berkeley campus, where Bill Cummings had made Phil's first tubes. That these tubes did not work was the fault of Phil's embryonic design, not the expertise of Mr. Cummings. Mr. Bob Hamilton, the man now in charge of the tube department was equally willing to help.

Our next concern was a place for the Rutherfords to stay. To reach Bolinas entailed an hour's drive on the narrow twisting road over Mt. Tamalpias. Helen was in poor health and we needed a place in East Marin County for them in order to avoid this drive.

Kirby did it again. The mother of a friend lived alone in a large home in San Rafael, a short distance north of the Golden Gate Bridge. This lady, Gloria Bettini, generously offered us the hospitality of her home. I kept Helen company while Tobe helped Cliff and Philo.

Philo and his crew had almost as much difficulty in finding old materials and equipment as had Phil in 1927 in improvising and building new equipment. As September 7th approached, it was a toss-up whether they would be ready. Philo had brought Paul Schatzkin and Georja Skinner-Schatzkin from Hollywood to help line up the media coverage. They had tried to interest someone in funding a television mini-series based on the first version of my book on Phil's life. At that time the question of who invented television was too controversial.

Philo and I were interviewed by an Associated Press reporter, in addition to Terrence O'Flaherty, columnist for the *San Francisco Chronicle*, who was caught up in our cause and wrote several very helpful articles. This resulted not only in many local calls, but the AP article brought in calls from many points around the nation.

CBS and NBC were to send crews up from Los Angeles on the sixth for interviews and then to cover the event on the seventh. There was tremendous relief in his voice when Philo called at ten p.m. on September fifth to say they were able to get a transmission. Cliff and Bob Hamilton had finished the tubes, but then it was necessary to get them pumped to a vacuum. There was no way to do this at Berkeley, so Cliff prevailed upon the good graces of a former associate at the Varian company for this.

While this was going on, Tobe took on the job of winding the magnetic coils necessary for scanning the image. He made a makeshift coil-winder, and with the assistance of Philo's son Mark wound the coils. He not only remembered the kind of wire to use, he knew the size!

The NBC crew headed by Jack Perkins was to arrive at nine a.m., Terry Drinkwater and his group at eleven-thirty, and then we were to make the hour-long drive to San Francisco for an ABC interview at 3:00 p.m. in front of the building at 202 Green Street where Phil had made his historic transmission fifty years previously.

On the morning of the seventh, we were detained by the constant ringing of the telephone. Mark was to drive us, and when Philo told him we were late, he said not to worry, he would get us there. I was sitting in the back of the Cadillac alone, and when Mark started tooling the car around those sharp curves as if it were a race vehicle, I found it necessary to brace myself with both feet and both hands to keep in the seat. There were no seat belts at that time. Fortunately Mark was so familiar with the road he could probably have driven it blindfolded.

We arrived, having somehow escaped the notice of the Highway Patrol, just one minute after nine, only to find that Mr. Perkins had called to say he would be two hours late! This meant that after our 3:00 o'clock appointment in San Francisco, we would have to drive back to Foothill College for NBC. Fortunately, these interviews all went smoothly, but we were very late getting home.

The day of the seventh was a huge success. We had a big crowd which included six of Phil's early helpers.

Despite the newsmaking arrival of Prince Charles in Los Angeles, we were well covered on the 6:00 and 10:00 television news.

This brought Phil and his lack of recognition into the limelight. A few months later, Philo was invited to accept on behalf of his father, a Northern California Governor's special "Emmy" award. Then the owners of 202 Green Street put a plaque on their building depicting Phil's accomplishments there. Shortly after this a group of civic-minded citizens led by Mrs. D. C. (Alice) Bryant and Mrs. Sarah Dunn, proposed that a Philo T. Farnsworth Foundation be formed to raise money for further honors. Phil's two sisters, Agnes Farnsworth Lindsay and Laura Farnsworth Player together with Philo and I, all accepted positions as directors of the Foundation.

It was the decision of the Board to first concentrate on getting the 202 Green Street building designated as an historical site. Unfortunately, this was not long after the assassination of Mayor Mosconi, and City Hall was still very jittery. There developed a controversy among the supervisors regarding who was the rightful leader of that body. The group broke into two factions, and our issue was squarely in the middle of the fray.

Mr. Guisti, spokesman for the owners of 202 Green Street, was against making the building an historical site, saying they would then be unable to make any structural changes thereto. The acting leader of the supervisors sided with him. The consensus of this group was that since the Encyclopedia Britannica gave the credit of inventing television to Vladimir Zworykin, Philo Farnsworth had no claim to fame.

Therefore, the City Landmark Board voted against us. The issue then was taken before the City Planning Commission. By this time I had talked to many of the nation's leaders who knew of Phil's work and letters began pouring in to Mayor Feinstein and the city planning boards and Board of Supervisors on behalf of Farnsworth. The City Planning Commission voted in our favor.

The final decision was with the Board of Supervisors. Once more we attended a hearing at City Hall. An issue to be considered among many others that day was a healthy raise to their salaries. We were determined to wait until our issue came up for a vote. At 1:00 a.m. they went into closed session not wishing to make the discussion of their salaries public. At 2:00 a.m. they came out and as motion was made to hear the Farnsworth matter. Our friend who lead the fight in the Planning Commission had stayed with us to present their findings, but she was not allowed to speak. A vote was taken and we lost by one vote. The newspapers the next morning had headlines about the large raise in salary the Board of Supervisors had voted for themselves. This caused such a furor they had to reduce this raise to a nominal amount.

We were of course very disappointed, but Alice Bryant was a fighter. She went over the city's head to the Governor. As a result, a California state monument was placed on the corner of Sansome and Green Streets on September 15th, 1981. The ceremony included the Navy Color Guard from Treasure Island Naval station and their Navy Band. The Institute of Electrical and Electronic Engineers (Phil was a Fellow of the Institute) were having their national convention and the incoming President gave our key address. The outgoing President and many other dignitaries were in attendance.

Our next campaign was to get Phil's picture on a United States postage stamp. We mounted a write-in campaign and letters began to deluge the Citizen's Stamp Advisory Committee. Finally the head of the committee said, "Please, no more! We hear you!" I had spoken to this gentleman several times. Now I called again. He said there were a number of other worthy men whose applications had been in for years. He suggested we make it a series of four inventors. I was calling from Philo's home in Bolinas, I turned to Philo and asked who he would suggest combining with Phil for an inventor's series. Without hesitation he said Nicola Tesla, Edwin Armstrong, Charles P. Steinmetz, and Philo Farnsworth. All had given much to society and received little credit.

When I repeated this to the gentleman on the telephone, he was very pleased. He said all of these men had long standing applications for commemorating stamps, and he felt this group had a good chance of passing the committee. This series issued on September 21st, 1983. My son Russell met me in Washington for the celebration.

In 1984 Phil was inducted into the National Inventor's Hall of Fame. Then in 1987, he was chosen as the second person from Utah to have a statue in Statuary Hall in our nation's Capital in Washington, D. C. The statue campaign was spearheaded by the sixth grade of the Ridgecrest Elementary School in Salt Lake City. They took a broad poll of the citizens in which Farnsworth led over all others. Then they lobbied the House of Representatives and the Senate. The first year it passed the House and was tabled by the Senate. The next year, after gaining more support, it passed both houses. Those smart young people just would not give up. The statue is nearing completion and will be placed in Statuary Hall on May 2nd, 1990.

The people of Rigby have been working since 1979 to raise funds for a Farnsworth Memorial Museum in Rigby to mark the birthplace of television. It was there that Phil, as a high school freshman, conceived the idea of all-electrical television and described it to Justin Tolman, his chemistry teacher in late February of 1922.

Despite all this, comparatively few people of the world know of Philo Taylor Farnsworth. It is hoped that this book, *Distant Vision, Romance and Discovery on an Invisible Frontier*, will change all this. We have brought the Philo T. Farnsworth Foundation from California to Utah. We hope to bring to fruition some of his many unfinished ideas he hoped would contribute to the betterment of life here on earth.

Phil making will-o-wisp for son Philo, playing with son Kent, 1950; after playing croquet with oldest and youngest sons, Philo III and Kent; biting Skee's apple while Philo III looks on; fishing with son Kent in Maine, 1952.

Top: Phil in 1968 (left) and with 1960 model of Fusor. (right). Center: Phil and Pem in daily morning planning session. Bottom: Phil and Pem at Kent and Linda's wedding, 1965.

Epilogue

In 1956, Phil and I participated in the centennial celebration of the town of Beaver, Utah, where Phil's cousin, Taylor Farnsworth, was the mayor. Also present were Taylor's wife, Kathleen, Phil's mother, Serena, and Elder Mark E. Peterson, of the LDS Counsel of the Twelve Apostles, who, along with Phil, was the featured speaker of the day. I did not realize the true importance of this event until the day after Phil's funeral, when I received a letter from Kathleen, which included the following:

When Elder Peterson spoke, he said, "How honored I am to be privileged to speak on the same program with Philo Taylor Farnsworth, one of the truly great scientists of the world. He is known and honored worldwide for his contributions to Humanity."

At the end of the meeting, Aunt Rena (Phil's mother) turned to me with tears in her eyes and said, "I just realized that a prophecy has been fulfilled. An Apostle of the church has announced that my son, Philo, is a world renowned scientist, and is known throughout the world for his contributions to mankind. Yes, my son has grown to be one of God's noble spirits."

Bibliography

Books

Everson, George. *The Story of Television - The Life of Philo T. Farnsworth.* W. W. Horton, 1949.

Eckheart, George. *Electronic Television.* Goodheart Wilcox, 1936.

Halloran, A. H. *Television with Cathode Rays.* Pacific Radio Publishing, 1936.

Waldrop and Borkin. *Television, A Struggle for Power.* William Morrow, 1938.

Dunlap, Orin E. Jr. *Radio's 100 Men of Science.* Harper Bros., 1944.

Morgan, Jane. *Electronics in the West: The First Fifty Years.* National Press Books, 1967.

Pardoe, T. Earl. *The Sons of Brigham.* Provo, Utah: Brigham Young University, 1968-69.

Abramson, Albert. *The History of Television, 1880-1941.* McFarland and Co., 1987.

Varian, Dorothy. *The Inventor and the Pilot.* Pacific Books Publishers, 1983.

Barnouw, Eric. *We Americans*, National Geographic, (1977).

Who's Who in America. Chicago: The A. N. Marquis Company.

Who Was Who in America. Chicago: The A. N. Marquis Company.

Magazines

Published articles by Philo T. Farnsworth:

Farnsworth, P. T. and Lubcke, Harry R. "The Transmission of Television Images," *San Francisco Engineers* (1930).

Farnsworth, P.T. "An Electrical Scanning System for Television," *Journal of the Franklin Institute* (1930).

Farnsworth, P. T. "Electron Multiplier Tubes and Their Uses," *Journal of the Franklin Institute* (1934).

Unpublished articles by Philo T. Farnsworth:

Farnsworth, P. T. "Peacetime Uses of Fusion Energy," (1966).

Farnsworth, P.T. "Advanced Concepts," (1966).

Articles by other authors:

Dinsdale, Arthur. "Television Takes the Next Step," *Christian Science Monitor.*

Halloran, Arthur H. "Farnsworth's Cold-Cathode Electron Multiplier Tube Uses Neither Grid nor Filament," *Radio* (October 1932).

"True Electrical Scanning Radical Television Step," *Christian Science Monitor* (September 27, 1928).

"Moon Makes Television Debut," *Christian Science Monitor* (August 25, 1934).

Cooley, Donald G. "Television Our Next Industrial Boom," *Modern Mechanix and Invention.*

Carskadon, T.R. "Phil the Inventor," *Colliers Magazine* (October 3, 1936).

"Banker Backed," *Time Magazine, Communications* (February 20, 1939).

"Boy Saw Television Clearly; As Expert Today He Pushes On," *Christian Science Monitor* (January 20, 1939).

"The Dramatic Story of the Father of Television," *BYU Alumnus* (August 1953).

"Edwin C. Hill Eulogizes Utah Television Inventor"

Wilson, Mitchell. "The Strange Birth of Television," *Reader's Digest* (February 1953).

Jones, Stacey V., "Farnsworth a TV Pioneer at 15, Gets Still Another Patent at 49," *New York Times* (July 14, 1956).

Minton, James. "Tom Swift in San Francisco, Philo T. Farnsworth and His Electric Television," *San Francisco Monthly* (November 1972).

Lovece, Frank. "Zworykin v. Farnsworth, The Strange Story of TV's Troubled Origins," (in 2 Parts) *Video Magazine.*

"Farnsworth Iatron Radar Projector Indicator Contributes To Air Safety As Well As To United States Defense," *Aviation Magazine.*

Selected Newspaper Articles

"Television Set Called Epochal," *Philadelphia Public Ledger* (August 14, 1934).

"New Amplifier Tube Amazes Group of Radio Engineers," *San Francisco Engineer* (March 5, 1936).

"Philo T. Farnsworth tells U.S. Monopoly Probers How Boyhood Dreams Of Television Became Actuality," *Washington Post* (1937).

"Former Utahn, Philo T. Farnsworth Gets Place on 'Top Ten' Young Men of 1939,"

Salt Lake Tribune (1939).

"Utahn Finds Way To Make Germs Visible," (1930).

Smith, Gene. "ITT Hopeful on Experiments To Harness the H-Bomb's Power," *New York Times* (January 4, 1961).

Williams, Ernest E. "Farnsworth's A-Power Unit Near Reality," *Fort Wayne News Sentinel* (January 3, 1961).

"Rewards of Real Faith Dwarf Television Magic." *Fort Wayne Journal Gazette* (November 9, 1969).

Schatzkin, Paul and Kiger, Bob. "Celebrating the 50th Anniversary of Electronic Television—The Story of Philo T. Farnsworth," (four part chronicle) *Televisions*. Vol. 5, No. 1, 2, 3 & 4 .

Hack, Richard. "Tele-visions," *The Hollywood Reporter* (September 7, 1976).

"Television Inventor Got Idea As Farm Boy," *UPI* San Francisco, (September 5, 1977).

Mead, Dale F. "Original 'Doctors' On Hand as Television is Born Again," *San Jose Mercury* (September 8, 1977).

Storino, Michael. "Father of Television Honored," *Foothill Sentinel* Los Altos, CA. (September 19, 1977).

Adams, Gerald. "TV's Birthplace goes Unenshrined," *San Francisco Examiner* (1979).

"Birthplace of Television Transmission Gets State Plaque," *San Francisco Chronicle* (1980).

"Philo T. Farnsworth Going First Class—on a Stamp," *Deseret News* September 20, (1983).

"National Inventors Hall of Fame Will Induct Four on Inventor's Day," *Washington Post* (February 5, 1984).

"Television's 50th Anniversary," *People Weekly* (Summer, 1989).

Lovece, Frank. "Is It TV's 50th Birthday—or Not?" *Channels* (June 1989).

"Hero Taking his Place in D.C. May 2nd, 1990" *Salt Lake Tribune* (1990)

"Bill Gives 'Father of Modern Electronic Television' Place in Capital Fame, Utah Authorized to Hold Ceremonies in the U.S. Capital to Erect Statue," *Salt Lake Tribune* (February 2, 1990).

Appendix

U.S. PATENTS ISSUED TO PHILO T. FARNSWORTH

FILING DATE	TITLE	PATENT #	ISSUE DATE
*1/07/27	Television System	1,773,980	8/20/30
1/07/27	Light Valve (split and refiled 11/07/27)	1,806,935	5/26/31
1/07/27	Electric Oscillator System	1,758,359	5/13/30
*1/07/27	Television Receiving System	1,773,981	8/26/30
1/09/28	Photoelectric Apparatus	1,970036	8/14/34
1/09/28	Fundamental Dissector Case, Television Method	2,168,768	8/8/39
*4/17/28	Electrical Discharge Apparatus	1,986,330	1/01/35
4/25/28	Synchronizing System	1,844,949	2/16/32
11/26/28	Method and Apparatus For Television	2,037,711	4/21/36
3/11/29	Admitance Neutralization Amplifier	1,986,331	1/01/35
3/03/30	Electron Image Amplifier	2,085,742	7/06/37
*5/05/30	Television Scanning and Synchronizing System	2,246,625	11/23/37
*5/05/30	Slope Wave Generator (P.T.F. and H. Lubcke)	2,059,219	11/03/36
6/14/30	Electron Image Amplifier	2,085,742	7/06/37
*6/14/30	Thermionic Oscillograph	2,009,846	11/23/37
7/07/30	Dissector Target	1,941,344	12/26/33
12/4/30	System of Pulse Transmission	2,026,379	12/31/35
7/14/31	Projection Oscillight	2,140,284	12/13/38
7/14/31	Scanning and Synchronizing System	2,051,372	8/18/36
7/22/31	Thermionic Vacuum Tube	1,975,143	10/02/34
5/31/32	Luminescent Screen (P.T.F. and B.C. Gardner)	2,098,000	11/02/37
*4/03/33	Scanning Oscillator	2,059,683	11/03/36
2/08/33	Luminescent Screen and Method of Use	2,104,253	1/04/38
4/26/33	Image Dissector	2,087,683	7/20/37
10/07/33	Electron Multiplying Device	2,071,515	2/23/37
4/26/33	Image Dissector	Re21,504	7/09/40
7/05/34	Oscillation Generator	2,071,516	2/23/37
*11/05/34	Scanning Means and Method	2,280,572	4/21/42
11/06/34	Projection Means	2,143,145	1/10/39
11/06/34	Projection Apparatus	2,091,705	8/31/37
3/09/36	Incandescent Light Source	2,089,054	8/03/37
3/12/35	Means of Electron Multiplication	2,143,262	1/10/39
3/12/35	Cathode Ray Tube	2,149,045	2/28/39
3/12/35	Oscillator (divided 4/26/37)	2,174,488	9/26/39

5/07/35	Incandescent Light Source		
	(P.T.F and H. Bamford)	2,066,070	12/29/36
5/07/35	Multipactor Phase Control	2,071,517	2/23/37
5/07/35	Means For Producing		
	Incandescent Images		
	(Farnsworth and Bamford)	2,155,478	4/25/39
7/06/35	Means and Method of		
	Image Analysis	2,216,264	10/01/40
7/06/35	Charge Storage Dissector	2,140,695	12/20/38
7/06/35	Cathode Ray Amplifier	2,228,388	1/14/41
7/06/35	Charge Storage Amplifier	2,233,888	3/04/41
7/15/35	Image Receiving Tube	2,118,186	5/24/38
8/10/35	Cathode Ray Amplifying Tube	2,251,124	7/29/41
9/07/35	Charge Storage Dissector Tube	2,141,836	12/27/38
9/07/35	Image Analysis Tube	2,100,842	11/30/37
*9/14/35	Charge Storage Tube	2,100,841	11/30/37
7/01/35	Electron Image Amplifier	2,292,437	8/11/42
2/10/36	Scanning Current Generator	2,214,077	9/10/40
2/11/36	Multipactor	2,135,615	11/08/38
2/24/36	Radiation Frequency Converter	2,107,782	2/08/38
3/09/36	Absorbtion Oscillator	2,159,521	5/23/39
3/24/36	Secondary Emission Electrode	2,139,813	12/13/38
5/16/36	Means and Method of Controlling		
	Electron Multipliers	2,140,832	12/20/38
5/16/36	Means and Method of Producing		
	Electron Multiplication	2,204,479	6/11/40
5/18/36	Electron Multiplier	Re20,759	6/14/38
6/01/36	Cathode Ray Tube	2,158,279	5/16/39
6/01/36	Multi-Stage Multipactor	2,141,837	12/27/38
6/18/36	Concentric Multiplier	2,147,934	2/21/39
10/31/36	Repeater	2,143,146	1/10/39
7/11/36	Image Source	2,213,070	8/30/38
8/18/36	Means and Method of Operating		
	Multipliers	2,128,580	08/30/38
8/18/36	Image Dissector	2,216,265	10/01/40
11/02/36	High Power Projection Oscillograph		
	(P.T.F and F. Somers)	2,109,289	2/22/38
11/02/36	Beam Scanning Dissector	2,124,057	7/19/38
11/02/36	Cathode Ray Tube	2,139,814	12/13/38
11/04/36	Cold Cathode Electron		
	Discharge Tube	2,184,910	12/26/39
11/09/36	Electron Multiplier		
	(P.T.F and F. Somers)	2,179,996	11/14/39
	Multiplier Oscillator	2,137,528	11/22/38
2/24/36	Multipactor Oscillator and		
	Amplifier	2,091,439	8/31/37
3/22/37	Multiplier Coupling System	2,140,285	12/13/38
3/22/37	Split Cathode Multiplier	2,217,860	10/15/40
3/22/37	X-Ray Projection Device	2,221,374	11/12/40
3/22/37	Self-Energized Alternating		
	Current Multiplier	2,174,487	9/26/39

3/22/37	Method of Operating Electron Multipliers	2,180,279	11/14/39
3/22/37	Diode Oscillator Tube Constriction	2,189,358	2/06/40
3/22/37	Two-Stage Oscillograph	2,216,266	10/01/40
3/22/37	Split Cathode Multiplier Tube	2,141,838	12/27/38
4/26/37	Detector	2,156,807	5/02/39
4/26/37	Amplifier	2,221,473	11/12/40
9/20/37	Means For Producing an Incandescent Image	2,179,086	11/07/39
1/05/38	Electron Amplifier	2,239,149	4/22/41
2/21/38	Radio Frequency Multipactor Amplifier	2,172,152	9/05/39
3/12/38	Dissector Tube (Original date 12/31/35)	2,235,477	3/18/41
6/13/38	Image Projector (Original date 12/31/35)	2,235,477	3/18/41
6/13/38	Shielded Anode Electronic Multiplier P. Farnsworth and R. Snyder	2,203,048	6/04/40
9/10/38	Image Analyzing System	2,254,140	8/26/41
12/31/38	Dissector Tube	2,153,918	4/11/39
4/05/39	Image Amplifier	2,257,942	10/07/41
4/05/39	Cold Cathode Electron Discharge Tube	2,263,032	11/18/41
4/24/39	High Efficiency Amplifier	2,223,001	11/26/40
4/25/39	Electron Multiplier	2,260,613	11/28/41
7/05/39	Electron Image Amplifier	Re22,009	1/20/42
	Electric Amplifier	Re21,818	6/03/41
2/15/40	Electric Recording and Reproducing System	2,304,633	12/08/42
2/23/40	Application and Method of Electron Discharge Control	2,274,194	2/24/42
3/05/40	Rectifier	2,287,607	6/23/42
3/11/40	Dissector Tube	2,264,630	12/02/41
4/03/40	Electron Control Device	2,286,076	6/09/42
7/25/40	Electron Control Device	2,311,981	2/23/43
9/07/40	Image Dissector	2,292,111	8/04/42
9/07/40	Television Projection System	2,315,113	3/30/43
10/09/40	Cathode Ray Signal Reproducing Tube	2,301,388	11/10/42
5/22/41	Deflecting System	2,297,949	10/06/42
7/05/41	Image Amplifier	2,291,577	7/28/42
6/20/42	Image Reproducing Device	2,355,212	8/08/44
7/29/50	Television Image Analyzing Tube	2,641,723	6/09/53
11/25/50	Cathode Ray Tube and System	2,754,449	7/10/56
5/18/54	Color Television Apparatus	2,921,228	1/12/60
3/03/54	Radio Translating Device	2,992,358	7/11/62
5/07/52	Light Translating Device	2,992,346	7/11/61
3/06/57	Cathode Ray Tube	2,941,106	6/14/60
3/07/62	Electron Gun in the Form of a Multipactor	3,201,640	8/17/65

11/05/34	Method of Manufacturing		
	Cathode Ray Tube Targets	2,286,478	6/16/42
4/26/37	Two-Stage Electron Multiplier	2,161,620	6/06/39
4/05/39	Image Amplifier	2,291,577	7/28/42
1/11/62	Electric Discharge Device		
	for Producing Interaction		
	Between Nuclei	3,258,402	6/28/66
3/29/62	Ion Transport Vacuum Pump	3,181,028	4/27/65
5/13/66	Method and Apparatus for		
	Producing Nuclear-Fusion		
	Reactions	3,386,883	6/04/68
4/19/63	Microwave Amplifier Utilizing		
	Multiplication To Produce		
	Periodically Bunched Electrons	3,312,857	4/04/67
	Electric Discharge Device		
	(Canadian Patent)	654,306	12/18/62
	Radio Frequency Amplifier		
	(Australian Patent)	102,330	10/22/37
	(Velocity Modulation per se)		

(All above patents were assigned to the Corporation, listed below are the only patents he owned personally)

6/09/64	Process and Apparatus For Drying		
	and Treating Lumber		
	(Vacuum process)	3,283,412	11/08/66
4/01/69	Lumber Drying		
	(Vacuum method)	3,574,949	4/13/71

* Denotes unusual importance.

The search for errant patents is still on. Located in 1987 are:

11/05/34	Method of Manufacturing		
	Cathode Ray Tube Targets	2,286,478	6/16/42
4/26/37	Two-Stage Electron Multiplier	2,161,620	6/6/39

Philo T. Farnsworth patents pending as of 1967.*

Case number 167	"Power Convertor"
Case number 168	"Multipactor Amplifier"
Case number 170	"Multipactor Flood Gun for use with Iotron"
Case number 171	"Tunable Infra-Red Source"
Case number 173	"Pendulator"
Case number 175	"Refluxor"
Case number 176	"Ion Propulsion Motor"
Case number 177	"Radio Frequency Power Generator"

(When Farnsworth went on medical retirement from ITT Farnsworth.)
It is assumed these patents issued later, and is concrete evidence that he was

still inventing. There were another six or eight disclosures beyond these that may or may not have been acted upon.

The following patents were listed in a Farnsworth Company brochure. They may have been filed under the name of one of the Farnsworth engineers, since no name is given, but they show unmistakable guidance of the master inventor of them all.

Patent number   2,099,846 -   Magnetic Focusing (an improvement)
                         2,155,479 -   Carrier Wave Modulation
                         2,163,966 -   On the Applications of Electron Multipliers
                         2,233,878 -   On more Application of Electron Multipliers
                         2,200,166 -   Improved Electron Multiplier for use in Image Dissectors.

<u>Philo T. Farnsworth's Most Basic Patents Used in Modern Television Receivers.</u>

<u>Television Receiving System.</u>
The second patent filed by Farnsworth (January 7th, 1927) covers the method of turning the electrical impulses back into a picture at the receiver. Patent number 1,773,981.

<u>Scanning.</u> (Termed the famous "Blacker than Black" case)
All modern television receivers utilize Farnsworth's basic system of scanning relatively slowly in one direction and relatively rapidly in the opposite direction, substantially extinguishing the beam in the picture tube during the rapid "retrace" parts of the scan cycles (See Farnsworth Patent number 2,246,625). In interference eleven years.

<u>Synchronizing.</u>
All modern television receivers embody Farnsworth Patent number 2,246,625 "Television Scanning and Synchronizing System." This also covers radar scanning, etc.

<u>Magnetic Focusing.</u>
Substantially all modern television receivers utilize Farnsworth's invention covered by patent number 2,099,846.

<u>Generation of the High Voltage from the Horizontal Scan Frequency.</u>
Single tube scanning wave generator, used universally for both vertical and horizontal deflection. Farnsworth patent number 2,059,683.

<u>Vertical Deflection Wave Generator.</u>
Almost all modern television receivers use this circut. Farnsworth Patent number 2,059,219.

<u>Maintaining Constant Black Level.</u>
Very widely used. Farnsworth Patent number 2,301,522 (Madison Cawein) for the Farnsworth Company. P.T. Farnsworth patent number 2,246,625 (see above).

Farnsworth Patents Used in Modern Transmitters, etc.

Television System.
First patent filed on electonic television. Farnsworth Patent number 1,773,980.
Filed January 7th, 1927. Patent Re 21,504 was a reissue of this patent to broaden the claims. This was one of the five cases that won interferences with RCA on their "Image Orthicon" tube. The only thing RCA can claim on this tube is the name. Patent numbers 2,254,140; 2,257,942; and 2,264,630 are three more cases of Farnsworth's covering the "Image Orthicon."

Magnetic Focusing.
This theory and method of focusing is used in every cathode ray tube, both in transmitting and receiving. Dr. Ernsest Lawrence (deceased), long time friend of Dr. Farnsworth, gave this patent credit for leading the way for his famous cyclotron and bevrotron the University of California at Berkeley. This Farnsworth patent is number 1,986,330.

Television Method. (The original method)
Filed January 9th, 1928. Provides a method of dissecting an image for electrical transmission. Patent number 2,168,768 (continuation of number 1,970,036).

Philo T. Farnsworth originated the Electron Multiplier art and had thirty two patents covering this field. Since this was such a new art, many of his patents covered the means and method of operation of these tubes.

The Farnsworth Iatron Series (electrostatic memory tubes) began with his Patent number 2,085,742, filed June 14th, 1930, and issued July 6th, 1937. One version of this tube was developed for use in the large telescopes, extending their reach out in space by some 50,000 times. Another use was for the first PPI scan in airport control towers to enable them to keep planes in the vicinity in patterns to prevent collisions.

Another tube in this series was Patent number 2,118,186, filed July 15th, 1935 and issued May 24th, 1938. This furthers the art of the Memory Tube and from this the Farnsworth Company produced the snooperscopes that made it possible for our Army trucks to move at night with infra-red light and the sniperscopes used on rifles that could shoot as well at night as in the day time.

Philo T. Farnsworth, in evaluating his work, felt that his two patents on producing fusion energy, Electric Discharge Device for Producing Interaction Between Nuclei, number 3,258,402 and Method and Apparatus for Producing Nuclear Fusion Reactions, number 3,386,883, were of more value than all the others combined. Unfortunately, he did not live to complete this work.

Index

"Fusor"   279
"I've Got a Secret"   263
"The Transmission of Television Images"   129
127 E. Mermaid Lane, Philadelphia Lab   148
1339 N. New Hampshire   48
1929 Stock Market Crash   120
29 Palms, CA   285
2910 Derby Street, Berkeley, CA   71
3208 Lyon St., Marina District, San Francisco   115
5166 Cottonwood Lane, Holladay   317
734 East State Blvd.   252

A Television Picture, D.K. Lippincott   207
Aberdeen Proving Grounds   226
Ace Pike III   240
Admittance Neutralization   113
Alexander Graham Bell   27
Allen, James   85
Amelia White Farnsworth   24
Anderson, John   323
Anderson, Dr. Rees H.   2
Anderson, Mrs. Lois Gardner   2
Arata, Dr. Justin   276
Arthur M. Gardner   5
Atomic Energy Commission   281

Bain, George   288
Baird Television, London, England   165
Bates Furniture Store   15
Baxter Park, Mt. Katahdin   200
Behn, Colonel Sosthenes   261
Bell Technical Journals   8
Bernstein, Mabel J.   182
Bertrand, and his Hispana, Suisa   186
Bishop, Roy N. S.F. Industrialist   59
Blum, 'Smiles', "Little Miss Television"   172
Boca Raton, and our 40th Wedding Anniversary   308

Bramhall, Dr. 232
Brigham Young University 5
British Broadcasting Company (BBC) 165
British Gaumont 165
Brolly, Arch 128
Bukata, Stephen 229
Buker, Lola, Cliff's Bride 108
BYU Honorary Dr. Degree 317

Cartlidge, Harry 47
Chapple, Dr. Charles C. 143
Chowdorow, Dr. 293
Christensen, Carl J. 88
Christy, Agatha/Murder on the Blue Train 185
Clark, Nathan, Farnsworth Engineer 121
Coke, Bruce 324
Conception of Phil's 'Electric' Television 37
Contracts from NASA 324
Corning Glass Company 160
Correspondence Course from National Radio Institute 39
Cosgrove, Thomas 210
Cramer, Mr. 172
Cranston, Mr. James, General Electric Co. 101
Cresheim Valley Road, Wyndmoor, Pa. 171
Crocker Laboratories, 202 Green Street 68
Crow, Kenneth 324
Cumming, Bill, UC Berkeley 76

Davis, Betty 47
Death of Lewis, January 8, 1924 41
DeForest, Dr. Lee 120
Delco Farm Power Generator 32
Dolores, 'Baby' Child Star 172
Dore, Dr. Kenneth E. 225
Downey, Nellie 330
Dumont, Allen B. Pres. Dumont Television 164
Dunn, Roger 230
Dunstone, Dr. 277
DuPlace, Roscoe 231

Eaglebrook Academy 235
Earthquake! 75
Eddy, Lieutenant William Crawford 151
Edison, Thomas Alva 27
Edward VIII, King of England 183
Einstein, Dr. Albert E. 266
El Rancho Vista Bonita 279

Elbow Beach Hotel and Bermuda 196
Electron Multiplier Tubes 160
Electron Multipliers 176
Electrostatic Inertial Confinement 289
Emitron, Marconi/EMI Camera Tube 165
Essays on Compensation, Ralph Waldo Emerson 41
Evans, Richard L. 271
Everson, George 6
Eyring, Dr. Carl, BYU Chemistry Professor 46

Fagan, James J., Exec. V.P. Crocker Bank 59
Farnsworth 1929 Television Receiver 121
Farnsworth Electronics 262
Farnsworth, Iris Fowler, Lincoln's Bride 175
Farnsworth, Joseph 248
Farnsworth, Kenneth Gardner, Born January 15, 1931 126
Farnsworth, Kent Morgan, Born September 4, 1948 253
Farnsworth, Philo T. Jr., Born September 23, 1929 123
Farnsworth, Russell Seymour, Born October, 5, 1935 171
Farnsworth, S. Taylor and Wife Kathleen 25
Farnsworth Television Broadcasting Station 171
Farnsworth Wood Products 227
Federal Communications Commission Created 134
Felt Electric Co. 6
Fernseh A. G. 179
Fernworth Farm 201
First All-Electronic Television Transmission via Radio 133
First All-Electronic Television Transmission September 7, 1927 90
First Farnsworth Patent Issued May 13, 1930 133
First Patent Application, number 159,540, December 21, 1926 82
First Television Test Blown up by Power Surge 53
First Television Transmission Attempt August 30, 1927 89
Fowler, Valdis, Carl's Bride 139
Franklin Institute Public Demonstration 160
Fryeburg Academy 230
Fuller, Leanard F., UC Berkeley 101
Furth, Admiral Frederick 279
Fusion at BYU 317

Gardner, B. Clifford 5
Gardner, Bernard Edward 5
Gardner, Alton F. 5
Gardner, Art 5
Gardner, Lois 5
Gardner, Olen 5
Gardner, Rhae (Thompson) 5
Gardner, Ruth (Wentz) 5

Gardner, Verona Alice (McCan) 5
Garn, U.S. Senator E. J. "Jake" 326
Gaskins, Gertrude 182
Geneen, Harold S. 284
Getchell, Letitia 228
Gillette, David 329
Golden Gate Bridge 248
Gorrell, Leslie 6
Greenbrier Clinic, W. VA 306
Greer, Sir Harry 167
Grimditch, William 140
Gust, George 287

Haggerty, Lawrence G. 262
Haley Farm, East Brownfield, Maine 201
Haley, Professor George 201
Hanna, R. J., Vice President Standard Oil of California 60
Harmon, Charles 221
Hart, Cornelius 323
Hasewinkle, Dr. 276
Heintz, Ralph/Heitz and Kaufman 76
Hewett, Diana 183
Highleyman, Lieutenent of U.S. Navy 131
Hirsch, Dr. Robert 296
His Majesty King George V. 32
Hitler, Adolph, Dictator of Germany 188
HMS Majestic Voyage Home 168
Hobson, Vern 325
Holden, Mr. St. George 115
Hollywood, California 5
Honn, Harlon, Engineer 60
Hoover, Herbert, Jr. 120
Huffnagle, George Jr. 242
Hugo Gernsbach's *Science and Invention Magazine* 34
Humphries, Robert 92
Huntress, Muriel 242
Huntress, Raymond 242
Hydrogen Bomb 236

Iconoscope 158
Image Amplifying Tube (Electron Microscope) 128
Image Dissector, Sensitivity Problems 85
Inertial Containment 264
Institute of Radio Engineers (IRE) 126
International Telephone & Telegraph 256
IRS Troubles 328

Jackson, Dr. Chevalier, Tracheotomy   143
Jensen, Utah   267
Johnson, Dr. Thomas H.   226

Kaplin, Rose   325
Karawada, Dr. U. of Tokyo   147
Keiser, Earl   321
Kennett, Robert   241
Kenny Dies March 6, 1932   143
Kenny Stricken with Strep Infection   143
Kent's Wife, Linda Douglass Farnsworth   1
Keyes, Dr. Elizabeth   115
KFI, Los Angeles   15
Kiesman, Dotty   311
Kiesman, Harold   311
King George V.   183
Klystron-type Tube   263
Knight, Dr.   267
Knight, Gordon   267
Knouse, Joe, Incident   141
Kruthers, Bonnie, Secretary/Announcer   172
KSL's Documentary   314
Kuhn, Loeb, & Company   179

LAPD, Hazel Keener   51
Latter-day Saint Church of Jesus Christ (Mormon)   23
Lawrence, Dr. Ernest O.   120
Lincoln National Bank   256
Lincoln's Accident   174
Linden, Bernard, Federal Radio Commission   111
Lindsay, Agnes F.   248
Lindsay, Claude T.   248
Lippincott, Donald K., Patent Attorney   126
Los Angeles, California   5
Low-velocity Scanning Beam Tube   207
Lubcke, Harry   103
Lyon, Leonard & Richard, L.A. Patent Attorneys   54

Maine Lab Crew   211
Maine, Introduction to   200
Man on the Moon   325
Man-Made Sapphires   299
March 11, 1971   331
Marconi, Dr. Guglielmo   120
Marshall, Dr. Milton, BYU Math Professor   46
Martin, Gene   242
Martin, Rachel   242

Phil Baptizes our Friends Bill and Linda Cramer   317
Phil on Medical Retirement   312
Phil Very Ill   331
Phil's First Press Conference September 1, 1928   108
Phil's Uncle Albert and Aunt Alice Farnsworth   33
Phil's Wonderful Dreams of our Future   86
Philco Radio Corp. Philadelphia, PA   135
Philco Television W3XE   145
Philo and New Wife, Diana/Baby Maya Aum   311
Philo T. Farnsworth Associates   316
Philo Wins Over Chemistry Teacher Tolman   38
Philo's Birth at Indian Creek, Near Beaver, Ut.   23
Philo's First Invention Wins Prize   36
Plane Crash   238
Player, Laura   172
Player, Lynden L.   172
Plaza Hotel   233
Poisson's Equation   277
Pond, Russell   184
Pool and Jacuzzi   320
Porter of RCA   131
Pouget, Dr. Pierre   186
Predictions for Fusion   297
President Woodrow Wilson   31
Press Club, San Francisco   260
Provo High School   13
Provo, Utah   5
PTFA in Trouble   329

Queen Mary   183

Radio Manufacturers of America (RMA)   216
Ramsen, Mr. Cornell, Jr.   325
Raytheon Tube Company   227
RCA's Image Orthicon Tube   208
RCA's Investment in Television 13 million   208
Reiber, Frank   266
Rigby Star Newspaer   36
Riggs, Dr. Benjamin   246
Riggs, Norma   246
RKO Picture Company   119
Roosevelt, Franklin D.   32
Ross, Nick and Orchestra   172

Sahley Defaults   327
Sahley, Lloyd W.   324
Salinger, Dr. Hans   287

Massachusetts Institute of Technology (MIT)   231
Mayo Clinic, Rochester   304
McAllister, Zeline   226
McCargar, Jesse, V. P. Crocker National Bank   58
McKay, President David O.   314
Meeks, Gene   280
Mentone, France   185
Method of Controlled Fusion   266
Metropolitan Opera   252
Midwestern Securities Corporation   321
Millay, Edna St. Vincent   19
Millikan, Robert A.   32
Millikan vs Einstein on Relativity   32
Miramontes, Frank, Farnsworth Engineer   121
Mix, Tom   47
Molinari, Bart   204
Moore, Garry   262
Mr. Bishop's Gift of Precious Meters   81
Mrs. McCoy, Science Teacher   36
Mrs. Thomas's Boarding House   6
Mueller, Dr. Rolf   189
Multipactor, Blue Glow   263
Mussolini   217

Nalder, Bishop Claude   117
National Guard   241
Navy Maneuvers off Puerto Rico   260
Navy, Annapolis Exams   42
Neutron Count Reaches 1.3×10^9 303
New York Stock Exchange   257
Newton Center   244
Nicholas, Edwin A.   284
Nicolson, Alexander M.   58
Nipkow, Paul, Inventor of the Nipkow Disc   61

Olpin, A. Ray, Bell Labs   132
Osterer, Mr. Chairman of British Gaumont Board of Directors 168

Papagayo Hotel, Acapulco, Mexico   277
Patent Office   285
Patents Two and Three Issued August 26, 1930   133
Patents, Farnsworth   176
Paul Weiss, Wharton, & Garrison   256
Pearl Harbor   223
Pennsylvania University Hospital   174
Peter Bent Brigham Hospital   219
Peterson, Elder Mark E.   25

San Francisco to Los Angeles Television Cable Link   260
Sanibel Island   313
Sarnoff's Buyout Offer Refused by Farnsworth   132
Sarnoff's World Fair Transmission in New York   213
Sarnoff, David, President of RCA   130
Saw-tooth Wave Scanning Form vs Sine-Wave Form   90
Scanning and Synchronizing, Problems of   106
Schairer, Mr., RCA V.P. in Charge of Patents   214
Scientific Films, Inc.   205
Sealed in the Salt Lake LDS Temple   317
Sears, Roebuck Catalog   27
Secondary Electron Emissions   115
Self-Digesting   321
Simpson, Wallace   183
Skeezix   225
Skogsberg, Hilma   250
Skogsberg, John   250
Skogsberg, Ruth   250
Slovak, Joseph   240
Smith, Elder George A.   25
Smith, Daniel   222
Smith, Dr. Mott, of Cal Tech   55
Smith, Gene Writer for the New York Times   288
Sony, American   327
SS Bremen   167
SS Hansa, German Cruise Ship   182
SS Queen of Bermuda   196
St. Petersburg Fla   261
Star Tracking   258
Stec, Charles   252
Stock Options   288
Stone, Ellery   257
Strauss, Louis, Kuhn, Loeb & Company   179

Tall, William   33
Television, Inc. of San Francisco   126
The Breaking Point   309
The Mary Ann   300
The Taming of the Shrew   46
Thompson, Wayne   248
Tihanyi, Dr. Kalman   158
Tolman, Justin, Chemistry Teacher   36
Travelers Insurance Company   327
Turner, Frank   151
Turner, John   324
Turner, Seymour   150
Twitchel, William   174

Tyner, Barbara Harmon   312

U-Bar Ranch   268
Ucon, Idaho   31
United Artists Film Company   123
United States Air Force   261
Utah Broadcasters Association   268

Valentino, Rudolph, The Sheik Premiere   52
Varian, Russell   126
Virus Removal from Culinary Water   321

W3XPF, Farnsworth Television   170
Walker, Garald   241
Walker, Hazel   241
Walt Disney's Steamboat Willie/Mickey Mouse   121
War Production Board (WPB)   227
Washington, D.C.   285
Webster, Dr. David   226
WGL, Purchase of   216
Wharton, John   255
Wiggins, Chester   256
Wild, Herr, President of Zeiss Ikon Optical   190
Wild, Rudolph   190
Wilkinson, Ernest L.   317
Williams, Ernest, Ft. Wayne Journal Gazette   288
Wilson, Woodrow   31
WLW, Cincinnati, Ohio   15
World War II   223
World War II, Armistice, Influenza Epidemic   31

Yancey, Olen Gardner   5
York, Donald   221
Young, Glen   330

Zeline Joins Mormon Church   317
Zenith, Television   256
Zobell, Dr. Claude   280
Zworykin, Dr. Vladimir of Westinghouse   128